C000143585

FOREIGN SHORES

SHORES

A True Story

Best Wishes

FOREIGN SHORES

A True Story

Stuart Crocker

Copyright © 2010 Stuart Crocker

The moral right of the author has been asserted.

Apart from any fair dealing for the purposes of research or private study,
or criticism or review, as permitted under the Copyright, Designs and Patents
Act 1988, this publication may only be reproduced, stored or transmitted, in
any form or by any means, with the prior permission in writing of the
publishers, or in the case of reprographic reproduction in accordance with
the terms of licences issued by the Copyright Licensing Agency. Enquiries
concerning reproduction outside those terms should be sent to the publishers.

Matador
5 Weir Road
Kibworth Beauchamp
Leicester LE8 0LQ, UK
Tel: (+44) 116 279 2299
Fax: (+44) 116 279 2277
Email: books@troubador.co.uk
Web: www.troubador.co.uk/matador

ISBN 978 1848 763 869

British Library Cataloguing in Publication Data.
A catalogue record for this book is available from the British Library.

Typeset in 11.5pt Palatino by Troubador Publishing Ltd, Leicester, UK

Matador is an imprint of Troubador Publishing Ltd

Printed in Great Britain by the MPG Books Group, Bodmin and King's Lynn

For Rosemarie and Layla

1

The Artist

Unshaven and shivering, the young man pulled the threadbare overcoat tightly around his body as a bitter east wind blew down the narrow street. His stomach protesting with hunger, he shuffled along pavements filled with plump and prosperous citizens making their way home through the murky remnants of the winter afternoon. Flurries of snow whirled in the grey sky, falling and clinging to the columns and domes of the grand buildings which filled this part of the city. He tucked an old leather portfolio case under his arm, pulled up his collar and made his way determinedly through the snow powdered streets for his last appointment of the day. Head down to avoid the icy blasts which came around every corner, he tramped through the streets of the city that had been his home for the past four years, the city he had grown to hate. Late for his appointment, the old man in the dingy shop on Herrengasse received him with ill-grace, directed him curtly to a small room at the rear and nodded for him to spread the contents of his folder upon the large table.

Fixing the shopkeeper with his piercing blue eyes, the young man obliged, spreading the pages of watercolours and sketches across the table. The old man placed a pair of gold, pince-nez spectacles on his hooked nose and studied the sheaves of papers spread out before him. Sniffing and muttering, shaking his head from time to time as if indicating that the wares on offer clearly failed to meet his exacting standards, finally he removed his glasses and shook his head.

"I cannot possibly sell any of these."

The young man quickly grabbed a watercolour from the sheaf and thrust it under the old man's hooked nose

"But this is one of my finest. It's better than anything you have on display in the window."

The old man looked impatiently at the scruffy young man, noting his long coat hanging damply down to his ankles with ancient patches on the elbows. He noticed the sunken eyes, the stubbly face and shock of unkempt hair, which had been hidden under a hat when he arrived. He put his glasses back on and studied the watercolour which the young man had thrust under his nose. The image of the cathedral was competent though uninspiring, but the inclusion of some small figures in the foreground appeared to have been an afterthought. Wooden and lifeless, they appeared to have no connection with or relevance to the picture.

The old man sighed.

"I can give you no more than ten schillings for this one. Five now and five if I ever sell it."

The young man frowned, barely concealing his contempt of the old man before grunting his acceptance of the deal, and began to gather up his paintings and slide them back into the folder. The old man counted the coins into his hand before he donned his hat and quickly disappeared into the gathering gloom of the late afternoon. As he strode along the damp pavements, he fondled the coins in his pocket. His rent was already two weeks overdue and Frau Blum would doubtless be waiting for him at the foot of the stairs when he returned to the boarding house, her grubby hand held out expectantly. His dingy room at the top of the tenement block was cold and damp, containing only the bare essentials, a bed, a clothes rail and a wash-stand. His own paltry possessions consisted of little more than a battered old suitcase containing a few spare clothes. A framed photograph of his dead mother was placed near the bed.

Passing the baroque splendours of the city centre with barely a glance, he headed north towards the river where his lodgings lay in a poor district beyond the railway lines. The pains gnawing at his stomach accompanied him like a faithful dog following its master. It seemed on days like this that he had been perpetually hungry for the past four years. As he passed a café he paused and once again fondled the coins in his pocket. Through the windows he could see people sitting at tables eating, plates piled high with meat and vegetables, bowls of steaming soup which looked thicker and more nutritious than the gruel he'd sometimes eaten in the soup kitchen beneath the church further down the road. He licked his lips and went inside.

He wanted to take his time, but the hot goulash scalded his tongue as he quickly devoured the contents of the bowl. To blow on it in order to cool it a little would have been sensible, but his stomach was an impatient master and would brook no delay. He mopped up the last, tiny droplets of soup with a crust of bread, savouring the last tasty mouthfuls. He looked up from his plate, feeling warm for the first time that day. He could easily have eaten three more bowls of goulash and still not been full, but at least the ache of hunger had retreated for a while. He sat back on the bench seat and allowed his thoughts to wander. The small café was filled with people calling in on their way home, but despite the glares of the other arriving customers he refused to yield his seat even though the waitress had long since removed his empty bowl. His piercing eyes stared off into space, oblivious to all around him as he focussed solely on his situation. As darkness fell, he finally came to his decision.

The glittering city in which he had arrived four years earlier had been a mirage; beneath its elegant veneer it had turned out to be nothing more than a chaotic mass of humanity, a polyglot of mongrel races from throughout the empire and beyond. The grand buildings were merely the physical relics of an empire which, like others before it, had grown decadent and corrupt, allowing itself to be taken over and destroyed by the very people over whom it had once held dominion. Mrs Blum, his grasping landlady, was one of those, so was the old miser Rosenthal to whom he had just sold his water-colour for the paltry sum of ten schillings, barely enough to cover the materials he had used.

His decision, in truth, had not been a difficult one. He had at last seen through the disguise and recognised the place for what it was; the facade of culture was little but a device to hide the true nature of its people who had become so lacking in culture themselves that they had failed to recognise his genius. He was now resolved to move away forever, to journey to a place where his talents might be recognised and appreciated, a place where he could live with some measure of decency, a place where he could forget the squalor of hostels and soup kitchens.

It was a propitious time for a change in the course of his life, for if the rumours were true, he might soon be called up by the military. If the authorities had known where to look for him, he might already have received his papers, but one of the few advantages of moving on every few weeks, apart from the possibility of escaping the payment of a week's rent, was that no-one could track him down. At twenty-five, he conceded that it was possible to see himself in uniform, but saw no honour in wearing the uniform of this corrupted empire. Who could fight for a state which had become diluted by an influx of foreigners, its strength ebbing away gradually as inferior peoples from across the empire relentlessly gained the upper hand.

Despite the continuing glares of the waitress, he remained lost in his reverie, lingering in the warm and steamy café as long as he could. It was now quite crowded and although the heady scent of food on the other tables was threatening to prompt a return of his hunger pains, he decided that it was better to remain inside rather than face the bitter cold outside. If he arrived back at the boarding house now, Frau Blum was bound to be there; besides, if he could delay his return until later there was a chance that he could slip past her door undetected. He didn't care about his few pathetic possessions, but he would have to return if only to collect the photograph of his mother. To the clear annoyance of the waitress, he ordered a cup of coffee and took almost an hour to drink it.

At seven-thirty he paid the bill and left the café. Walking along the Jager Strasse he turned into the dark, cobbled street that ran beneath the railway line, turned left and approached the dingy boarding house in Meldemann Strasse. He had timed his arrival to coincide with the Blums normal mealtime in the hope that she would not hear him. The front door was usually left unlocked and so it was this evening, and sure enough the light in the downstairs window indicated that the Blums were busy with their evening meal. Quietly opening the door, he entered the hallway and crept up the stairs, carefully avoiding the creaky third tread. Making it up to his room without attracting any attention, he quickly threw his things into the old suitcase. Wrapping his mother's photograph in an old shirt, he placed it in the case and then crept slowly back down the staircase. He moved silently past the Blums door and then out into the night.

As he walked towards the railway station, he fondled the coins in his pocket, calculating the amount he had left to the last pfennig. He calculated that he had just enough for the ticket which would take him away from four years of misery and disillusionment. He boarded the train and stared out into the darkness as it pulled away from the detestable city and sped him towards a different destiny.

2

I have never been blessed with a great deal of patience, a shortcoming apparent from the very beginning in my eagerness to leave the confines of my mother's womb. I entered the world four months prematurely, and weighing a paltry two pounds, I bore more resemblance to a scrap of red, raw flesh one might find on a butcher's slab rather than any kind of human form.

In those days babies were born at home without teams of hospital staff on hand to cope with any complications which might arise. Frau Stiedle, the midwife, had delivered everyone under the age of forty in the surrounding area and in all that time she had never encountered anything as pathetic as the sight she beheld on the night of April 24th 1925. Fearing that I had been stillborn, she first probed, then prodded and finally slapped before she was able to detect the faintest signs of life. She immediately placed me in the arms of my mother and instructed my father to run and fetch the priest for I was unlikely to last the night.

The priest duly arrived, hastily christened me and then administered the last rites. The name chosen was Theodor because an uncle of the same name had told my mother that it would bring me luck. After the priest had departed, my mother snatched me back and clasped me tightly to her breast where she held me continuously for the next forty-eight hours, refusing to set me down or allow anyone else to hold me until exhaustion finally forced her to relinquish her grip.

Frau Stiedle visited the house every day for a month and although she never wavered from her initial prognosis that I would not remain long on this earth, she was delighted and amazed each day to find me still clinging tenaciously to life. I slept most of the time, feeding little, but gradually growing stronger. It wasn't until I was three months old and had at last achieved the weight of a typical new-born, that Frau Stiedle conceded that I had confounded her prediction. She was not the kind of woman who could easily admit to being wrong and she did not admit it on this occasion, declaring to my parents that a miracle must have taken place and from that day on she always referred to me as her 'little miracle'.

This 'little miracle' took place in Westphalia, the flat, fertile part of the north German plain bisected by the mighty Rhine as it flows in one stream before dividing and sub-dividing then spilling into the North Sea. Although my family had lived in that part of Germany for two generations we were not considered by the authorities to be German. My paternal grandfather had settled in the region after moving from his native Holland during the time of Bismarck. Under German law people took their nationality from their father regardless of any other consideration and so my father was a Dutch citizen simply because his father was and I was also considered Dutch for the same reason.

My grandfather had been the second son of a peasant farmer with a handful of acres near Buurse in the eastern part of Holland close by the German border. As he grew to maturity, he realised that his elder brother would inherit the small parcel of land and that he would have to seek his livelihood elsewhere. At that time northern Germany was a magnet for people throughout Europe; the mines and industries of the dynamic and newly united nation had an inexhaustible hunger for labour and materials. It was still an era when people rarely travelled more than a few miles from their birthplaces. Most of those living under the rule of the Iron Chancellor didn't consider themselves to be 'Germans' at all, they considered themselves as Bavarians, Saxons, Hessians or Prussians. They were citizens of the myriad small duchies, bishoprics, landgraviates and various free cities which comprised the German-speaking swathe of central Europe. A man arriving in Westphalia from Holland would arouse no greater curiosity than someone arriving from Berlin or Leipzig and so my grandfather quickly learned the language and was soon assimilated into his new surroundings.

He took on a variety of jobs before settling on his skill at clog making to earn his living. An itinerant clog maker could earn a living almost anywhere, but he eventually settled in the village of Ostinghausen which lay in the rural area to the east of the industrial cities of the Ruhr where chimneys belched out the acrid, sulphurous fumes which hung heavy in the air, turning day into night.

Clogs were almost universally worn by working men and women in those days and though the trade would never make his fortune, it provided a steady income. As clogs gradually went out of favour, he was able to turn his hand to leatherwork and produced the shoes and boots which the people increasingly preferred to wear. It was while making shoes that he met a girl in the village who was looking after her invalid, widowed father. A visit to the house to measure the old man up for a new pair of shoes led to a courtship which resulted in marriage. They began their life together in her father's house and lost no time in starting a family of their own. Their first son, my father, was born as the years of the nineteenth century slipped away.

My father's name was Bernhard and though under the law he was considered to be Dutch, he barely gave this any thought as he grew up and went to school in the village where he was born. He was treated like everyone else, spoke German with the same accent as everyone else and was indistinguishable from all the other boys of his generation. It was only when rumours of war began to circulate in 1913 that he remembered that he was not the same. He paid little heed at first and like most fourteen-year-old boys, was far more interested in girls and sport than politics, but the rumours would not go away. The newspapers were full of stories about an impending conflict and it was widely forecast that conscription would be introduced at any time.

My father was still too young for military service, but he knew that if the call did come, he would not be required to pull on the field-grey uniform of the Imperial German Army. Months of increasing tension passed before the shots fired by Gavrilo Princip in Sarajevo finally caused the tectonic plates of imperial and military alliances to shudder into each other. Everyone was of the opinion that it would be over by Christmas, but no-one remembered to specify which Christmas. The initial euphoria which greeted the declaration of war and the swift invasion of Belgium soon evaporated in the marshes of the Marne and the Yser. Mothers and wives began to realise that their husbands and sons might not be coming home by the year's end after all. They would soon realise that they might not be coming home at all.

On his seventeenth birthday, when the war had been grinding on for more than two years, my father at last received his call-up papers stating that the King of the Netherlands required his services. He slipped away from Ostinghausen one night and made his way over the border into neutral Holland with his father's blessing and his mother's sighs of relief. He spent the remainder of the war guarding an airfield near Eindhoven, never firing a shot in anger nor having to shelter from the relentless pounding of artillery shells. His days were filled not with death and terror, but with the tedious routine of drill and guard duties. He would not return home until the end of the war, but as far as my grandparents were concerned, it was a negligible price to pay for the knowledge that he was out of harm's way. Enquiring neighbours were told merely that he was 'away in the Army' and that God willing, they hoped to see him once again when it was all over.

At the end of the war, many of those who had survived vowed that such a terrible thing should never be allowed to happen again, but many felt betrayed by their leaders. What had been won with blood and steel had been lost by a traitorous stroke of the pen. What had not been yielded in the mud-filled trenches of the battlefield was now given away in the mirrored halls of royal palaces. As the Kaiser journeyed into exile in Holland he passed my father travelling in the opposite direction, returning in the night just as he had left. When he at last made it back to the family home in Ostinghausen, he went directly into the garden and burnt his uniform.

3

The War Hero

The millions who had been in uniform returned home to become the millions of unemployed. Reward for years of service and sacrifice was a place in the queue at the thousands of soup kitchens that sprang up overnight in towns and cities across the land. The artist who had left behind his Vienna days five years earlier returned from the front a war hero, but defeat and betrayal left a bitter taste in his mouth which not even his gleaming Iron Cross could diminish. Along with many others he believed that his adopted country had been stabbed in the back; the supporting facts were hazy, but the myth grew strong and who needed to digest the truth when the myth was so much easier to believe?

Confusion reigned. While the victorious allies divided the spoils, those they had defeated argued among themselves and searched for someone to blame. Men who had fought bravely and with honour blamed the November criminals who signed the surrender which had brought dishonour upon the whole nation. Marginal political parties and movements that had acted democratically before the war, now saw an opportunity to seize power by other means. The old certainties had gone, the Kaiser had fled, the old guard of the Army allowed the politicians to take the blame for their own actions and the Bolsheviks, egged on by Lenin, began to agitate for change.

The government in Berlin found itself with little support and activists in the regions, disillusioned with a central government unresponsive to the people's needs, talked of a break-up. Better to have an independent regional government of one's choosing rather than some remote discredited cabal in the capital. In Munich the socialists had acted first, proclaiming a Bavarian 'Peoples' State' after marching through the city with a few hundred men and taking over parliament without a shot being fired. When their leader was assassinated three months later, the more radical of his followers proclaimed a soviet republic.

The war hero looked upon this turn of events with increasing horror. He knew that the nation's real enemies were not to be found in London and Paris, but in the towns and cities across Germany. Here, there were far more dangerous enemies, enemies who could not be distinguished by any uniform, enemies who hid in the shadows waiting to stab people in the back. Had he not fought bravely for the past four years? Had he not been almost blinded with gas, so badly burned that his eyes became glowing coals so that even now he felt the pain? Had he not been prepared to give his life for the Fatherland, for the ideal of one strong nation?

When he first learned of the surrender while in the sanatorium, he had been devastated. As soon as he had been able to leave, he had journeyed back to the place where his military adventure had begun, drawn inexorably to the city where he had arrived full of hope five years earlier. He had survived the horrors of the trenches to see a city full of workers' councils and soviets, where Bolsheviks and communists flexed their muscles while the spineless democrats in Berlin did nothing. The nation was fragmenting before his eyes and in his pain and fury he resolved to devote all of his energies to prevent it happening. He silently vowed that he would do everything possible to ensure that the criminals responsible for the infamy of November 11th would be overthrown and punished for their treachery.

Yet what could he do? Citizens were more concerned with where their next meal was coming from rather than with political agendas. He knew that the only people who could change things were people with power and he knew that he had none. A lowly corporal, no matter how highly decorated, was still a lowly corporal. Those with influence were the leaders of political parties or the captains of local militias. He was weak and they were strong and if he tried to act alone they would crush him.

Agonising over his impotence, he frequented the bier-kellers where politics were fiercely debated by the multitude of fringe parties, splinter factions and pressure groups that sprang up and disappeared virtually overnight. Night after night he would listen as various speakers decried the state of the nation and declared their certain remedies to cure all its ills. Every crank in the city had a recipe for salvation which they were prepared to share with anyone who frequented these raucous and often violent gatherings in the city's hostelries. Rarely did his nocturnal wanderings assuage the pent-up feelings of frustration and anger. The countless speakers had no remedies at all, they sought power for the sake of power, revolution for the sake of revolution, they were proud and they were vain and they did not understand the problem.

His despair and melancholy grew in equal measure until the night he heard Drexler talk. At last he listened to a speech that struck a chord and when he read the grubby pamphlet the locksmith had thrust into his hands afterwards, he knew. These were the same truths which were in his own mind. After listening to the cacophony of a thousand confused and competing voices, here at last was a voice he recognised. Here at last was someone who made sense of the confusion, someone with a message that rang out loud and clear, a message which cut to the very heart of the matter. The only problem was that the author of the pamphlet seemed to be as powerless as he himself.

The small run-down tavern in the Herrenstrasse was a far cry from the immense, crowded halls of the Hofbrauhaus and the Burgerbierkeller, but this was the appointed place for his meeting with the locksmith and the small band of confidants who comprised his 'party'. Even among the myriad political factions of the city, it was so small and ill-organised that it was almost laughable. The war hero recognised this as a severe problem, but no matter how great his passion, a man such as he with a poor education and a lack of powerful friends was not able to stand alone. Events were continuing apace, he could no longer drift while they overtook him. If he was ever to have a chance of making a difference it would have to be now and so it was with this group of poorly educated men in the dimly lit back room of a small inn that the war hero and former artist threw in his lot.

4

My mother was born Wilhemina Theele in Dortmund, Westphalia and before she married my father, she was a housekeeper for the Weismanns, an elderly couple who lived in the smart suburb of Bad Sassendorf near Soest. Mr Weismann was a dentist and although they had no children, they lived in a large house that was his wife's pride and joy. Perhaps it was the absence of children that made Mrs Weismann so house-proud for she was fastidious in every respect and my mother was employed to clean and cook and generally keep the place in the pristine condition desired by her employer.

During the week, my mother would live in the house, returning home only on Saturday afternoons in order to spend that evening and Sunday with her parents. It was Mrs Weismann's custom to pay her wages just before she left and after clearing away Saturday lunch. The old lady had a soft spot for my mother who had been with them for the past three years and was as scrupulously neat and tidy as they were. She would count out the bundles of notes, each one of them tied with a small red ribbon and each week there would be an additional bundle. The time had gone when people bothered to count the notes individually or even bothered to check that each of the neatly wrapped bundles actually contained the number of notes scribbled on the uppermost note.

A few years earlier, the twelve bundles that Mrs Weissmann gave her would have represented a considerable fortune which would allow a life of utter luxury, but now it was barely enough to buy a few essentials and perhaps, if she was lucky, a few items for her forthcoming wedding. My mother and father had met a year earlier at a dance in Soest and had seen each other regularly since then. They became engaged when she discovered that she was pregnant; doubtless they would have married in any case, but the fact of it hastened the announcement. She had started to save what little she could for the wedding, but had soon realised that saving was pointless; the fifty marks she had managed to accumulate over the past six months wouldn't now even buy a loaf of bread and so, like everyone else, she spent her wages as soon as she was paid.

On Saturday afternoons my father would wait for her outside the big house. Waving Mrs Weissmann farewell, my mother would skip down the steps and embrace my father before he took her heavy bag and they walked off arm in arm towards the centre of the town. At each shop they would stop to see if there was anything that they might be able to buy. They would often search in vain for items that they needed and if there was nothing that they needed themselves then perhaps there might be something they could buy which could be exchanged later for something they did need.

People had begun to visit the shops with bags and cases full of bank notes, some even used wheelbarrows when the bundles became too heavy. People emptied their bank accounts and used the money to buy anything they could lay their hands on; even if it was of no use to themselves, it might be bartered for other goods at a later date. This meant that shops held virtually no stocks, usually selling their entire inventories within hours of opening their doors; which in turn pushed prices up still further. Shopkeepers had even abandoned the practice of putting a price on their wares as they would change them several times a day.

Queues would form outside the butchers and bakers before they opened in the morning because those who left it until midday or later would probably have to pay double or triple the morning price, or more likely find that the shelves were completely bare. The wheelbarrows and suitcases used to carry money to the shops were also used to transport goods back to the house where items would be stored in readiness for future transactions. People re-arranged their furniture in order to accommodate the sheer quantity of goods they had purchased. In the centre of towns, queues would form spontaneously on the rumour that something might be in stock and on some occasions people who had merely stopped to chat outside a shop would find a queue of anxious shoppers forming behind them.

The young couple managed to buy a few items that they managed to find on the otherwise bare shelves before walking back to her parents' house. It had become a Saturday routine for the couple to meet, go into town and then return to the Theele's house where the soon-to-be-married couple would share a meal with the rest of the family. My father would always bring some little gift, usually food, perhaps some cured ham or a cabbage, for his future mother-in-law. This was not considered in any way to be an insult as it might have been in former times; shortages of everything, especially food, removed any sense of shame and made everyone grateful for such small gifts.

My father's family was not a wealthy one, but some years earlier, before the war, old Johannes, my paternal grandfather had bought a small plot of land behind his house from a local farmer and had turned it into a vegetable garden. It had been more of a hobby rather than a means of supplementing the family income at the time, but it had now become necessary for survival, the difference between living and merely existing. They usually had all the vegetables they needed and were even able to trade their surplus for items that they could not produce themselves; a goat provided milk and cheese and he had recently acquired a pig which would feed on the scraps.

Everyone agreed that things had not been this bad even during the war. There had been shortages of course and even rationing of some things, but at least money still had a value. It hadn't been necessary to take a wheelbarrow full of notes to complete even the most modest of transactions; there had been no need to buy things merely because they were available rather than because they were required. The entire country was working on the basis of a barter economy the like of which had not been seen for more than a thousand years. A couple of eggs bought a pair of boots, a pound of butter bought a new coat. Lead was torn from the roofs of buildings and handles torn from doors to be used as payment, anything instead of the worthless bundles of banknotes that the government kept printing.

It was all the fault of the war. In 1918 the victorious allies had not only insisted on the abdication of the Kaiser, the cessation of Alsace-Lorraine and Schleswig, the granting of a sea corridor to the Poles, but more critically the reparation of five billion dollars in gold marks. The effect of this, though inevitable, was not immediate. The reparations proved impossible to pay and the mark began to fall inexorably against other currencies, slowly at first, but rapidly gaining in pace. By 1921 it took seventy-five marks to buy one dollar, the following year it was four hundred and by the beginning of 1922 it was more than seven thousand.

The government begged for a moratorium, asking for time in which they would be able to make the reparations in full, but the French would not hear of it and so the government was forced to default. The French occupied the Ruhr, the industrial heart of the country, the occupation in turn triggered a general strike, completely strangling the economy and causing the mark to fall even more catastrophically. By January 1923 it took 18,000 marks to buy one dollar, by the middle of the year it took 160,000 and by August one million. The lunacy continued apace and by November it took four billion marks to buy one dollar, and thereafter people lost count and lost hope. Salaries were worthless and people's life savings were wiped out; it was as if a monumental fraud had been perpetrated upon everyone in the land.

It was in these less than ideal times that my mother and father embarked upon their matrimonial life.

5

The Philosopher

The prisoner's visitor picked up a pen as he sat at the desk placed against the whitewashed stone wall of the cell. The prisoner had been banished there for his part in a rebellion against the government and it was here that he began dictating the first words of his book to his faithful friend. He stood at the small window, his eyes shining with zeal as he expounded his theory which outlined his four and a half years of struggle against lies, stupidity and cowardice. There were parts of his life he chose not to mention; he remained silent about his family and those early years when he had vainly tramped the streets of Vienna looking for artistic acceptance. The matters upon which he was not silent were his ambition, his beliefs and the nature of the nation that he wished to create.

There was no lack of candour or any failure to clearly outline his intentions. The agenda was not hidden, it was clearly stated. Much later, foreign leaders and diplomats would claim surprise and astonishment at the actions that he laid down clearly and precisely in these prison visits. He spoke of the need to restore the nation to its former glory, the need to allow for the expansion of its people, the need to remove the nonsensical cacophony of democracy and particularly he spoke of the need to remove the spineless government that had betrayed the people it purported to represent. Strong nations required strong leadership, leaders who would not be deflected from their unflinching long-term purpose by the passing whims of popular sentiment.

A strong nation also had to be a pure one, free from the ethnic and cultural divides which troubled other lands, a nation which would never permit itself to be governed or influenced by inferior peoples. Had he not seen this with his own eyes as he walked the streets of Vienna? A once great empire had allowed itself to become diluted and debased, an empire that remained an empire in name only, a large apple that had rotted from within. This rot had been allowed by weak leaders blind to the manoeuvrings of socialists and Bolsheviks, political movements originated and engineered by inferior peoples whose overriding aim was to bring down their superiors.

It was this superior people who had raised mankind to its current state of mastery over the other beings of the earth, this people from whom the divine spark of invention and culture had sprung forth to illuminate the darkness of the world. The Aryan alone was the highest form of human evolution and without the Aryan, the world would descend into the chaos from which it sprang. It was both the right and the duty of the Aryan to protect and preserve his species for the greater good of mankind and this could only be possible by exercising mastery over the lesser races. These lesser races had their purposes; after all, the Aryan was only able to accomplish so much and had only become supreme by trampling on those beneath. It was the natural order of things. Just as in the animal world, the fittest survived at the expense of the weak, so it must be in human society. The strong were only strong because of the weak.

Only by retaining this mastery would culture be preserved and increased.

If the Aryan gave up the purity of his blood, he would become submerged in a weak racial mixture and lose his cultural creativeness; this was the reason that so many old cultures died out. Cities became states and in turn states became empires, adding territories and dominions populated by less advanced peoples who were allowed to become citizens of the empire. Thereafter, they gradually and stealthily mixed their blood with that of their conquerors until they achieved that objective which they had not been able to achieve in war, namely the downfall of the superior culture. These ancient cultures did not disappear through lost wars, they disappeared because they allowed themselves to become contaminated and infected by lesser strains.

These thoughts brought our philosopher to the meaning of the state. What was the state, but a collection of individuals? For a nation to function efficiently, each of its citizens must also function efficiently; if the nation was to be strong, the people must also be strong. Thus he expounded his view of life through seven hundred and eighty-two pages, devoting many of the pages to the way in which individuals in the new state would be required to conduct themselves. Only the healthy must beget children, indeed it would be their duty to do so; the weaker, contaminated strains would be allowed to die out. It would be considered reprehensible, a crime even, to bring anything but pure, healthy children into the world. Marriage must be raised into a consecrated institution within which perfect images of the Lord may be produced.

And so, throughout the months of imprisonment within the thick, stone walls of his cell, the philosopher committed his thoughts to paper. For all his vision, the philosopher was also a practical man, he knew that his dreams would never become reality merely through the publication of a book, no matter how brilliant. The pen may be mightier than the sword, but he knew that the time was near when he would have to put down the pen and take up the sword.

6

When women got married in those days there was rarely any question of them continuing to work. The place for a wife was in the kitchen and in the bedroom. In the former, they would clean, cook the food and generally look after their husbands and in the latter, God willing, eventually fill that home with children. And so my mother left the employ of the Weismanns three days before her wedding. Mrs Weismann paid her final week's wages, carefully adding another two be-ribboned bundles of marks to the number she had received the previous week.

The old lady's eyes were moist as she pressed a small box into my mother's hand and kissed her on the cheek. After receiving a gentle admonishment not to open the box until her wedding day and not to forget her and to come and take tea occasionally, my mother bade her a fond farewell, skipped down the steps of the Weismanns' house and into the arms of my waiting father. On her wedding night my mother opened the small box given to her by Mrs Weismann; it contained a small silver pendant in the shape of a star which she put around her neck.

Until they found a place of their own, they moved in with my grandfather, Johannes. It wasn't a large house, but there was enough room for the two newlyweds and the child that would arrive in a few months' time. A little girl was born late that year, they called her Anna and they doted upon her. She was a sickly child, however, and my mother constantly nursed her through a succession of illnesses. She found time to become pregnant once again, but when she was six months into her second pregnancy, little Anna died when just nine months old. My mother grieved over her loss and worried and fretted that the baby still inside her womb might also be as cruelly taken away from her as her first born.

Three months later, my elder brother was born strong and healthy. The demands of a new baby prevented my mother dwelling too long upon her loss. They named him Johannes after his grandfather, but the younger Johannes would always be known as Hans. Though the birth of their first son brought my parents great joy, following so closely upon their earlier loss, times were becoming increasingly hard. The great machines of industry and commerce remained at a standstill, ground to a halt by a lack of the oil that was a convertible currency. Bands of jobless men roamed the land looking for work or food and many had no qualms about taking what they could not obtain legally. Hunger drove honest men to steal, men with medals for valour who had survived the trenches of the Somme and Verdun were reduced to begging and petty crime. The government had no answer to the chaos which had been unleashed and instead of grasping the economic nettle, took the expedient route of printing ever more banknotes in ever more exotic denominations.

Amid protests, strikes and rallies, political parties formed and dissolved overnight as the forces of left, right and centre sought to make political capital of the government's ineptitude. The parties squabbled and as the situation grew worse the voices became increasingly louder and increasingly radical. Serious problems, it seemed, required radical solutions. The communists claimed to have all the answers and many men, driven by hunger and despair, flocked to their rallies, but there were also a number of other 'workers' parties, each with their own ideas of how the situation could be retrieved.

My father had little time for politicians, considering them all to be scoundrels regardless of their political stripe. Difficult though things were, my father still counted himself among the lucky ones. People always needed new shoes or at the very least had to have their old ones repaired and for payment they would bring not money, but instead a rabbit, a cabbage, a bag of potatoes or perhaps an article of clothing. We fared better than many, the plot of land behind the house continued to provide food which could either be eaten or used as payment for other commodities which we could not grow ourselves. Ownership of such a plot was not entirely without its problems for, after a few thefts during the night, my father and grandfather took turns to keep watch through the hours of darkness and acquired a large and ferocious Alsatian dog.

I was born two years after my elder brother and one year after that my mother gave birth to my younger brother, Bernhard. There were now three boys in the family and we were running out of space at my grandfather's house. When my mother again became pregnant eighteen months after Bernhard was born, it was no longer possible for us to remain there. My father couldn't afford to buy a house and there were none available to rent at the time. It was then that my father managed to find a job with Beckmann's distillery in the small village of Beckum some five miles away. It was a small distillery and the money wasn't a great improvement, but more importantly the job came with a house and for this reason my father decided to give up shoemaking. Moving away from the house in which you had been born and in which you have spent the first years of life is a big event for a young boy and it is one of my earliest memories. I can clearly remember the day we moved, one of my enduring images being that of my mother sitting in a carriage, little Bernhard sitting on her lap while she held aloft an ornate birdcage containing Willi, our yellow canary.

Our new house was not particularly large, but even so, we had far more space than we had ever had in my grandfather's house. When we arrived, Hans, Bernhard and I raced excitedly around the house looking in all the rooms, inspecting our new bedrooms. I can remember that when we were upstairs, we heard an almighty roar, so loud that it seemed that the house itself shook. We ran down to our mother in fright, but she laughed and pointed through the window where an express train was hurtling past on the main railway line that ran at the bottom of the garden. What joy! I had never even seen a train before, let alone been this close. I ran outside, disappointed to see the last carriage disappear down the line, but I didn't have to wait very long before the next train came hurtling along in the opposite direction. I stood and marvelled at the clouds of steam belching from the locomotive and the clanking of the iron wheels upon the track. The sights and sounds of the railway would become an integral part of my childhood.

Despite the hardship of the times, my parents were happy; they now had three sons and shortly after we moved into our new house my little sister Wilhelmina was born.

7

It was a two-mile walk from my house by the railway line to the small redbrick schoolhouse that stood among open fields at the edge of the village. When I was six years old, my mother kissed me goodbye, instructed me to take my brother's hand and sent us off through the village, to begin my first day at school. I had been eagerly looking forward to this day for a long time and now at last I would be able to join in all the things which Hans had told me about every day when he came home. Hans had been attending school for more than a year and he was enormously proud to show me off to his friends on that first day of term as we walked through the schoolyard and into the classroom.

Like most village schools, the school in Beckum had only one teacher, Herr Schonemann, who had taught there since 1916 when he had been invalided out of the army with shrapnel wounds in his legs. After he had been dragged screaming from the shell hole, he was told that his wounds were so severe that it would probably mean amputation, but miraculously gangrene had not set in and his legs were saved. They remained scarred and twisted however and fifteen years later still caused him a great deal of pain, particularly during the cold of winter when the metal splinters that could not be removed ground pitilessly against muscle and sinew.

The boys and girls often made fun of his strange and

awkward gait and I'm sure he knew that some of the boys mimicked his walk as he shuffled across the schoolyard, but he pretended not to notice. Old and twisted though his body was, he could remember when he was their age and that anyone considered to be in some way out of the ordinary was fair game for tricks and mimicry. He knew that such young innocents, with healthy bodies so full of life, could not possibly know or understand the pain and horrors he had experienced. Despite his deformity and pain, Herr Schonemann was a kindly man who taught the rudiments of education to the village boys and girls that he knew would leave school at fourteen without any significant attainments other than a tolerable ability to read and write and with only the most basic knowledge of arithmetic, geography and science.

I wasn't the brightest in his class, but I was far from being the dullest. I was very small for my age and would have been picked upon had it not been for Hans who was one of the tallest boys in the school and who assumed the role of my protector, despite the fact that when we were at home we would fight and squabble in the way that brothers do. My father had instilled in us the idea that we were to look after each other and that no matter what happened at home, in the outside world, the family always came first. Hans, however, could not always be around to protect me and so I had to develop my own defences, namely an ability to run very fast, to think quickly on my feet and a finely tuned instinct for self-preservation which was to stand me in good stead in later years.

My younger brother Bernie started school a year after me; he was doubly fortunate to have both Hans and me to guard him against the attentions of any school bully, particularly the unruly Muller boys who were the scourge of pupils and teacher alike. Bernie was a typical younger child in a family, mischievous, funny and completely irresponsible; but for all his failings it was impossible not to love him and although my parents treated us all very fairly, my mother's eyes always seemed to have a particular twinkle when she looked at Bernie.

A few months after Bernie started at the school, I remember a winter day at the end of January. Snow had been falling steadily all morning and by the early afternoon it had begun to pile up outside; with no sign of it abating, Herr Schonemann decided to close school early in order that everyone could get safely home. Naturally everyone was thrilled at getting out of school early, but we were in no hurry to reach our homes and took advantage of the enchanting, white world into which the village had been transformed. Our journey was frequently interrupted in order to engage in snowball fights along the way, taking great pleasure in ambushing the other boys and girls.

When Hans, Bernie and I eventually did get home some two hours after Herr Schonemann had let us out of school, we bounded into the kitchen bragging of our prowess at snowballing and building snowmen, but mother hushed us to be quiet and pointed to our little sister who lay sleeping near the fire. Wilhelmina, who by now was three years old, had been ill again; it seemed to me as though she was always ill and mother looked pale and drawn after a succession of sleep-interrupted nights. The three of us ravenously helped ourselves to some slices of the black loaf that was usually left on the kitchen table before returning outside once more to play in the snow.

It was almost dark when my father came home from Beckmanns, which was normally the sign that dinner would soon be on the table, but when Hans and I went back into the house, we found the kitchen table bare and, more strangely, our parents in the sitting room listening intently to the radio. My father used to listen to the radio in the evening, but never when he came in from work. I knew instinctively that something important must have happened, but couldn't quite understand what it was all about except that the voice mentioned something about a new government. More concerned with my empty stomach than with any news on the radio, I returned to the kitchen and while my parents were still in the sitting room, cut myself a slice from a large sausage. When my mother eventually re-appeared a few minutes later she looked pale and distracted and instead of the expected scolding for helping myself to the sausage, I received a kiss on the forehead.

We always sat down as a family to the evening meal at the scrubbed oak table that stood in the middle of the kitchen. Normally there would be lively conversation as we ate, usually revolving around what we three boys had been up to at school and my mother, despite laughing at the tales of our antics, was always concerned that we had behaved ourselves. She was always insistent that we should not be disruptive in school for she knew that Herr Schonemann had enough difficulties in his life without us making them any worse. This particular evening, however, my parents were strangely subdued, they ate in silence. They did not ask us about school or even comment upon the wintry weather that had been the cause of the school's early closure. The atmosphere in the kitchen seemed to be just as chilly as the weather and we three boys instinctively ate our meal as quickly as possible, exchanging barely a word, and I can remember going to bed later that evening with a strange sense of foreboding.

8

The Leader

The last and final stage of the metamorphosis was complete. The artist had first become a warrior, then a philosopher and finally he had become a Leader. No longer would there be a struggle for his voice to be heard, no longer would he have to accept the sneers of those who thought him inferior, the slights of people who thought him a preposterous upstart corporal. Now those same people would be required to seek *his* indulgence, the important men in the land would flatter and dissemble in *his* presence. The entire population would tremble at *his* name and many would curse the day they snubbed and derided him.

The Leader was not content to sit back into the torpor of someone who has achieved his ambition of power. Power was fine, good even, but it was not an end in itself. Now that he had thrown out the craven, traitorous, vacillating politicians who had presided over decades of decline and humiliation, he would act. He would move decisively to replace chaos with order, disarray with unity; he would impose his iron discipline and above all he would inspire his people to achieve greatness. He did not mind that the majority of his people had opposed him, they would soon see the error of their ways and they would come to recognise his qualities, as the nation was reborn in his image.

Like all leaders without a true mandate from the people, he was acutely conscious of the machinations and subterfuges that had brought him to the pinnacle of power and he knew what was required to maintain his still tenuous grip. That he had many enemies he had no doubt; they would be dealt with in due course, but a man's most dangerous enemies are often those who call themselves friends and who lie close at hand. Enemies whose intimate jealousies and rivalries posed a far more urgent threat than any stated political adversary, and it was these that had to be dealt with first of all.

Together with the very few men that he trusted, he set in motion an apparatus that would eradicate any lingering threat to his position. As he had written prophetically some years earlier, he had proved himself to be the natural leader, a man who had overcome almost insurmountable obstacles to rescue his people. It was his divine mission to lead the people out of chaos into a stronger, brighter future. The nation needed him at the helm, a strong leader who would never be deflected from his purpose, a leader who would steadfastly lead his people on to achieve things beyond their imagination. To remain at the pinnacle of this new order was not merely a sense of self-preservation, it was his solemn duty to the people and he would annihilate anything and anyone who stood in his way.

9

Things were definitely getting better, even my parents said so and they normally never had a good word to say about the Leader and the people who were now running the country. No longer were bands of jobless men roaming the country, stealing from hen houses and digging up vegetable plots in the dead of night. Paper money had a value once again and people, even those who had seen their life savings wiped out a few years earlier, once more began to trust the banks and open savings accounts. Everyone always said that the trains had began to run on time, although I had never been on one. The nearest I ever came to them was as they thundered by on the line at the bottom of the garden. It certainly seemed to be true that most people had a job if they wanted one and no-one had to go to school without a pair of shoes on their feet. It seemed that a miracle had occurred and despite the misgivings of some, everyone seemed pleased with the way that things had turned out.

I would sometimes listen to my parents discuss such weighty matters, but I confess that I didn't understand most of it. I remember we used to laugh in disbelief as my father told us stories of the bad old days, not so many years earlier, when it had taken suitcases full of money to buy just a loaf of bread, and of how some men carried a revolver on pay day. It may have been true that things had improved for the country as a whole, but I knew for certain that things had got a lot better for my brothers and me. Our teacher, old Herr Schonemann had retired and been replaced by a much younger man who looked as though he had not long been out of school himself. He was tall and handsome, vital and athletic - everything old Herr Schonemann had not been. Suddenly we had activities, lots of activities, and like any ten-year-old with energy to burn, I couldn't get enough of them. We spent less time in the classroom in order to concentrate on football matches, athletics tournaments, wrestling competitions, camping trips, hikes and parades. I particularly remember the parades; we would march proudly from the school and through the village behind our new teacher with scarlet banners fluttering in the breeze. The young teacher seemed more like one of us than a teacher; sometimes he even joined in our football matches and was able to outrun any of the boys over the distance of a mile.

The fact that he wore a scarlet armband with an odd shaped, crooked cross upon it and came from a different part of the country where they spoke with a strange accent, didn't make any difference to us. He was always eager to tell us about the glorious new chapter that was unfolding in our lives and how we were an important part of this new life. We children were to be the inheritors of this earthly paradise to which the Leader would inevitably take us. I wanted to join in everything and in order not to miss out on all the fun, on my tenth birthday, along with all the other boys my age, I made the following oath:

In the presence of this blood banner, which represents our Leader, I swear to devote all my energies and my strength to the saviour of our country. I am willing and ready to give up my life for him, so help me God.

Now we were proud new members of *The Youth.* but

none of the boys who stood in the classroom that day could possibly have suspected that in the years to come, the Leader would fully expect us to honour our oath in the most literal sense. Some boys wore the special uniforms and though my mother always promised that she would get one for Hans and me, somehow she never got round to it. Perhaps the reason was because money was tight now that there was another baby in the house, for she had given birth to another boy that summer.

Whatever the reason, it didn't bother us greatly, uniform or no uniform we threw ourselves into everything and no-one seemed to mind that we dressed in the same old clothes in which we went to school. No-one was left out of the activities, no-one excluded for any reason and everyone was made to feel an important and necessary part of the team. The emphasis was always upon teamwork and healthy outdoor activities and nothing sounded sweeter to the ears of a ten-year-old than to hear, as we often did, that afternoon lessons were cancelled so that we could build a rope bridge over a nearby stream or take a ten mile hike through the forest at the end of which would be food and a singsong around a blazing bonfire.

I remember that one day the teacher brought some photographs into the class. The photographs were of a huge building site that was being prepared for a stadium to welcome the outstanding athletes from around the world. Germany had been chosen first from among all the nations of the world to host this competition and the teacher told us that everyone would come and marvel at our re-born country. We were encouraged to train diligently at sport for although we were too young to compete in these games, they were sure to be such a great success that they would probably be held in our country for evermore. We might have the opportunity to compete for medals in future games and it was the least we could do to repay the Leader for all that he had done for us.

Hans, Bernie and I would return home from school every day, full of excitement and chattering enthusiastically about what we had done and what the teacher had told us. Times were so exciting that we had completely forgotten about kindly old Mr Schonemann and his funny twisted gait; we were full of admiration for his young replacement who seemed almost to be one of us and who constantly kept us enthralled with stories about all the wonderful things that were happening in our country. Although he kept a strict discipline in the classroom, it was rare for any of the boys to misbehave, as we would be letting our Leader down and none of us wanted to do that.

My baby brother was named Heinz and there were now five children in the house, but I was so busy enjoying myself at school and in the Youth that the arrival of my new brother barely touched my existence.

10

Even after we had moved from my grandfather's house to our new house in Beckum, my mother had still kept in touch with her former employers, the Weismanns, who lived five miles away in Bad Sassendorf. The Weismanns never had any children and I think that's why they liked my mother so much, treating her in some respects like the daughter they never had. She would often visit them on Sunday afternoons and occasionally she would take me or one of my brothers with her. I remember that their house stood in a tree-lined road in the best part of town and it was grander than any other that I had ever been in. The stout double doors of the front entrance opened onto a hall that had a beautiful wooden floor; the hall itself was bigger than any of the rooms in our house and the walls were decorated with silk wallpaper upon which hung magnificent paintings. I particularly remember the Iron Cross which Herr Weismann had earned as a lieutenant at Verdun and which was proudly displayed in a small case on the mantle.

My mother had worked for them for three years before she married, living there during the week, and she had come to think of it as a second home. One Sunday afternoon, not very long after my eleventh birthday, I was out in the garden at the back of the house when my mother called me. I had been given some jobs to do while my father had taken Bernie and Wilhelmina to my grandfather's house. Hans had gone to visit a friend so apart from baby Heinz, my mother and I we were the only ones at home. I found her in the kitchen busily filling a wicker basket with food. I watched intently as she placed a loaf of bread, some slices of ham and a jar of pickled gherkins in the basket before covering them with a cloth. She told me to put on my coat, as I was to accompany her to Bad Sassendorf.

My mother carried my baby brother while I carried the heavy basket for three miles to the village of Benninghausen where we caught a tram to the Weismanns' house. I wondered why we were bringing food to the Weismanns, as they were far richer than we were and it was usually my mother who left their house weighed down with gifts. We went up the steps and rang the bell, but it was several minutes before the door opened and Frau Weismann appeared. She smiled at the sight of my mother and glancing nervously down the road, ushered us in. It had been some time since I had been to the big house, but I was surprised at the change in the appearance of Frau Weismann who didn't appear to be her normal immaculate self; she was still smartly dressed, but she seemed to have aged, the lines on her face had deepened, her eyes were surrounded with dark rings and a few wisps of grey hair had escaped from the tight bun she normally wore and hung loosely around her ears.

I was left alone in the drawing room while my mother took Heinz and went with Frau Weismann into the kitchen with the heavy basket that I had carried all the way from home. The house seemed strangely bare in comparison to my previous visits; many of the paintings had disappeared, the wallpaper leaving a telltale pattern of different faded colours. I noticed too that the magnificent silver seven-headed candelabra, which had always fascinated me and which used to stand on the finely carved oak dresser, had also disappeared.

I wandered out into the hall where I stopped, straining to hear the hushed conversation of my mother and Frau Weismann in the kitchen. I moved closer to the closed kitchen door to try and hear what was being said and overheard Frau Weismann mention something about them moving away. I moved quickly away when I heard the door handle turn and hurried back into the drawing room and a few moments later my mother and Frau Weismann came in. Mrs Weismann gave me a hug and I could see that both my mother and the old lady had tears in their eyes when we left, but when I asked her why she was upset, my mother she just shook her head and spoke not one word during the entire journey home. I didn't pursue the matter further for I could she was biting her lip and trying desperately to hold back further tears.

That night after I had gone to bed, I was woken by the sound of raised voices from the next room. I could hear my parents in their bedroom, my mother was crying and my father was shouting, something he rarely did in the house. I knew that something was seriously wrong so I crept out of bed and into the hall to listen outside the door. I heard him say something about her being irresponsible and that it was dangerous to go and see the Weismanns and that even if she felt that she had to go then she certainly should not have taken Heinz and me with her. He told her that anyone might have seen her going in or coming out of the house and that she was never to go there again. I crept back into my bedroom in case I was discovered eavesdropping and myself become the object of my father's fury. I couldn't understand why my father was so upset at such an innocent visit and lay awake for some time listening to my mother sobbing before I eventually drifted off to sleep.

I didn't give the incident much further thought until some weeks later in school. The teacher told us about a certain type of people who were living among us who were evil and were being sent away to live in another country so that they wouldn't be able to damage the vital work being done by the Leader in re-building the country. He said that although they didn't look much different to anyone else, they were little more than parasites and that everyone would be better off without them. He said that we were lucky where we lived in Beckum because there were none in the village and not too many of them at all in our part of the country, but in some of the bigger towns and cities there were large numbers of these evil, dangerous people. Thanks to the foresight of our Leader in identifying this menace, matters were in hand to prevent this threat to our very survival.

I mentioned this to my parents one evening as we ate our evening meal and was surprised that they just looked at one another and said barely a word. I told them what the teacher had said about these people, that these enemies who lived among us, looked like us and even talked like us might murder us in our beds. I thought they might have been shocked or frightened by this revelation, but although they listened politely, they didn't seem unduly concerned and I was surprised that they didn't seem to take this news very seriously. Perhaps my teacher had been right, not too many of these people lived in our part of the country so there was little need to worry, but the poor people who lived in the cities must have been very lucky to survive such a deadly threat.

It was many months later that I learned that Weismanns

had left their lovely house in bad Sassendorf and gone away. A neighbour told my mother one day that she had seen them together with some other families being taken to the railway station, carrying their possessions in suitcases. It was only then that I discovered that the Weismanns were some of these wicked people they called Jews and that they were our enemies. I was confused. If these people were enemies then why had my mother been helping them and why had Frau Weismann always been so kind to us? It was hard to believe that such a kindly old lady and her husband, who had fought for Germany during the Great War and had been decorated with the Iron Cross, were in fact our enemies.

Shocked and disturbed, I never again mentioned the subject to my parents and certainly not to my teacher who was constantly telling us in class that we had to beware of anyone who might sabotage the collective national purpose. I was frightened that if anyone found out about the Weismanns and us we might also be considered traitors and punished for our transgressions.

11

Karl Muller was no stranger to the police. He had spent many nights in the cells at Lippstadt police station and on one occasion had been jailed for three months in Soest prison. He was a stocky, bull of a man standing five feet eight inches high. He walked with a slight limp, the result of childhood polio, but he was nevertheless a powerful man. Broad in the shoulder, he had over the years acquired a significant girth as a result of spending so many hours drinking beer in Brandt's, the village bar whose proper name was the Gasthof zur Post, but everyone referred to it after the name of the owner Peter Brandt. As well as his awesome physique, Karl Muller also had a fearsome reputation for violence, particularly when in drink and it was a brave man who would pick an argument with him when he was in that condition. My father told me that he had once seen him simultaneously lift two men off the floor before hurling them against the wall.

The Mullers had three sons and they were exactly like their father both in appearance and temperament and they had been causing trouble at the village school from the day they started. They had run completely wild when old Mr Schonemann was the teacher and it was only when he had been replaced that they were brought under some semblance of control. Needless to say, most of the people in the village gave the Mullers a wide berth. They lived at a small farm at the edge of the village where three ferocious dogs ran loose in the yard of the ramshackle house. Everyone believed the dogs were there to frighten off the police rather than any potential intruders. When Karl wasn't working his small parcel of land he would be drinking or just as likely engaged in some petty criminal activity. He would also earn a bit of legitimate money by performing odd jobs around the neighbourhood which required a strong pair of hands, though many claimed that their valuables had a habit of leaving the house at the same time that he did. There were others who said that his dark hair and swarthy complexion were due to the amount of gypsy blood running in his veins, but no-one would ever have dared to say it to his face, and especially now.

But Karl Muller had undergone a radical change, on the outside at least. His last brush with the police regarding the possession of some stolen chickens seemed to have had an extraordinary effect upon him. Rather than the usual ticking-off and perhaps an appearance at a minor court, he had been held at the police station for over a week without any charges being brought. Someone said that when they saw him the day after his release, he appeared pale and even more dishevelled than normal. He wasn't seen for weeks following his release from detention; even the regulars at Brandt's saw neither hide nor hair of him. This temporary disappearance was all the more surprising because after his previous arrests, he would invariably end up in the bar drunkenly bragging to everyone how he, Karl Muller, had once again outwitted the forces of law and order.

A month passed before one day he strode into Brandt's dressed in a brown shirt complete with scarlet armband and gave the party salute to the astonished landlord. Karl Muller was a new man, a reformed man. Nobody ever found out what had transpired during his detention at the police station to effect this sudden change in character and appearance, but this petty criminal and erstwhile scourge of the authorities had apparently seen the light and recognised the error of his past ways. He intended no longer to be an irritant to society, but would henceforth be its protector; instead of being a man who used his strength to bully and intimidate, he would use it to uphold the law and protect the new order.

Karl Muller was proud of his new uniform. The uniform gave him legitimacy, transforming him into a figure of importance and respectability; it gave him status and gained him the acceptance that had never been accorded to him throughout his miserable life. If the people in the village had feared him before, they feared even more this unlikely champion of social order and if anyone still dared to raise a voice of dissent in public, they were careful not to do so when Karl Muller was present.

It was the custom for the village boys to help the local farmers at the busy times of harvest and planting, and we would even be given a day off school to help the farmers in return for a couple of marks and a hot meal in the farmhouse when the work was done. One day in autumn, Karl Muller came to the school to ask for volunteers to pick potatoes at his farm the following day. This was unusual because he usually did the work himself, helped by his sons and even his wife, hardly ever did he pay anyone from outside to come onto his land. Nevertheless, Hans and I were always keen to volunteer for this kind of work as it gave us the chance to earn some money, and even though we didn't care for Muller it still meant a day out of the classroom. Bernie was considered still too young for this kind of work so, much to his disgust, he had to go to school the next day.

The following morning, Hans and I, together with two other boys from school, walked out to the farm where Muller handed us spades and pointed to the potato field. It was a warm day and we soon worked up a sweat as we dug down into the thick clay, wrestling the potatoes from the clinging soil before throwing them into sacks. The leaves and stems were left on the ground for the pigs that would be released into the field directly after our work was done. By mid morning we had harvested about a quarter of the field and Mrs Muller came out with a large earthenware flask of beer. It wasn't often that the farmers offered us anything stronger than lemonade, but we didn't mind, after all we were doing men's work and it was only right that we should be treated accordingly. I didn't care much for the taste, but nevertheless drank copiously, the beer tasting marginally better because I knew that my parents would not have approved. At lunchtime Mrs Muller produced another pitcher of beer together with some bread and cheese that were both speedily devoured.

By five o'clock, despite all the beer that we had drunk, the field had been cleared and we leaned on our shovels to survey our handiwork. The cart was groaning with the weight of the full sacks of potatoes that Muller had been loading throughout the day and the discarded plant tops lay in rows across the field. We were tired and hungry, our backs and legs ached, but we had enjoyed our day out in the fields. With spades slung over our shoulders we trudged back towards the Mullers' house where Mrs Muller had prepared a large cauldron of goulash. We filled our bowls and spooned the hot liquid into our mouths, dipping crusts of bread into it so as to mop up every last drop.

It was almost dark by the time we assembled at the front door to await our payment. We noticed that Muller had changed out of his work clothes and donned his brown party uniform. He shook us all by the hand, but our outstretched palms were ignored. Instead he treated us to a short speech saying how much he appreciated our sacrifice for the fatherland and that furthermore he would personally take it upon himself to tell our teacher how diligent we had been and would inform him that we were a credit to the nation. He completed by giving us the party salute that was duly returned.

"Bastard! " said Hans as we left. "We've slogged our guts out all day long and he hasn't paid us a pfennig."

Even the meanest of the farmers around the village wouldn't have dared to refuse payment, even if it had only been one mark. Our sense of burning resentment grew as we walked wearily home and by the time we arrived home our resentment had turned into a plan for vengeance. The following day was Saturday and we knew that Muller would be taking his crop to the market so Hans and I awoke early, crept out of the house before anyone else was awake and made our way back out to Muller's farm. The closer we got the more scared I became and I began to express my doubts over the wisdom of this expedition to Hans, but he merely told me to shut up, he was determined that Muller would be punished for his failure to pay us for all our hard work. As we neared the cottage, the dogs began to bark. We could see that the cart had not yet been brought into the yard and was still standing in the corner of the potato field where it had been left the previous evening. There was no sign of movement around the cottage, so we crept into the field and towards the cart. We kept glancing anxiously towards the cottage, but still no-one came out to see why the dogs were barking.

I still wondered exactly what Hans intended to do and I

watched nervously as he took a penknife from his pocket and crawled beneath the cart. Using the blade of the knife, he began working loose the split pin that secured the wheel to the axle. He eventually managed to loosen the rusty pin, first from one wheel and then the one from the other side. He was careful not to remove them altogether, but made sure that any movement would be sure to make them fall out. The job completed, we crept away. I was ready to run all the way home just as fast as I could, but Hans held me back.

"This will be no revenge unless we can see it! " he hissed as he pulled me back.

On the other side of the road that ran past Muller's cottage was a water filled ditch and beyond that an embankment lined with willows. We leapt across the ditch and hid behind one of the larger trees to wait. It wasn't too long before Muller appeared, cursing and kicking out at his dogs as he crossed the yard with his usual swagger. He brought his skewbald pony out of the stable and led it into the potato field where he hitched it up to the laden cart. He jumped up onto the board and with a flick of the whip the pony began to pull the cart out of the field and onto the road.

We watched the spectacle unfold, staring, transfixed as if we had never before seen a pony and cart. Despite the uneven surface, the cartwheels seemed to be turning steadily. I looked at Hans, but he merely smiled; he knew that we wouldn't have to wait much longer and sure enough, Muller hadn't gone more than another twenty yards before one of the wheels finally worked loose from the axle and as the horse whinnied, the cart slewed crazily to one side as one of the wheels broke loose, spectacularly spilling Karl Muller and his load of laden potato sacks onto the road. Amid his cries and curses, the sacks burst open with the force of the impact rolling potatoes in every direction, many of them rolling into the water filled ditch below us with a satisfying splash.

Karl Muller swore so loudly and violently that I swear he could have been heard in Soest. He kicked the cart, kicked the sacks and even kicked his pony. Hans had to stick a handkerchief in his mouth to stifle his laughter, but I could see the tears running down his cheek. As Muller frantically tried to retrieve his potatoes the horse, clearly distressed at the accident and its subsequent treatment, pulled forward, dragging the cart a few yards further along the road before, inevitably, the other wheel fell off. The cart collapsed onto the road with a sickening bang, waking the rest of the Muller family who emerged from the cottage bleary-eyed to see what all the commotion was about. It was time to make our getaway so we dropped down the other side of the embankment before making our way home across the fields well out of sight of any of the Mullers.

Hans had little need to swear me to secrecy. If Muller had known that we had been responsible and that it had not just been an accident, I swear he would surely have killed us.

"That was worth more than a couple of lousy marks." said Hans "Remember Theo, nobody takes advantage of us ter-Horsts".

We had got our own back on Karl Muller, the village bully. He might continue to strut and intimidate his neighbours with his newfound authority, but we had put one over on him and he never did suspect that the collapse of his cart was anything other than an unfortunate accident.

12

It was a time of rallies and parades. Every week the Youth would form up and march through the village, banners fluttering, sometimes the marches were held at night when we would each carry a flaming torch to light the way. Occasionally we would join together with other groups in the vicinity and parade through the local town of Lippstadt, cheered by townspeople lining the route. It seemed that every day at school we were told what a fine thing it was to be German, how other countries looked up to us once again now that the Leader had re-built the nation and restored our pride. We were told also of our nation's cultural riches, the great composers, writers, artists and engineers who were respected and admired throughout the world. We were also taught about our great military traditions and of how there would have been no united German nation had it not been for the army.

There was thus great joy when it was announced that our armies had marched into the Rhineland, an integral part of our nation from which we had been forced to withdraw under the unjust terms of the Treaty of Versailles. The Youth held a rally the following Sunday, at the end of which we were told that this was only the first of the many wrongs which were to be righted. We were told that Germany had never been defeated on the battlefield and that we had been forced to accept the armistice only because of international conspiracies and the enemies in our midst, the communists, the democratic back-stabbers and the Jews. The Great War, we were told, was something in which we should take pride and should not be regarded as a matter of shame. Hadn't the Leader himself fought valiantly in the trenches and been almost blinded by gas? We were told to go home and ask our fathers about their exploits during the war and to listen carefully while they told us of the sacrifices they had made while fighting for the fatherland.

When we sat down to our meal that evening, Hans duly asked my father to tell us about the war and what he had done. He pursed his lips, then looked first at my mother before turning to Hans, Bernie and me.

"There is something that you should all know." he sighed, putting down his knife and fork.

We waited with baited breath, wondering what momentous tale he was about to tell. A story of heroism perhaps, of courage under fire, a story which I would be proud to tell to the whole class the following day. I waited excitedly for him to begin.

"It's about time I told you something about this family. It never seemed very important before, but things have changed. My father, your grandfather, came to this country from Holland."

He stopped for a moment so that we could digest this fact, but it was something that we already knew, for grandfather had often mentioned it to us.

"Under German law, nationality is determined by your father. If your father is German then you are German, if your father is Dutch then you also are Dutch. My father is Dutch therefore I am Dutch and if I am Dutch then............"

I saw Hans's eyes widen. "We are Dutch?" he said, scarcely able to utter the words.

My father nodded.

"And during the war?"

"I did my duty. I was called up and I served in Holland. Holland was neutral, it was not at war with Germany," he added as if this somehow made it alright.

I threw down my knife and fork, ran out of the kitchen and up to my bedroom. I felt physically sick. I was proud to be in the Youth and had felt part of this wonderful spirit of renewal, eager to play a role in this new adventure, this new beginning that the Leader had promised. Now I was devastated to discover that I was a foreigner and couldn't really be a part of it at all. It didn't matter that my mother was German, that her parents were German and as far as I could tell, all the previous generations of her family had been German as well. It didn't matter that I had been born in Germany, as had my father; it didn't matter also that we spoke no other language than German and thought of ourselves as nothing other than German. Just because my grandfather had been born in Holland then under the law, we were foreigners and would it seemed always be foreigners – even my mother was, due to her marriage, no longer considered German.

I cursed my elderly grandfather for his ancestry; I cursed the laws that forced you to take the nationality of your father and his father before him. I ran back downstairs and bawled and shouted at my father until he silenced me with the back of his hand. I had fondly imagined myself standing up in front of the class the next day and proudly telling everyone about my father's heroic deeds, anticipating the rapturous applause that would surely follow the hair-raising tales of bravery and sacrifice which I would relate. I had even thought that perhaps my father may have won a medal for gallantry which, in his modest way, he might have kept secret; he would remove the honour from its secret hiding place and allow me to take it into school. How could I stand up and tell the whole class that my father, instead of the war hero I had fondly imagined him to be, was little more than a traitor?

13

Although the discovery of our true nationality caused my brothers and me no little discomfort, it was soon to have a more tangible impact. Hans was now fourteen and, in his last year at school, had turned his thoughts to how he was to earn a living. My father was keen for him to get a proper trade rather than joining him at Beckmann's distillery, so he approached a number of local companies who were keen to take on hard-working young men and would also teach them a skill. Finding a job wasn't difficult at that time, the nation was becoming more prosperous by the day, roads and factories were being built throughout the land and the military were always looking for new recruits for the rapidly expanding army and to man the magnificent new battleships and cruisers that were being launched each month in the shipyards of Kiel and Hamburg.

A boy of fourteen leaving a village school such as ours in Beckum could do no better than obtain a good trade and in those days that could only be obtained by serving an apprenticeship. It was almost unheard of for anyone to go on to a technical institute or art school, much less a university. My father spent many days visiting local firms who might be looking for a bright young boy to become a joiner, a plumber or electrician. It was quickly apparent that there would be no difficulty in finding a job, but there was a major stumbling block to obtaining an apprenticeship; under new laws that the government had passed, only German citizens were permitted to serve a skilled apprenticeship and Hans, along with the rest of us, was not a German.

My father was thus forced to do something that neither he nor his father had ever bothered to do before; they decided to apply for German citizenship. He first made enquiries with the local burgermeister regarding naturalisation and obtained the necessary application forms. I can remember him sitting in the study by the light of a small lamp, carefully filling in the many pages with family details. The forms were duly witnessed, signed by the burgermeister and posted off to the Interior Ministry in Berlin. One month later we received a letter bearing a government crest stating that the application had been successful. At a stroke the whole family became German citizens instead of Dutch ones, even little Heinz who had only just started to walk had his nationality changed without knowing a thing about it. My father was always a practical man and though he may have had some misgivings about our changed status, he realised that in the present times it was for the best, although I do remember him complaining bitterly at the amount of money he'd had to pay for the little piece of paper that confirmed our new nationality.

My father always used to say that the family was more important than any country or political party and that whatever might happen, we should take care of each other before anything else. I was nevertheless relieved that I could now hold my head up high at school and in the Youth, more importantly, it removed the secret fear I'd had for the past two years…. that we might one day be taken away on a train like Mr & Mrs Weismann.

Hans left school and took up an apprenticeship with a local joinery firm, but even though he'd started work, he still remained a member of the Youth. Even though we were now as German as the other boys, our parents never seemed to be able to find the money to buy the smart uniforms that many of the other boys wore, together with their bright armbands. We were easily put off because we knew that money was tight and we knew also that my mother was expecting yet another baby. Although we continued to join in with all the sports competitions and other activities, when the parades and rallies were held, we were usually hidden away in the centre of the ranks and consequently were never given the honour of carrying one of the flags at the head of the parade.

Ever since the time we had lived at my grandfather's house in Ostinghausen, we had grown our own vegetables. It had been a necessity during the difficult times when it was impossible to buy food in the shops and though this was no longer the case, the routine of planting and harvesting had been continued. The garden at the back of the house was not large, but the rich, black soil produced healthy crops of potatoes, cabbages and beans. My father had constructed a small pen at the bottom of the garden next to the railway line and twice a year, he would buy a piglet that we fed on vegetables and scraps from the house.

When he had first brought a piglet home, in order to get out of the chore of feeding it, Hans and I had told our sister Wilhelmina who was about five at the time, that it was her pet, so she christened the animal 'Peter' and every morning come rain or shine, she would religiously go down to the bottom of the garden and feed it with scraps from the house. One morning she had gone to feed it as usual, but a few minutes later she ran back into the kitchen screaming and crying that it had disappeared. Hans, Bernie and I roared with laughter and told her that 'Peter' had not disappeared, but had merely been transformed into the tasty rashers of bacon which mother was frying for our breakfast.

Poor Wilhelmina was inconsolable and I don't think she ever forgave my father for killing her precious Peter. It was a long time before she would ever touch bacon and when father brought the next piglet home a few months later, she would have nothing to do with it. The piglets were kept for a few months until they had grown fat, then a butcher from the village would come and slaughter it before transforming the animal into numerous joints of pork, several large hams, sides of bacon and a multitude of sausages and salami. The butcher used to joke that the only part of the pig he couldn't turn into food was its squeal.

I remember one Sunday morning that the butcher arrived with his leather bag full of sharpened knives, hooks and cleavers. He was enjoying a glass of schnapps with my father at the kitchen table before he went out to perform his grisly task and as I came inside from the garden, I overheard them discussing something in hushed tones. I stopped by the door and was shocked when I heard the butcher say that he wished he could cut off the head of the Leader rather than the pig at the bottom of the garden. How, I wondered, could he say anything like that about the man who had done so much for us all? I fully expected my father to be as outraged as I was, but I was even more shocked to hear him laugh at the butcher's jest.

I heard them getting to their feet and quickly made myself scarce, wondering if I should mention this conversation to my teacher, who always encouraged us to tell him about anyone who might not fully support the Leader in order that the error of their ways might be explained to them. I thought about it for much of the afternoon before deciding that perhaps they had only been joking; besides it would have been hugely embarrassing if the teacher had come to the house and explain to my father the benefits the Leader had bestowed upon us, not to mention the fact that I was a little frightened of feeling the back of my father's hand for my trouble.

My father spoke very little about politics; he would read the paper and listen to the news bulletins, especially those describing the civil war in Spain where our Leader was helping the gallant Spanish people to resist the communists. I knew also that he listened to the Hilversum channel on Dutch radio in the sitting room late at night, for he remembered enough of the language to understand. He didn't realise that I was aware of this, but sometimes I would go down when he wasn't there and turn on the wireless to find it still tuned to a Dutch language station from the previous night. I couldn't understand a word of Dutch so I wouldn't have known what was being said, but I suspected that they were probably spreading lies about our country and the Leader. The teacher and some of the other leaders in the Youth had warned us that foreign radio stations and newspapers were spreading lies because they were afraid of us becoming a strong nation once again. In fact we were warned not to read any foreign papers or listen to any foreign broadcasts because their aim was to try to fill our heads with doubts. The only believable news was that which was printed in the German newspapers, everything else was probably a lie.

Perhaps it was my greater awareness or just that things had slowly and imperceptibly changed, but it was around this time that I became aware that people had begun to speak in whispers. The men who drank in the bar at the Gasthof and in the beer garden, during the summer, weren't usually slow to complain about one thing or another, but it seemed that people no longer had any complaints. I thought at first that it was because people had very little to complain about; after all, almost everyone had a job, the police had clamped down on crime and in the summer we were no longer plagued by the bands of gypsies who came to help the local farmers with the harvest and at the same time help themselves to the contents of peoples' homes during the night. No-one seemed to quite know where they had gone and in truth no-one really cared, except the farmers, of course, who had to pay higher wages to those they could find to help with the harvest.

If people wanted to talk about anything that might reflect badly upon the government or the country in general, they would talk in hushed whispers, looking over their shoulders to make sure that none could overhear their conversation. The newspapers had long since ceased to publish anything which might be considered critical or print stories that might cause people to question the direction in which we were being taken. The absence of hard facts created fertile ground for rumours: stories were leaked by those in the know or who claimed to be in the know, and passed on, suitably embellished. There were rumours of war, rumours of people being taken away by the police during the night, rumours of every kind imaginable.

14

I left school when I was fourteen, deciding that the benefits of higher education were not for the likes of a village boy like myself. I'd had enough of schooling, and like most boys, was impatient to be a man, I wanted to earn a wage and do the things that men did. I had already begun smoking regularly by the time I was thirteen, regularly at least, in the sense that I would steal from my father's cigarette packet that was often left lying around the house. Hans had been doing the same thing for even longer than I and although I'm sure my father suspected, he never said anything. Almost everyone over the age of sixteen smoked in those days, so it was not a matter of huge importance if some of us started a little earlier.

I hadn't been keen on following Hans into an apprenticeship as a joiner, the thought of spending the rest of my days in the dusty confines of a workshop or a factory held no appeal. I wanted a job that would get me out of doors in the fresh air so the natural choice was to join the building trade and become an apprentice bricklayer. I was apprenticed to Timmermanns, a building company in the nearby town of Lippstadt. My father had taken me to their head office to see the foreman who commented that I looked a bit on the small side, but after reading the glowing testimonials contained in the letter that my teacher had written, agreed to take me on.

The company was extremely busy at this time with a host of construction contracts which they were having difficulty fulfilling due to labour shortages caused by the military call-up of many men over the age of eighteen. I was given a variety of tasks to perform which in other times would not have been the lot of a fourteen-year-old apprentice, but I loved it. I revelled in the freedom from the discipline of school and most of all I looked forward to my wage packet at the end of the week even though I was required to hand it, unopened, to my mother who would pay me an allowance and keep the rest. The allowance was sufficient for cigarettes and a few other luxuries, although I was not yet old enough to join my father and the other men in the bar at Brandts.

The government had recently introduced a scheme whereby young men under the age of military service were required to join the work corps called Arbeitsdienst which was run on military lines and required boys to work on various projects throughout the country. I had only been at work for a few months when Hans was called up by this organisation. Employers had to release these boys, who left with the guarantee that they would resume their apprenticeships on completion of the service, which normally lasted for six months.

It was the first time that any of my family members had left home and although I was busy with work, it still seemed strange not to have Hans around. Even my mother, busy as she was with my younger brothers and sister, Wilhelmina who was ten, Heinz who was now five, and six-month old Eugen, obviously missed her eldest son. She would eagerly open the letters which he sent each week from his barracks, located somewhere near Hannover, in which he would describe his work and life in the camp.

I knew that I too would probably have to perform this service in a couple of years' time, but in the meantime I continued learning my trade, for I was ambitious and always kept in mind what my father had once told me; that no one ever got wealthy working for other people. Somehow I knew that one day I would be working for myself. I was still a member of the Youth and continued to enjoy the games and activities organised by my old teacher, who was now assisted by Karl Muller. My father continued to take a dim view of Muller as did everyone else in the village, repeatedly warning me to beware of him and anyone else in a position of authority, though I had long ago abandoned the crazy notion of ever reporting anyone who said anything critical of the government, especially a member of my family.

Shocked as I had been those years earlier when I overheard my father and the butcher talking in the kitchen, I was totally unprepared for some of the conversations I heard at work. Unlike the classroom, where the teacher had imbued his pupils with a youthful passion about the new order of things, I rapidly became aware that with one or two exceptions, my workmates were noticeably less enthusiastic. Although nearly all of them agreed that most things had improved under the Leader, many disliked him and I had even sometimes heard men call him the 'carpet-chewer' describing him as if he were some kind of lunatic. I never argued with anyone about this, but wondered whether this was part of what growing up and being a man meant; not getting carried away with the euphoria on the radio and in the newspapers. The older people seemed more wary and seemed to be worried about unfolding events. I put it down to the fact that they had lived through the last war and had experienced the times of hardship, the unemployment and hunger that followed.

I was convinced that their concerns were unfounded and that the Leader would look after his people and achieve his aims without any catastrophe befalling us. Everyone had seen the pictures the previous year of the army marching triumphantly into Vienna to finally re-unite the peoples of Austria and Germany and our joy knew no bounds when some months later the enslaved people of the Sudetenland were liberated from the tyranny of the Czechs. There was surely nothing our Leader could not achieve and despite the comments of some people, and the carping of some ungrateful souls, I felt sure that the majority of people had nothing but praise for the way in which the nation was being transformed and had once again been given the respect it deserved.

I was learning a great deal more about my trade than a boy of my tender years had any right to expect. I had learned from Hans that in the first few months of an apprenticeship, I was likely to be given a succession of largely menial tasks and be required to instantly respond to demands from the older hands for more coffee, but things had changed. With so many experienced employees away in the army or the Arbeitsdienst there just weren't enough hands to go round and hiring further workers was out of the question. Most firms were in the same position, particularly in the building trade with full order books and not enough men to do the work. I was therefore given lots more responsibility than would normally be the case. The chargehand took a liking to me, finding time to show me the tricks of the trade and as a result I learnt more in my first year at work than most apprentices would learn in five.

It was about this time that we kept hearing on the radio and in the newspapers that the Poles were causing problems – there was a lot of fuss over some kind of corridor that I didn't fully understand, but I was sure that our Leader would manage to get the problem resolved despite the objections of neighbouring countries. One of my workmates told me that he had already succeeded in Austria and Czechoslovakia and there was no reason to doubt that he would succeed in Poland.

Many of the older hands who had fought in the Great War avoided getting caught up in the hysteria. One day the foreman told me a story about the time he had served in the trenches and had lost his best friend, seen him cut down right in front of his eyes. He'd been trapped for days in a forward redoubt and knowing that he couldn't get back to the main line, had buried his friend in a shell hole, only to find the following morning that further shell fire had disinterred the body. He buried his friend once again, but the same thing happened the following night. This sequence was repeated for a further three days until he managed to get back to the main line. He never found out what happened to the body of his best friend. Many men of his age seemed worried about another war and though they didn't often talk of the things they had witnessed, I learned something of its horror from the look in their eyes.

I was not unduly concerned, however; the Leader himself had served in the trenches and surely endured such injury and privation. Surely he would not drag the nation into the same catastrophe. I was sure that he knew what he was doing, after all he had seen for himself how weak the leaders of our enemies were. Despite the obvious worries of many, I had every confidence that he would succeed and in any case, like every fifteen-year-old, I had more important things to worry about than great affairs of state. I was far more concerned with whether I would be picked for the village football team on Saturday and whether or not Maria

Kolche would be waiting for me outside the Gasthof on Saturday evening.

Having a wage packet, even after my mother had taken her cut, had given me an incredible feeling of independence. I could now afford to buy my own cigarettes instead of stealing them from my Dad's pocket and I could afford to buy soft drinks for some of the girls in the village – especially Maria Kolche who had been known to let some boys 'go all the way'.

One Sunday morning in September, I came down for breakfast and found my mother and father listening intently to a news bulletin on the radio. I could hear the voice of the Leader telling the nation that in the face of Polish aggression and a refusal to agree to our few simple demands, there had been no alternative but to launch an attack. Even now our victorious troops were advancing deep into enemy territory and sweeping all before them.

I let out a whoop of delight at the news before I was quietened with a stern sssshhh! from my father.

"People are fighting and getting killed!" my mother snapped.

The truth was that I hadn't given it a great deal of thought. I hadn't really connected the events we were hearing about on the radio with real people, it all seemed so impersonal.

"I'm sure it will be alright," I said. "Things are going well by the sound of it."

I could see they were upset so I disappeared into the kitchen, leaving them listening to the radio broadcast.

15

For days the newspapers and the radio bulletins had been full of news describing the visit by Prime Minister Chamberlain to see the Leader in Munich. I had always been told that England was a powerful nation and I somehow expected their leader to epitomise this strength, so imagine my surprise when I saw a picture of a strange, gaunt looking figure in a rumpled black suit, with a ragged moustache, clutching a bowler hat. He looked more like an office clerk than a great statesman and standing next to our Leader, resplendent in his grey uniform, made the leader of the supposedly mighty British Empire appear all the more weak and elderly.

It was clear to see who was the strongest and I had every confidence that our Leader would prevail in his mission to release our people from their slavery in the East and there was nothing that this shabby, weak old man could do to prevent it. The newspapers reported that our Leader was doing everything humanly possible to avoid conflict and had bent over backwards to accommodate the British, even going so far as to dilute still further our already moderate and legitimate demands. It seemed that despite the reasonable approach of the Leader, the allies, who had imposed such harsh and unfair conditions upon us at Versailles, were up to their old tricks again, attempting to grind down the long suffering German people. This time, however, the newspapers reported that things were different, for we were singularly fortunate to have our Leader at the helm and he would ensure that the infamy of 1918 was never repeated.

Austria had already joined the Reich, uniting our peoples and saving them from communism. Our cousins in the Sudetenland were also saved from slavery and persecution at the hands of the Czechs while Chamberlain returned to London from Munich waving his ridiculous piece of paper. There had of course been talk of war, but the Leader had always prevailed in his discussions with the British and the French. There would be further talks, but no-one could fail to notice that it was always the French and British leaders who travelled to Germany, a sure sign of their weakness.

If anyone might have had any lingering doubts about the Leader's greatness, none now remained. He had forced the British and the French to accept the manifest destiny of the German speaking peoples and for the first time we were a strong and united nation. Those who feared that we would be dragged once more into a horrific conflict in the west had been proved wrong; the Leader had secured all his objectives without a single shot being fired. Surely there was nothing that could not be achieved under the guidance of this brilliant man.

Geography was not my favourite subject, but at school I had been able to point out most of the countries on the large map of Europe that hung on the classroom wall. I could locate some of the major cities, Berlin of course, Paris and Rome, but if I had been asked to place my finger on a city by the name of Danzig, I would undoubtedly have failed. It was a missing part of my geographical education that would soon be remedied, for soon we were all to learn in newspaper columns and from our teacher, that this Baltic city in East Prussia was home to Germans like ourselves, but they had been surrounded by a foreign country and under the grossly unfair terms of Versailles had to remain separated from their countrymen by a land corridor which allowed Poland access to the sea.

We were outraged. How many more Germans were there in Europe who had been 'stolen' by the iniquitous provisions of Versailles? How many of our folk were sentenced to a life of exile from the fatherland, dominated and persecuted by foreigners? Our Leader said time and time again that if these poor people were liberated peacefully then there would be no need for war, yet the Poles, supported by the British would not concede to this legitimate and reasonable request.

As the warm days of August drew to a close, my father listened with increasing nervousness to the broadcasts from Hilversum. We had been told that there would be no war; that all our objectives would be achieved peacefully and the people had believed the talk of peace, drunk on the heady wine of bloodless victories achieved thus far. We were led to believe that these victories would continue, while the Leader made his plans for war, a war not just with Poland, but a war with Britain and France and Belgium and Holland, a world war. The Leader broadcast to the nation on the last day of August, it was a Thursday. He spoke in the distinct voice that had become recognisable to everyone in the land, that he had received no answer from the Polish government in response to his generous offer of peace and that the responsibility for any conflict lay with them. We went to sleep that night trusting that at the eleventh hour the Leader would achieve our aims without recourse to war, just as he had done so many times before.

The following morning we heard with alarm the news

that in response to an unprovoked attack upon German soil by Polish forces, the Leader had had no alternative but to retaliate. Throughout the next three days the excited radio bulletins broadcast every hour, reporting that our forces were advancing rapidly towards Warsaw and that the Polish army was in retreat. It wasn't until Sunday evening that we were informed that Britain and France had declared war upon us. Even those who believed that because of the intransigent attitude of the Poles we would have no alternative but to attack them before they attacked us, never believed that Britain or France would take up arms to defend them. Everyone thought they were bluffing and we had seen before that our Leader was capable of calling their bluff. The Poles were being smashed and our people in the east liberated from their oppressors. Why would Britain and France fight to save a country that had already been beaten?

We were confident that the Leader would come to some arrangement with them, but in the meantime there began a feverish building of air raid shelters while shops in some cities ran out of food as people made stockpiles. Bernie and I helped my father insert heavy timber props in the cellar and filled sacks with sand and soil to place against the walls. I thought this was unnecessary, but my father was convinced that these precautions were necessary.

While Poland was being invaded, it had been made an offence to listen to foreign broadcasts. Ignoring the new law was punishable by death, but my father would still listen in to Hilversum late at night. He never spoke about what he had heard, although he knew that we were aware of his nocturnal practice. I'm not sure whether it was because he didn't quite trust us or whether he didn't want to put any of us at risk for the less you knew, the safer you were.

Despite all the frantic preparations that were made for

war, the building of shelters and the stockpiling of food, absolutely nothing happened. There was lots of talk, but there was no action, Britain and France didn't attack us after all and as far as I knew we never attacked them. Poland had been beaten and for most people the Leader had pulled off yet another incredible victory at next to no cost. We felt as though we were lords of the earth.

Over the next couple of days people seemed more relaxed. I was working overtime at work as we continued to have full order books and insufficient hands. All the men were working at least sixty hours a week, but we were happy because we had bulging pay packets. Some of the men with memories of being hungry and unemployed just a few years earlier eagerly volunteered for additional hours; they would be able to buy a few treats and besides, who knew how long this time of plenty might last?

Just two weeks before my fifteenth birthday, our troops were sent to occupy Denmark and Norway – the papers said it was to protect them from attack by the British - and it seemed that once again the prospect of a general war loomed large. It seemed incredible to me that Germany had enough soldiers to go around, first Czechoslovakia, then Poland, now Norway and Denmark. My incredulity reached new heights when just one month later our soldiers overran France, Holland and Belgium in a matter of just a few days.

My father had been listening to the increasingly bellicose broadcasts from Hilversum for the past few weeks. It was all bravado; my father knew probably better than anyone in the neighbourhood just how ineffective any resistance might be against the onslaught of our armies. He considered himself a German, but he was a German who had served in the Dutch Army during the Great War and he seemed filled with despair when the news came through.

The news of the encirclement and collapse of the French army came as a surprise. It seemed amazing that our forces could take on the largest army in Europe and defeat them so swiftly and easily. Now it was the turn of the victors of the last war who had imposed intolerable conditions upon us in 1918 to have similar terms imposed upon them. The whole country was jubilant, it seemed that there was nothing we could not accomplish and our Leader was worshipped all the more.

The Youth held a number of torchlight parades in his honour and to honour our valiant forces who had smashed our enemies. At work everyone was buoyed by the news of our victory and although England had not yet fallen, it could only be a matter of time and then we would have a just peace and Germany would walk tall again and no-one would ever doubt that we were first among nations.

16

The fire brigade in small villages like Beckum was a voluntary organisation. The local authorities purchased the equipment and uniforms, but it was the men of the village who manned the appliance in emergencies. Most of those who had performed this task had been called up into the forces or were working longer hours in the factories that were essential for the war effort. Although service was voluntary, we all knew that in the present circumstances, anyone without very good reason not to volunteer would soon receive a visit from the police or Karl Muller and some of his thuggish friends.

In the absence of those away fighting, the older men and young boys like myself, normally considered too young to undertake such potentially dangerous work, were expected to fill the gaps. I was pleased to answer the call, not so much for the small allowance we received, but because at the end of the training sessions which took place once a week, the brigade members went along to Brandt's where the burgermeister paid for all the drinks. I wasn't old enough to legally drink alcohol in the bar, but as a member of the Feuerwehr it was an entitlement that could not be refused. I had just turned sixteen and although the uniform I was given was a little too large, I felt like a grown man.

The fire appliance which was kept in a building at the village crossroads was horse drawn and had a manual pump operated by four men alternately pulling and pushing on two great wooden oars. Although the fire engine was designed to be drawn by horse, by the time the horse had been brought in from the nearby field and hitched to the wagon, any fire would have been beyond control. It was quicker and simpler for six men to take hold of the shafts and simply pull it along themselves.

It had been over a year since the war began and despite the assurances of the government that there would be no attacks on German soil, there had already been some air raids in the Ruhr which lay only twenty miles or so to the west. As members of the Feuerwehr we were expected to act as air raid wardens as well as being prepared to cope with any emergencies such as the dropping of bombs. It was hard to imagine that a sleepy little backwater like Beckum, which consisted of no more than one hundred and fifty dwellings and one distillery, might be a strategic target of any British bombers, but you could never tell what might happen in wartime. A stray aeroplane from one of the increasingly frequent raids on Dortmund or Essen could well drop its deadly cargo on us all.

No-one was surprised when the postman arrived one warm June morning carrying a brown envelope bearing the eagle and swastika insignia containing Hans's call up papers. He had only just returned from Arbeitsdienst and although not yet eighteen, the authorities had calculated that he would be by the time he had completed his basic training. Like most other mothers throughout the land, my mother had resigned herself to his going; other mothers' sons were going off to war and she had no reason to believe that her family would be any different. She had become used to Hans being away after his year in the Labour Service, though she knew of course that the worst that could befall him was that he might hit his thumb with a hammer or cut himself with a saw, but this was different. We had now been at war for almost two years and though things continued to go well, bullets were far more deadly than hammers and nails.

The letter ordered him to report to Soest barracks in one week's time where he would be given further instructions. My mother packed the one small suitcase he was permitted to take with him and my father, Bernie and I walked with him to the nearby station at Benninghausen. A few other young men, obviously fellow conscripts, were already waiting at the station, looking rather sheepish in the company of their parents who had come to wave them off. The varied clothing and motley collection of bags and cases of the new recruits contrasted with the smart, grey uniforms and regulation backpacks of a couple of soldiers who were also waiting for the train.

My mother had intended to go with us, but at the last moment had chosen to say her farewells at home rather than in the impersonal surroundings of a railway station. Looking at the other conscripts standing by their weeping mothers I could see that Hans was relieved to be spared this embarrassment. As the train pulled in, my father pressed a packet of cigarettes into his hand together with a small silver crucifix which his own father had given him years before when he had departed for Holland to serve that country during the last war.

"I hope that this protects you from harm as it once protected me" he said, hugging his eldest son.

We stood on the platform and waved as the train pulled away, Hans's arm was soon lost in a flurry of others as the men on board waved farewell to wives, sweethearts, fathers, mothers and children. My father was not an emotional man, but as I looked across at him I saw a tear trickle down his cheek before he quickly wiped it away. We trudged home without speaking a word, each of us lost in our thoughts. Despite Hans's attempt at high spirits on the way to the station and my own youthful optimism about the outcome of the war, an air of trepidation had settled upon us.

We reached Beckum and as we passed by Brandt's, Karl Muller stumbled down the steps and into the road. He was clearly worse for drink and gave us the party salute, which I returned immediately, but which my father pointedly ignored. Muller took note of this and swayed towards my father with a sneer upon his face.

"Why don't you salute like your son?', he sneered. "Not good enough for you eh?"

Despite his transformation from petty criminal into the village's leading party member, Muller was never able to command the respect that he felt his uniform deserved among the people of the village and he knew it. I could sense that his resentment burned inside him.

I noticed my father clench his fists as Muller approached. Muller stopped in front of him, swaying as if moved by a breeze that he alone could feel. If his brain hadn't been so addled by the amount of beer he had consumed, he might have been able to articulate his displeasure at my father's disinclination to salute him. I could smell Muller's beery breath as his mouth opened and closed without making any sound. My father stared at him and I could see that, the mood he was in, he wouldn't have hesitated to punch him even though Muller undoubtedly was the stronger man.

The two men stood in silence, each with a look of disdain. I waited anxiously for one of them to make a move, but at that moment one of Muller's drinking cronies emerged from the bar and shouted for him to return to the bar.

Muller swayed uneasily as he looked around. He turned back to my father and at last the power of speech returned to him.

"I'll ignore your insult for now," he said, then saluted once again. My father didn't move, just continued staring at him. This time I made no effort to return the salute. Muller scowled at us then lurched away back up the steps to join his friend in the bar. My father's eyes burned with anger as we continued our walk home, but he said nothing. He had said before that the behaviour of men like Muller wasn't worth the words of decent people.

Mother had dinner ready when we returned and although the young children chattered away throughout the meal, my parents, Bernie and I ate for the most part in silence. We were thinking of Hans and wondering when we might see him again. It was more than a month until we received our first letter from him informing us that he was fit and well and undergoing basic training near Wuppertal. His training was scheduled to last for three months after which he would be assigned to an operational unit.

We all clung to the belief that there would not be the need for any further fighting. It seemed that most of the Leader's objectives had already been achieved. Poland had been conquered, Norway, Denmark, France and the Low Countries were all occupied. Only the British were still resisting and everyone felt that they would eventually see sense and sign a peace treaty. It seemed that we owned the whole of Europe and that our soldiers would be required not to fight, but merely to maintain order in the many conquered lands beyond our borders. I went to sleep that night with the happy and comforting thought that I had no need to worry too much about Hans or the millions of others who now wore uniform, for it seemed that the war was already won.

17

I was cycling home from work the day after seeing Hans off at the station. It was a warm summer's evening and as I approached the railway crossing a few miles from Beckum, the old man who controlled the barrier shuffled across from his hut to lower the red and white striped wooden pole. I came to a halt and as we waited for the train to pass, he asked if I had heard that Russia had been invaded. I could scarcely believe it; even after all our victories this was a step into the unknown. It only served to deepen the trepidation we all felt when we had waved goodbye to Hans at Benninghausen station.

I remembered the map of the world hanging on the classroom wall at school and thought of how vast Russia was, stretching eastwards from Poland half way around the globe to the borders of China and even to the far shores of the Pacific Ocean. Surely it wasn't possible to invade such a large country and succeed, this was not Denmark or even France, countries that had been occupied and subdued within a matter of weeks. Russia was vast and its people were numbered not in millions but in hundreds of millions.

My thoughts were temporarily interrupted by the approach of an eastbound train, belching steam and smoke as it accelerated down the straight. I automatically raised a hand to wave at the carriages as they sped by. I saw a blur of field grey uniforms behind the windows, heading who knew where, Russia perhaps, to try and cover the endless steppes and the forests of Siberia beneath a field grey blanket; it was absurd. I cycled home as fast as I could to tell my father the news, but I could see from his expression when I entered the kitchen that he already knew.

My father had always feared that the Leader would eventually make a miscalculation. He'd thought that the invasion of Norway was a mistake, but had been proved wrong, he believed the invasion of France to be an even bigger mistake and had been proved wrong again. Over the years, like many people who were doubtful of the Leader's abilities, he had been so encouraged by our successes so far that even he had allowed himself to believe that the Leader might indeed be superhuman and that under him the German people could achieve anything.

The doubters had long since learned to keep their thoughts to themselves of course; for as long as I could remember no-one ever publicly said anything bad about the Leader and even if they were so unwise, their comments would be whispered and veiled in innuendo. No laws had been passed, no notices banning the freedom of speech had ever been posted, but everyone knew that to speak out in a critical manner invited a knock upon the door at night. I had occasionally heard someone in Brandt's say something derogatory when worse for drink, but he would be quickly hushed by those around him, not perhaps for the safety of the man concerned but because the others were afraid of guilt by association.

I saw little to criticise. The Leader had restored our pride and if he had taken a few gambles now and then, they were gambles that had always paid off; but after today's news I was no longer sure.

18

Throughout my young life I had never been further than twenty miles from my home in Beckum, but this was about to change. When I was almost seventeen, I received my call-up papers for the Arbeitsdienst. Although in a way I was sorry to be leaving the building company, I was filled with excitement at the prospect of seeing something other than the familiar surroundings of home. I knew that Hans had enjoyed his time in the corps, so I packed my bags and reported to the office in Soest. With a dozen others who had also received the call-up, we were instructed to board the westbound train for Saarbrucken. The carriages were full of soldiers who spent a large part of the journey amusing themselves by telling us the gruesome and horrific stories of their adventures in the war. If their intention was to scare us then they certainly succeeded for we young lads must have listened to their stories with mouths agape. Leaving the soldiers to continue their westward journey into occupied France, we disembarked in Saarbrucken.

I joined over two hundred excited teenagers milling about the station platform awaiting further orders. A Labour Corp sergeant eventually led us to a line of trucks which took us to a camp near the small town of Quierschied which lay some five miles to the north of the city. On arrival we assembled into something approximating a column before marching in through the gates of the camp. We were certainly a motley crew, some were dressed in ordinary work clothes, some were wearing their Sunday best while others wore the uniform of the Youth. As in any group of teenagers, there were considerable disparities in height and build; some of the boys were well over six feet tall and, to judge from their features, had been shaving regularly for some time, others like me were considerably smaller with only a hint of soft down upon their cheeks and upper lips.

The camp lay at the edge of a large forest that cloaked the undulating land. A fast flowing stream ran alongside the wooden fence that enclosed twelve rows of wooden huts arranged in two rows of six facing each other across an open grassed area. At one end of the grass stood the cookhouse, the canteen and the commandant's hut, on the opposite side stood the laundry and shower block. We lined up our bags and cases in front of us while the commandant made an address.

He welcomed us to the Labour Corps, telling us that we should be proud to have an opportunity to play our part in serving the nation, especially at a time when everyone was being called upon to make sacrifices. Our names were then called out and we were divided into groups of thirty, each group being allocated a hut. They were dark and gloomy inside, illumination provided only by four small light bulbs hanging from the rafters and a row of eight tiny windows along each side. The huts contained rows of bunk beds, fifteen along each side each with one small cupboard at the side which was supposed to contain all our personal things, but which were far too small for the purpose. At the centre of the hut stood a wood-burning stove, a metal chimney leading from the rear and disappearing up through the roof.

As we were not directed to a specific bunk, I threw my small case on a lower bunk as near to the stove as possible.

I could judge from the size of the stove, the ill-fitting windows and doors that the hut would not be a cosy place. Each hut had a leader who watched us securing our berths with great interest. He approached me, looking down at his list of names on a clipboard:

"Terhorst! I'm glad you found yourself a comfortable spot near the stove. I always like to see that my charges are thinking ahead."

"Thank you, sir" I replied, pleased that my initiative had been recognised.

"You obviously like to be warm."

"Yes Sir!" I replied.

"Good. Then while you are here, it will be your duty to obtain the firewood. I expect you to ensure that the stove never goes short of fuel."

As he strode away, the others could barely contain their mirth. I cursed him under my breath.

That night I spent six restless hours scratching beneath the single uncomfortable rough blanket with which we had each been provided. We were woken at dawn when the hut leader came past, loudly ringing a bell by each bunk. Those not immediately out of their bunks were treated to a vigorous ringing of the bell close to their ears. We were ordered to strip and then went outside where we had to run through a line of cold showers set up at one end of the parade ground. At the double we raced back into the hut to dry off and dress in the new khaki uniforms we had been allocated; it wasn't quite an army uniform, but the nearest thing to it.

I got used to the itchy blankets by the end of the week and I never had any difficulty sleeping after that first night because I was so exhausted at the end of each day that sometimes I almost fell asleep during the evening meal. The weeks passed in a blur of drills, physical training, long distance running and digging with a spade. Most of the work however was to be at the 'hill', a half-hour march away from the camp. The 'hill' was in fact a large field rising from the valley bottom towards the edge of woodland. Due to some strange geological process, the soil at the top was stony and largely infertile, whereas it had been 'discovered' that beneath this upper layer, the soil was light and would allow any crop to be grown, and at the present time when every piece of ground was required to grow crops to sustain the war effort, this was considered essential work.

I had never heard of such a thing where the lightest, most fertile soil could be found anywhere but at the surface and felt that this was a 'make work' exercise to keep a group of young adolescents occupied, exhausted and compliant. We all came to hate the 'hill' by the time our stint had come to an end because our work consisted of attacking the hill with our spades in order to turn over the infertile topsoil for the richer soil lying beneath. The regime was spartan and the work was hard, but at least the food was good and plentiful. The commandant told us that the purpose of the service was to prepare us for the greater sacrifices still required by the nation and that we should be adequately nourished to see us through more difficult times ahead.

Spring was turning to summer and the days began to lengthen. As the weather turned warmer, my duty to gather firewood from the forest became less arduous, for all through March and April, the hut leader was true to his word and each evening, when we had returned to our huts, I was required to go off into the forest and gather firewood. I always had the help of a couple of others, who were ordered to help, but it was always me who had to lead the expedition and many were the evenings when I cursed him.

The cleanliness and tidiness of each hut was never left to an individual, but was the collective responsibility of us all. If anyone was found guilty of leaving something lying around or failing to properly make up his bed then the whole hut was punished. One unfortunate youth in my hut had one day neglected to remove his boots as he entered the hut and had left muddy footprints across the floor. The collective punishment was for the entire floor of the hut to be scrubbed and disinfected, an operation that took more than three hours when we were already exhausted from our normal daily activities. The subsequent beating we handed out to the culprit was a salutary lesson not only to him, but to us all.

I managed to get into trouble myself on a few occasions, but fortunately my punishment was individual rather than collective, thereby avoiding a double punishment. After one extremely wet and soggy expedition to the 'hill', rather than leaving my muddy, saturated boots at the entrance to the hut with all the others, I decided to place them on top of the stove in order to thoroughly dry them out for the next day. Unfortunately I forgot to remove them before dawn and awoke the following morning to find them not only thoroughly dried out, but that the leather had cracked and the sole separated. I reported this mishap to the hut leader who promptly marched me together with my useless boots over to the camp commandant's hut.

After informing me of the necessity of keeping my uniform and equipment in good condition, I was sentenced to three days in the guardhouse on a diet of only bread and water. The guardhouse was really just another hut behind the equipment store. It contained just one bunk bed, a small table and a chair. Light came through a small window high up in one wall and a skylight in the roof; it was impossible to see out. It wasn't comfortable, but at least I had three days respite from digging, but most of all, I was relieved that the commandant had not seen fit to hand out a collective punishment to the hut. Being locked in the guardhouse gave me a kind of celebrity status among the others and one evening, knowing that I was surviving on a meagre ration of bread and water, some of the other boys climbed onto the roof and dropped some food in for me through the skylight, which they had saved from their own meals.

When I got out, I was treated like a hero. The commandant must have taken note of this, for when a similar incident happened in one of the other huts some time later, all the occupants were put on strict rations and the culprit, rather than being the hero, became the villain. Despite such incidents, the regimentation, discipline and hard work, it was difficult to dampen my spirits. It was the first time I had been away from home and I was enjoying the sense of freedom that came from having more responsibility away from the normal restraints of family life.

I returned home at the end of May after completing a four-month stint, but I found that things were not well at home.

19

I discovered upon my return that Hans had been taken ill. When my father told me that he had been taken to hospital, I assumed that he would soon recover; after all, Hans was my big brother, and he had always been strong and robust with never a day's illness in his life. My father knew of his illness when he received a letter from the commanding officer at the Solingen garrison stating that Hans had been moved to a hospital in Wuppertal, an industrial city about fifty miles away from Beckum. The following day my father had caught the train and visited him in the hospital where doctors told him that a bad cold had turned into a case of pneumonia.

Two days after my return from Labour Corps my father went once again to visit him and when he returned that evening he told us that Hans had looked very weak and feverish. It was only after Wilhemina, Heinz and Eugen had gone to bed that my father told Bernie and me that throughout the visit, Hans had been lapsing in and out of consciousness, feverishly mumbling something about punishment duty and standing to attention for hours with a heavy sand-filled knapsack on his back. I had heard stories of the punishments handed out to soldiers for even the most trivial breaches of discipline, men being forced to stand at attention with weights of up to eighty pounds for hours on end, and I suspected that this might have happened to Hans.

After hearing my father's description of Hans's condition, my mother insisted on visiting the hospital herself, so she and my father caught the train to Wuppertal the following morning. She was clearly distressed when she returned, but remained tight-lipped in reply to our questions about Hans, while father went into the sitting room and hid behind his newspaper. Three days later my father once again caught the train to Wuppertal and returned with even greater concern showing on his face, but once again he brushed off our questions with the simple statement that the doctors were doing everything possible.

He would not allow my mother to accompany him on any of the further visits he made to the hospital. Each time we prayed that he would bring news of signs of recovery, but each time he would return with no word of comfort. Instead of Hans being on the mend, it seemed that the fever, which was gripping him, was gradually taking greater control and on my father's last visit, Hans had remained unconscious throughout the entire hour permitted for visitors. The doctors told him that it was meningitis and that, despite their best efforts, they could do no more than hope that the fever would pass. Two days later we received a telegram informing us that he had died.

Many families in the village and throughout the land had suffered the loss of a loved one, but now, after more than three years of war, it was the turn of our family to be touched and we too discovered just how hard a thing it was to bear. Despite the overwhelming sense of loss, it felt in a strange kind of way, that we had also been cheated. In times of war, young men go off to fight, to take part in the cruel lottery that decides who will live and who will die. It is a macabre game of roulette, in which death is the banker and every gambler has only one chance to win and many chances to lose.

Hans was denied his opportunity to spin the wheel of fortune. Before he could take his chance with the guns and shells of the enemy, he had succumbed to an invisible foe that had no need of rifles or heavy ordnance to win the day. He had died a serving soldier, but had never seen the enemy, never fired a shot or left the soil of his homeland. The bitter compensation for our loss was a funeral, a proper funeral with full military honours, for although Hans had not died on the field of battle, he was a serving soldier and the army would give him a soldier's funeral. Unlike the many thousands killed at the front for whom there would only be a forgotten grave beneath the mud of a foreign field, the army would bring Hans home and he would have a proper resting place.

A troop of eighteen soldiers led by a sergeant brought my brother's coffin by train from Wuppertal to Benninghausen station and then carried it shoulder high in solemn procession to our house. I remember waiting outside with my parents, my mother dressed from head to toe in black. It seemed as though the entire village was on hand to pay their respects as the guard of honour placed the coffin, draped in the black, white and scarlet flag, upon a horse-drawn hearse. Many of those who tearfully offered their condolences to my parents had lost one or more of their own, but they had not been able to say farewell to their loved ones and it seemed from the throng of people that in some way we were burying not only my brother, but the dead of the entire village.

The sergeant handed my father the silver crucifix that he had given Hans to wear around his neck for protection and in turn my father gave the sergeant and each of the soldiers who had borne the coffin a glass of schnapps. A neighbour looked after the little ones while Bernie, Wilhelmina and I followed behind my mother and father, walking at the head of the long procession that slowly made its way towards the church in the neighbouring village of Horn. As I sat in the front pew reserved for the immediate family while the service proceeded, it was hard to imagine that Hans, big strong powerful Hans, my friend and protector since I was born, was lying lifeless in the flag draped coffin just a few feet away. Surrounded by the rest of my family and the people of the village that I had known all my life, I had never felt so alone.

I didn't hear a word of the priest's eulogy, I was absorbed in thoughts of the times Hans and I had spent together, some of them in this very church where we had incurred our mother's wrath by telling each other jokes and making faces at the other boys and girls in the congregation when we should have been singing hymns or saying our prayers. Today there were no jokes or laughter, no light-hearted pranks and the admonishment of the adults, just the gentle sobbing of women and the weary sighs of men.

As Hans's coffin was lowered into the grave outside, a chill wind blew through the churchyard and into all our hearts. The tragedy of the war had touched my family at last and I knew that nothing would be the same again.

20

The Stoic

The snow-clad mountains of the Obersalzburg shone gold in the brilliant rays of the morning sun. On the balcony of the Berghof the Leader was relaxing with his aides, but this was a different Leader from the one they had seen before. There had always been the staring eyes that could pierce as surely as any dagger, but there was a palpable dullness behind them now, whether it was the dullness of insanity or the dullness of defeat, none of his aides could be sure.

Some had long thought him mad, even though they had been afraid to voice their fears, but he had always proved them wrong. An endless series of stunning victories had confounded those who forecast that his adventures would result only in defeat and disaster. They had become as intoxicated as the Leader himself by the heady wine of conquest and they too had begun to think that he might indeed be invincible. His increasing belief in his own invincibility had caused him to drop the measured, calculated approach that had seen him rise so far. The risks he had taken in the past had merely been punctuation marks in long paragraphs of measured scheming and calculation, a way of avoiding the many roadblocks set in his path, a last, desperate throw of the dice when no other alternative existed.

Now, like the drunkard who loses any sense of peril, he believed that his risks were not risks at all, but part of a calculated strategy. If he willed something to happen, then it would happen and his own commanders and those of his enemies would be powerless to stop him. He was the absolute leader of an empire, the like of which had never been seen. His empire covered the face of Europe from the steppes of Russia to the Atlantic Ocean and he believed that in histories yet to be written, his conquests would be mentioned in the same breath as those of Alexander, Caesar and Ghengis Khan.

Cowards had never built empires. Empires were created by bold, imaginative men who were blessed with brilliant and incisive minds. The recent defeats on the eastern front were due not to any strategic failure on the Leader's part, but to the inability of lesser men, the generals and commanders in the field who had failed to carry out their orders properly. The entire Sixth Army had been lost to the nation by such failure, but even failure could be turned into victory if the example of heroic self-sacrifice could be held up as a beacon around which the nation could rally. The encirclement by the Russians at Stalingrad would have provided a splendid opportunity for such a sacrifice.

Even when all was lost, it was important never to give up the struggle. At the eleventh hour, the Leader had bestowed upon von Paulus the title of Field Marshall so that he might die with even greater honour. In the end however he had been unwilling to fight to the death, as the Leader himself would have done, and had cravenly surrendered to the Soviets, disobeying a direct order not to give up. Nevertheless, the truth was not as important as the message that would be relayed to the German people. They would not of course be told of any surrender, they would hear only of the heroic sacrifice made by the Sixth Army, which would serve as a beacon for the nation and in a thousand years people would still talk of the heroes of Stalingrad.

As a third of a million men trudged away to Siberian prison camps from which they would never return, the nation was told on February 3rd that the Sixth Army had fought to the last and all had died heroes' deaths. Sombre music was played on the radio and the Leader proclaimed four days of national mourning.

Defeat was a word which did not exist in the Leader's vocabulary and so Stalingrad was not allowed to become a defeat, it was merely a temporary setback caused by the incompetence of those around him. Defeat was something only contemplated and permitted by weaker men like those who had allowed the nation to be defeated just twenty-five years before. The heady wine of victory and triumph was still coursing strongly through the Leader's veins, obscuring the peril around. A mere setback was not the time for introspective reflection and a change in direction, it was a time for resolve and determination, a time for reinforcing the national will and for the message to go out to all commanders that every inch of occupied soil must be held, regardless of the cost.

And so the order was sent, promises were made of re-inforcements and deliveries of arms and material. The German people were at their best when faced with adversity, the Leader would give them the opportunity to show their true mettle and they too would also see that in such times, their Leader would also be at his best.

21

After Hans's funeral I returned to work, resuming my apprenticeship at the building company in Lippstadt, but found that the company was suffering from an even more acute shortage of workers than it had been when I had left some months earlier for the Arbeitsdienst. Men with whom I had worked previously had been called up for military service and it was not just the young ones, some men who were in their late forties had also received the call. Most building projects were well behind schedule and firms frantically scoured the area in a desperate search for the skills they required to complete them. Men who had retired years earlier were put to work with a number of inducements, underpinned as always by the hint that it would be remembered if they did not play their part in the war effort.

February 1943 was the coldest month in living memory. The snow which had fallen in January still lay frozen upon the ground, piled high in crusty, dirt-streaked piles by the side of the roads. In the six months since I had returned from Saarbrucken, I had seen my brother buried and watched my parents age almost overnight; my eighteenth birthday was fast approaching and I knew that my call-up couldn't be far away. The demands of the military were now so great that the age of conscription had been reduced and boys, instead of initially serving time in the Arbeitsdienst as I had done, were now being directly drafted into the army.

For many years we had realised that the newspapers and radio reports rarely told the truth, but when even these official organs began to speak of 'certain difficulties' and 'strategic withdrawals' people sensed that things were going badly wrong. We didn't need to be told about the situation in far away Russia and North Africa , we could see with our own eyes the devastation being visited upon towns and cities throughout the land by the nightly visits of a thousand enemy bombers. I had seen for myself, on the train journey back from Saarbrucken, that great swathes of the industrial heartland in the Ruhr had been reduced to mounds of rubble. It wasn't so bad for the likes of us living in a small rural village, but it was still frightening to hear the drone of the planes during the night on their way to rain death upon some hapless town or city, but occasionally we were reminded of our vulnerability when we heard the crump of explosions coming from the direction of nearby Soest or Lippstadt.

As I was eating my breakfast one morning a radio announcement, preceded by the playing of sombre music, stated that the battle for Stalingrad was over and that true to their oath to fight to the last man, the Sixth Army had finally been overcome by an enemy that significantly outnumbered them. The Leader proclaimed four days of national mourning, but it was only much later that we learnt that despite the fact that he had forbidden the commander, von Paulus to surrender his forces, the Field Marshall had surrendered and a third of a million soldiers had been marched away to their death. When my call-up papers arrived the following day, my parents' misery was complete.

There was never an alternative to entering the military

for young men like myself. I wasn't in a reserved occupation or considered in any way medically unfit, besides I never looked for an escape; I was proud to do my duty and fight for my country as so many others were doing. The only choice I had over the course of my immediate future lay in which branch of the military I joined, and even in this regard the choice was limited due to operational necessity. It seemed to me that the life of an infantryman in the Army was likely to be harsh and short, the Navy similarly held little appeal, particularly if it were the claustrophobic life of the submariner. When the possibility of joining the Air Force as one of its elite paratroopers was mentioned, I was therefore immediately interested.

I certainly didn't choose the paratroopers for my love of flying, for I had never been in an aeroplane, let alone leapt out of one. Unlike paratroops in many other countries, German paratroopers were not part of the Army, but of the Air Force, and one of my reasons for joining was that I had been told that conditions were better than in the Army or the Navy, with better pay and better rations. This was allegedly due to the fact that Goering was head of the Air Force and because he was so close to the Leader, he was given the pick of everything. Whether this was true or not, I don't know, but when given the choice between Army and Air Force I unhesitatingly chose the latter.

The last time my mother sent a son off to war, she had stayed at home rather than accompany him to the station, but this time she came along with the entire family to Benninghausen station where I was to catch my train. I was determined to appear happy and carefree, striving manfully to hide any sign of the apprehension that churned inside. On the long walk to the station I played games of chase with my two younger brothers, Heinz who was seven and little Eugen who was almost four. I thought that my mother would cry, but she remained dry-eyed, her determination in not allowing her emotions to show, mirroring my own. Only the quiver of her lips gave her away as I gave her a final embrace. I hugged and kissed them all before climbing aboard the train and as it began to move off I stuck my head out of the window, watching them turn into a small knot as they receded slowly into the distance.

I was initially sent to an airfield at a small place called Heiligenhafen, 'the holy harbour', which lay on the Baltic coast, but when I stepped off the train it was an unholy wind that blew off the cold, steel-grey sea. I had never been to the coast before and my first shivering glimpse of the wind-tossed waves in the chill of a cold February morning made me glad that I had not volunteered for the Navy. The other new recruits and I were kitted out in our splendid new uniforms: the smart blue tunics and grey-green trousers certainly made us stand out from the drab field-grey that it seemed almost everyone else in the country was wearing. We were considered elite troops so it was only right that we should be distinguished from the rest.

The ten days consisted of filling out endless forms, frequent roll calls and the requisitioning of those parts of our kit that were not immediately available from the stores. Once we had been fully kitted out and had learnt to stand in a passably straight line, we were despatched to a variety of locations. My orders were to attend basic training at a base not in Germany, but near Eindhoven in occupied Holland. It coincidentally turned out to be the very place where my father had been based during the Great War when he had been a member of the neutral Dutch armed forces. Now here I was, his son who had also been a Dutch citizen until just a few short years ago, wearing the uniform of Germany as part of an occupying force. I had changed from being a fellow countryman to one of the despised enemy as far as the local population was concerned.

Fortunately, I never had to contend with any local hostility as we were never permitted to leave the airfield perimeter, even when off-duty. I was there for basic training and that could be done within the confines of the base; when we weren't being drilled or trained in the use of our weapons, our duties were to help guard a large ammunition dump located in the middle of the sprawling site. I was told that there had been a number of incidents where local resistance members had tried to break in, and as a result we were on high alert. As I paced back on forth during my watch with a loaded rifle and orders to shoot on sight, I wondered how it would feel to actually pull the trigger and whether I would hesitate at the thought of killing another human being, a Dutchman perhaps, to whom I might even be related. The time would come when I would know only too well what it was like to pull the trigger and I wouldn't think twice about it.

My questions went unanswered for the time being as there were no incidents during my short stay. With my head full of drill routines and the techniques of firing and maintaining my weapon, I was sent to complete the next phase of my training back on home soil. Gardelegen, situated in the eastern part of Germany, between Magdeburg and Berlin, was an immense military transit camp complete with its own railway station at which hordes of soldiers embarked and disembarked on an almost hourly basis.

Upon arrival, I was assigned to the kitchen where for three weeks I seemed to do little else but peel vegetables. Mountains of potatoes, carrots and turnips would be delivered by truck every day to feed the thousands of soldiers who were resident at any one time. Soldiers would arrive from the west and after a few days depart towards the east, others in turn would complete the journey in the opposite direction; the only constant thing about Gaderlegen was the perpetual change. Everyone had either just arrived or was about to depart for somewhere else. I assumed that someone in high authority understood and was responsible for this apparently random movement of men, but to the casual observer it presented a picture of utter chaos.

Before embarking on the next part of my training, I was surprised and pleased to be given a leave pass. The pass was only valid for five days and that time ran from the moment you passed through the barracks gates to the moment you arrived back. It was never a fair system, particularly for those who had to travel a great distance. Once the clock started running it would not be stopped even if trains were cancelled or delayed; no allowances were made for a late return and although most men would have deemed a few days in the guardhouse on reduced rations to be a reasonable price to pay, it was the penalty of no further leave passes which ensured a prompt return.

Often, men who had been given leave passes found that due to transport delays they had to turn round and return to Gaderlegen before reaching home, in order to make it back before the time expired. I was more fortunate than many as my home lay not too far from the main railway line. I managed to get there within the day and surprised my parents, sister and brothers by walking in unannounced while they were sitting down to the evening meal. Father got out the beer and bottle of schnapps and we spent the evening catching up on each other's news. That night the sound of enemy bombers vaguely disturbed our sleep, but we thought little of it as by now the sound was as familiar as a passing thunderstorm. It was only on the following day that we discovered that the target had not been the cities of Dortmund or Beilefeld, but the Mohne Dam which lay fifteen miles away to the south of our village.

There had been a great loss of life as the dam was breached and the land below inundated with millions of gallons of water from the reservoir. My sister and brothers were at school and my father had to go to work that day, so with nothing better to do, I borrowed my father's bike and went to see the damage for myself. I had only been to the dam once before, even though it lay just a few miles on the other side of Soest. It had been a hot summer's day some years earlier when Hans and I had gone there on an outing with the Youth for a picnic and swimming in the lake.

I put on my uniform, put some bread and sausage in my pack and pedalled out of the village in the direction of Soest. I passed through the town centre and was leaving the outskirts when I recognised the familiar uniform of a paratrooper walking towards me. He waved and I stopped. He told me that he had been down to the dam, but had come away because the police were rounding up every able bodied man to help with rescue and recovery. He advised me to turn back because they weren't making any distinction between civilians and men in uniform. He, like myself, had a leave pass and had to get back before it expired. He knew that being forced to help with the emergency would be no excuse when he eventually got back to his base. I thought about it for a few moments, he was probably right, but I decided that I had to see the devastation for myself.

I cycled further down the road, but two miles short of the dam I hid my father's bike behind a hedge and proceeded on foot across the fields where I was less likely to be challenged. I climbed the low hills on the northern shore and reached the crest. I gasped at the sight that unfolded below me. The blue lake of memory was now a vista of rocks and islands of mud amid pools of brackish water. It looked as though someone had removed an enormous plug and allowed it to empty, leaving only the sediment. Across to the western end, I could see two jagged stumps of concrete, all that remained of the proud and robust dam that had once stood there.

I couldn't see very far beyond the spot where the dam had once stood as the ground fell away and I tried to imagine what it must have been like to be suddenly engulfed by a wall of water that must have poured through the breached dam. Gangs of workers were already beginning to move piles of broken concrete around the dam, while further down the valley, out of sight, no doubt bodies were being removed from the inundated towns and villages that had lain in the path of the deluge. I dared not approach any nearer for fear of being forced to help in the work, not that I would have objected to helping, but like the fellow paratrooper I had met earlier, I too was conscious of getting back to Gaderlegen on time.

I remembered Goering's boast that the enemy would never be able to bomb the country. The boast had been made years earlier when the war had only just started, when it seemed that we were able to beat our enemies with ease. Now, we were being bombed every night and increasingly during the day. Hundreds of thousands of Germans had been killed or burned in towns and cities across the land and now this and other dams had been hit, creating new and different kinds of death for those unfortunate enough to be in the way.

I lay there on the hilltop eating my crust of bread, and as

I surveyed the empty lake below, for the first time in my life I began to fear for the future. I finished eating and, taking one last look, walked back down the hill, retrieved my bicycle and pedalled home. My remaining few days at home passed all too quickly and I returned to the barracks at Gaderlegen with six hours to spare on my leave pass.

Just when it seemed that the whole point of my training to date had been to provide me with the ability to peel and slice vegetables, the reality of my decision to join the Luftwaffe as a paratrooper began to sink in. After weeks of making me perform humdrum tasks, life was about to become more exciting. They were going to make me jump out of an aeroplane.

22

I was sent to an airfield at nearby Stendal where the training initially took place in a large hangar, the floor of which had been covered with thick, padded mats. The new conscripts began by standing on the floor and were instructed how to bend knees and roll on impact. We rolled forwards, backwards and sideways before progressing to a platform some six feet from the ground, and endlessly repeated the procedure for a whole day until our legs were aching. Our rolling techniques perfected, we graduated to a much higher platform from which we would jump in a harness to get the feel of being suspended beneath a parachute. We were taught how to swing our legs and pull on the harness ropes to manoeuvre ourselves into position before the harness was released and we dropped onto the mats below.

The next stage in our training was to practise jumping out of a plane, but this would not yet be in the air. An old fuselage with a door aperture was rigged up on a platform at one side of the airfield, into which we would climb and attach our harnesses to the overhead wire. With parachute packs on our backs we would jump out of the door in rapid succession and land some ten feet below in a sand pit. The instructors constantly stressed the necessity of following each other rapidly out of the plane to ensure that the entire 'stick' of paratroopers landed as close together in the drop zone as possible.

After two days practising these 'jumps' we were considered sufficiently trained to make our first falls from an aeroplane, but first we had to learn how to control our parachutes after we had landed. To practise this technique a 'wind donkey' was used. This consisted of a propeller engine mounted in an old Junkers airframe which was used to create a strong, artificial wind. We were instructed to lie on the ground with our parachutes unfurled and then the engine would be started up, our chutes would gradually fill and we would then be dragged along the ground. The objective was to get to your feet as quickly as possible, run around the other side of the chute and gather the silk into a ball.

It was easier said than done. On my first attempt I was dragged, kicking and rolling for over fifty yards before I finally managed to scramble to my feet and get the parachute under some kind of control. When I eventually managed to roll the yards of material into a ball, the wind donkey seemed an awfully long way away. The instructor was clearly unimpressed with my efforts and told me that if I was that slow in a real battle situation, I was more likely to kill the enemy with my flailing body than with my rifle. I had to take my turn repeatedly until I met the instructor's requirements and by the end of the day the trousers of my uniform were in shreds. I had bruises too numerous to count and though every part of my body ached, I slept well that night.

I was still not ready to make my first jump for I had to learn how to fold and pack the parachute. This was the scariest part, for you knew that your life depended upon this procedure being done correctly; all the other techniques I had learned would count for nothing if the 'chute didn't open. It would have somehow felt more comfortable to believe that my parachute had been packed by some anonymous 'expert', but the thought that you alone were responsible for saving your own life certainly concentrated the mind.

One of the hangars was filled with rows of incredibly long tables upon which parachutes were draped and I watched as the silks were folded then rolled, the lines neatly coiled before the whole thing was stuffed into a bag no bigger than a regular rucksack. We all rolled, folded and coiled the maze of ropes and endless yards of silk, then unpacked and repeated the procedure over again until we felt confident. It took half a day to pack them at first, but with repetition we eventually managed to accomplish the task in less than an hour. By the time we had packed the 'chutes for the tenth time, it was announced that these were the parachutes we would be using the following day. A mixture of fear and excitement prevented me falling straight to sleep that night, as I contemplated the following morning. I would not only be making my first flight in an aeroplane, but would also be jumping out of it. Despite all the training I had been given, I wondered if, when the moment arrived, I would be scared.

The following day we marched out onto the airfield. I tried hard to stop my hands shaking as I entered the rear door of the Junkers JU52 with twenty other new recruits. I had never been this close to an aeroplane before and as I climbed aboard I drew no comfort from the fact that the flimsy looking fuselage appeared to be constructed out of a light corrugated material, not unlike the roof of my father's garden shed.

We would not have the luxury of pulling our own ripcords as the 'chutes were attached to a static line which ran overhead along the length of the cabin. It would not be left to chance, the line would automatically pull the ripcord on the parachute after we had fallen thirty meters out of the plane. The sergeant barked out his instructions for us to sit down in lines along each side of the fuselage, and when the last man sat down the pilot wound up the engines from a mere roar to a high-pitched scream. The aircraft begin to roll, bouncing down the grassy runway as its speed increased.

The sergeant sat down next to one of the recruits, Kaussen, a spotty youth from Berlin who had earlier asked what he should do if he was too afraid to make the jump. The sergeant had bellowed with laughter before informing the unfortunate youth that it was not a question of whether he had the nerve to jump or not, but only a question of whether he jumped himself or whether the sergeant would have to throw him bodily out of the plane. I sat and watched beads of sweat forming on his face and felt much better knowing that at least one person on board was as frightened as I was.

The plane shuddered and vibrated as it turned and climbed away from the runway. The noise made any attempt at conversation impossible and so we contented ourselves with making encouraging smiles and grimaces at one another with the occasional raised thumb to keep our spirits up. My ears popped as the plane continued its slow climb into the heavens. There were only a few windows cut into the sides of the fuselage and although some faint shafts of light filtered through, only the dim red glow from a single light above the rear door illuminated the frightened passengers.

Some fifteen minutes after take-off, I heard the engines being throttled back and sensed that the plane had levelled off. We were to jump out at three thousand feet above the airfield. Now all the hours of classroom instruction were about to be put to the test. I mentally ran through the sequence of events: jump clear, arms and legs spread, face down, raise arms to hold harness straps when 'chute has deployed; if 'chute fails to open pull on reserve 'chute toggle – as I fingered it for re-assurance I wondered if perhaps the Army might have been a better option.

The sergeant got to his feet and began attaching our parachute cords to the static wire. He worked his way down the cabin until he reached the rear door, which he pulled open. There was a horrific noise as the howl of air rushing past the opening combined with the roar of the engines. We waited for the pilot to indicate that we were above the drop zone by turning the jump light to green. I was ten men away from the door so I knew that the petrified Kaussen would jump before me.

The engines throttled back a little more and the light changed to green. The sergeant motioned for us to get to our feet, and unsteadily we arose and began shuffling towards the door. The sergeant stood by the door and gave the first jumper a gentle push, then one after the other as they each disappeared through the door. As I slowly made my way down the fuselage, I saw the sergeant take a firm hold of the Berliner and throw him out of the door. Now it was the turn of the youth in front of me, my mouth was dry and my chest felt tight. The boy in front of me disappeared and I felt the firm grip of sergeant's hand on my shoulder; the noise was deafening. I paused momentarily in the doorway and then I was out, falling and tumbling towards the earth below.

There was a sudden shock of silence as I fell away from the frantic howl of the aircraft's engines. Remembering my instructions, I stuck out my arms and legs to stabilise my tumbling only seconds before an urgent jolt arrested my fall. I gasped and gripped the straps of the parachute tightly, looking up in relief to see the white silk umbrella opening above my head. After a moment or two I relaxed and looked around to see the others around me descending slowly from the pale blue cloudless sky and then nervously down at the ground below. After what seemed no more than a few seconds I looked down to see the grass of the airfield rushing up towards me at an alarming speed. .I prepared myself for impact, then hit the ground and rolled over. A stiff breeze caught the parachute and dragged me across the grass for a few yards before I managed to unclip the harness.

I stood up and yelled at the top of my voice. I can't remember what I shouted. I could find no words adequate to describe the feeling of relief, excitement and sheer thrill of what I had just done. All the tension and nerves came flooding out as the fellows landing around me burst into laughter and whoops of delight. Only Kaussen remained on the ground, kneeling and vomiting on the grass. At last I'd done it and what's more, I wanted to get right back in the plane and do it again. Next time I would enjoy the whole jump and not just the few calm seconds before I hit the ground. At least that's what I thought, but the instructor had other plans.

23

The remaining two weeks I spent at Stendal were weeks of tedium and routine, punctuated only by the brief excitement of the practice jumps. As the group became more proficient, we jumped at progressively lower altitudes; the sergeant told us that in combat, if we floated gently down over enemy territory from more than three thousand feet there would be no need to worry about our landing technique because we would already have been shot.

We became more confident with each jump, even Kaussen, the spotty Berliner, was able to jump out without waiting for a firm shove in his back from the flight sergeant. The problem with the lower altitudes was that there was less reaction time, especially if the reserve 'chute had to be deployed, but even if all went to plan, the ground seemed to rush up and hit you very quickly. Many of the recruits had severe bruises and sprained ankles to show for their efforts, despite the fact that we were becoming more proficient.

Oberleutnant Kruger was in overall charge of jumping practice. A scarred veteran of numerous campaigns, his own jumping days had come to an end when he had taken a bullet in the leg while parachuting into Crete. It was three days before he was found on a remote hillside and by that time gangrene had set in. His left leg had been amputated above the knee in a makeshift field hospital and he'd returned home an embittered man with an obsession that high level parachuting should be avoided at all costs - the costs being the broken limbs and other injuries suffered by the trainee paratroopers in his charge whom he commanded to jump at heights which were almost suicidal.

After we had made half a dozen jumps from varying heights and in different weather conditions, Kruger informed us that our last jump was to be made at a mere eighty meters. In our pre-jump briefing I could see that the sergeant who accompanied us on the flight was nervous, and as experienced as he was, he himself had never jumped from less than one hundred and fifty meters. Technically there was no reason why a jump could not take place at such a low altitude in good weather. The 'chute would deploy as soon as the paratrooper was out of the plane, the jump would take place in nothing more than a light breeze, but it would be a short drop and there was absolutely no margin for error.

We knew the routine by heart as we trudged out towards the faithful Junkers for the short flight. There was a fairly low cloud base that day, but very little wind. I looked up to the sky before I pulled myself into the plane, we wouldn't even be halfway up to the cloud base before we jumped out. It seemed as though we had barely taken off before the light above the exit door turned from red to green. I was to be the first out this time and I edged towards the open door at the rear. I glanced out and saw the ground below looking perilously close; it seemed more like the view of the ground from the roof of a building rather than from an aeroplane. I felt the sergeant's hand on my shoulder, took a deep breath and threw myself out. I had only fallen a few feet when I felt the familiar jolt of the chute opening above me. My instinctive sigh of relief was cut short by the sight of the ground rushing up towards me. I had only a couple of seconds to think about it before I hit the ground and rolled over. It was a very hard landing, but I heard no cracks of breaking bone and felt no shooting pains. As I pulled in the lines and gathered up my 'chute, my comrades dropped around me and it was clear from the screams and shouts that many of them had made far harder landings than I.

Oberleutnant Kruger stood at the edge of the drop zone inspecting the events through his binoculars. The flight sergeant who had jumped last was running around the drop zone, checking the troopers, many of whom remained on the ground. I then saw him run up to Kruger, gesticulating wildly. I moved nearer and was shocked to hear the sergeant shouting at his superior officer. He continued to bellow at him for some time while the officer stood, saying nothing. Having had his say, the sergeant strode away leaving an apparently shocked Kruger standing motionless and silent.

It took the ambulance twenty minutes to pick up all the injured from the airfield. Out of the thirty who jumped, two had concussion, six had fractured bones requiring hospitalisation and a further twelve had sustained severe bruising. I was miraculously unscathed. I later heard that Kruger was court-martialled for putting the men under his command at unnecessary risk. It appeared that all the months of training we had undergone to produce urgently needed troops for the war effort had been undone in the space of ten minutes by the recklessness of one officer. Instead of being fully trained and ready to go to the front, a third of the company were in hospital and another third had been placed on sick leave; the confidence we had gained from repeated jumps had been shattered by this one moment of madness.

It was March 1944 and the war was well into its fifth year. I had promised to write home once a week, but had only managed one hastily scribbled note every two weeks, although I had received more regular letters from home. My father usually wrote the letter, though my mother would often add a few lines at the end. They kept me informed of events at home, of how Wilhelmina was enjoying being a member of the 'Maidens' League' a youth movement for girls, of how Heinz was doing well at school and of how little Eugen was excitedly looking forward to starting school in a few months' time.

In one of his letters my father said that Bernie had now been called up and had joined the SS Panzer Corps. I wasn't sure what to make of this. The SS were despised by many other branches of the military for their harsh discipline and because of their reputation for brutality. I couldn't imagine a man less likely to join the SS than little Bernie, a gentle soul more at home with the horses on the farm than with members of an elite fighting force. It was only later that I discovered that he hadn't really been given much of a choice, he had only been given the option of either the SS or the Navy submariners, and I supposed that he had chosen the SS because he could not have endured the claustrophobic conditions of a U-boat. If Bernie had been given a real choice, he would have chosen not to join anything at all, he would have remained on the farm looking after the animals and returning home every night to his mother's cooking. I worried for Bernie.

In the meantime, those of us who had completed our jumps and were still able to walk, returned to Gaderlegen and were allowed to go into town and celebrate before we received our postings, which would inevitably come through in a matter of days. Putting thoughts of Russia or Italy to the back of my mind, a dozen of us walked the two miles into town where we spent the afternoon drinking in the various bars in the centre of the town. The beer was weak, but we compensated for that by drinking greater quantities, for nothing was going to prevent us having a good time while we were still able. None of us knew what the coming days would bring, but we had a shrewd idea that it wouldn't involve the pleasures of drinking German beer in a cosy bar on home soil.

The afternoon and evening was passed in singing songs, telling jokes and in devising ever more absurd drinking games. We drank copiously in all the bars until, with our pooled finances perilously close to exhaustion, we staggered into Renschler's Bar for a final drink. Renschler's bar was on the outskirts of the town, quite close to the airfield and most of his customers naturally were men from the base. It was otherwise deserted as we ordered a final round of beer and schnapps. We toasted one another and, as was customary, downed the schnapps in one go.

"Sheise!" roared one of our number, a large Bavarian called Bernsmann. "This isn't schnapps, it's water."

Bernsmann slammed the empty glass on to the table. Despite the general level of inebriation, others had also detected the weakness of the drink and complained similarly. Bernsmann got unsteadily to his feet and went to the bar to make his complaint to Renschler, but he dismissed the accusation that he had watered down the schnapps with an imperious wave of his hand. Some others joined Bernsmann at the bar to support his claim, but Renschler was as unmoved as he was unwise. A bar full of drunken paratroopers, about to be sent to fight and possibly die for their country, were not a group to be trifled with. Instead of apologising and offering another drink on the house, Renschler cursed us for our audacity at complaining about the quality of his schnapps.

I didn't see who threw the first chair, but it was quickly followed by the sound of breaking glasses as our table was upturned and the glasses crashed to the floor. The bar was soon transformed into a riot of broken glass and smashed furniture. Renschler had prudently disappeared and the mayhem continued until we had satisfied ourselves that no piece of furniture was left unbroken and that no glasses remained intact. Continuing to shout our curses at the odious and unpatriotic bar owner who had attempted to short change the nation's elite troops, we kicked open the door and staggered outside into the gathering dusk.

We linked arms and sang on the walk home, but the cool breeze blowing into our faces had a sobering effect and by the time we reached the barracks, some of us were beginning to doubt the wisdom of our actions in Renschler's bar.

24

A bitterly cold wind swept in from the east, across the flat countryside, cutting through my uniform and chilling me to the bone. I shivered and pulled my greatcoat tightly around me. It was almost April, but winter lingered and I was glad that I wasn't headed for the East. I had already been waiting on the platform for more than three hours for the train that was supposed to take me to France when a paratrooper approached me, lit two cigarettes and handed me one.

"Fucking Officers ! We could have been warm in our barracks for a few more hours instead of freezing our arses on this godforsaken railway platform."

I pulled on the cigarette that he had given me.

"Better here than in the guardhouse" I replied, unconvincingly.

The man spat.

"At least it would have been warm in the guardhouse. I'm Rudiger Frischke" he said, thrusting a meaty palm towards me. "Call me Rudi."

We shook hands as the icy wind blew across the platform. At least the cold air was beginning to make my headache disappear. I had noticed this man Frischke in the camp before, he was hard to miss, standing well over six feet tall with a mane of black hair. A good five years older than me, he had been in the paras for three years and had seen action in Crete and the Balkans. Why he'd turned up at

Gardelegen wasn't quite clear; I suspected that he too had been involved in some breach of discipline, but whatever the reason, he'd also found himself posted to France.

There were about a dozen other paratroopers on the platform, some trying to sleep and others sitting around in small groups smoking and playing cards. Braun, the Feldwebel who would accompany our little group, had disappeared into the warmth of the sentry hut, the bastard, but at least he wasn't out on the platform to make a nuisance of himself. Trains would periodically pass both eastbound and westbound, some were full, but others were largely empty. Often, a train that rumbled past in one direction would shortly return an hour later going in the other direction. I supposed that someone somewhere knew what was going on, but to me the movement of trains and the soldiers on them seemed entirely random and without purpose.

It was well past midnight when yet another train trundled up to the platform. It seemed no different to any of the others that we had seen over the past four hours except that this one stopped. The Feldwebel stirred himself, pulling on his overcoat as he emerged from his cosy lair. Everyone on the platform took this as their cue, hastily gathering their packs and rifles and getting into something resembling an orderly line. The Feldwebel ordered us to number off before allowing us to clamber aboard the train. Rudi and I jumped on, finding the carriages virtually empty and in the absence of any direct orders, we grabbed a compartment at the rear, as near to the kitchen wagon as possible. The carriage was unheated, but in comparison to the icy platform it felt like heaven.

Rudi deposited his gear on one of the bench seats before disappearing to see if anything was happening in the kitchen-wagon. He returned a few minutes later grinning from ear to ear, his mess tin filled with some cold potatoes and a watery stew.

"Food's supposed to be ready in an hour so I took these to be going on with while the cook wasn't looking."

It didn't take too long to realise that Rudi had an unerring ability to lift things that did not belong to him and I guessed that if he were not in uniform, he would more than likely be in prison. As I gratefully helped myself to the food he had brought for me, I kept my thoughts to myself.

We wolfed down the cold potatoes as the train lurched and shuddered into life with a squealing of wheels. The barracks, which had been my home for the past six months, slid slowly away out of sight and I wondered what the Commandant had told the police when they arrived. Perhaps they were in his office right now. He would probably send them away with a flea in their ear for he was a man who believed in looking after the men under his command and was the only officer at Gaderlegen about whom the men ever had a good word to say.

It was some hours after we had returned to our barracks the previous evening and sobered up a little, that we realised that Renschler would certainly complain to the police about his wrecked bar. We had decided to go and see the Commandant before he received a visit from the police and tell him what had happened. He'd listened to our story impassively and without interruption until we finished. To say he wasn't pleased was putting it mildly, but when he finally did calm down, he told us that he had far more respect for men who might shortly be dying for their country than for an odious cheat like Otto Renschler who apparently had a long history of short changing his customers.

We didn't escape punishment entirely, but instead of throwing us in the guardhouse, he had a stamp placed in each of our *soldbuchs* indicating that we had been guilty of a misdemeanour. He told us that he would make sure that by the time the police knocked on his door we would be long gone. It would mean a last minute change in orders and instead of our group being sent to Italy in two days' time as originally planned, we would be split up and leave on the first available train from Gaderlegen that night.

The train chugged through the darkened countryside, clattering along slowly with frequent stops in the middle of the countryside for no apparent reason and on numerous occasions it was shunted off into a siding to allow other, faster trains to pass. By dawn we had only just made it through Hannover when the train ground to yet another stop. I got up and leaned out of the window to get some fresh air when a few moments later an express with shiny black carriages and opaque windows flashed by on the main track, heading east in the direction of Berlin. I wondered who could be in such a hurry, while we who were headed for the front were moving so slowly.

Rudi must have read my thoughts.

"Don't be so impatient Theo, we'll get there soon enough. Look at it this way, we're warm and dry, the food's not so bad, there are no officers ordering us about and no-one's shooting at us, so count your blessings."

He was right of course. The occupants of the express train would probably never be sent to fight at the front, perhaps that explained their hurry. Our westward journey continued, much of it completed during the hours of darkness to avoid enemy air raids. The unlit train crawled onwards, passing through countless darkened towns and cities across northern Germany until dawn broke, when we

would invariably be shunted into a siding for the remainder
of the day. Our orders were not to leave the train, but these
we ignored in order to get out and stretch our legs, relieving
the monotony by walking along the carriages and talking to
other soldiers. The problem was that we never knew when
the train was going to move off again, so venturing very far
from the tracks was out of the question. The consequences of
missing the train and being returned to Garderlegen were
too fearful to contemplate - even if the fuss at Renschler's
Bar had blown over there was a distinct possibility that we
might be shot for desertion.

And so it went, countless days of inactivity, nights spent
trundling along in the darkness and the steady stream of
soldiers joining the train at various halts along the way. I
wondered if our route might take us along the railway line
that ran at the back of my house in Beckum - it was
incredible to think that though I was headed for the front, I
might pass within yards of my home. I would peer out into
the darkness, searching for any familiar sign or building that
might indicate that I was close to home, but I recognised
none. Perhaps we had taken a different route or perhaps we
had passed close by my sleeping family while I too slept.

Rudi told me something of his time in Crete and Greece
where he had made a number of jumps when our forces had
taken control of the region. As I suspected, he told me that
he had been sent back to Gaderlegen after a series of
discipline breaches, including punching an officer. He had
been expecting a posting to Russia ,which was frequently the
punishment for such misdemeanours, when he had a stroke
of luck. An old friend of his from Hamburg happened to be
working in the CO's office and had managed to delete his
name from the list of men due to leave for Russia and
inserted it in the list of those bound for France. He had been

as anxious as I was to get away from Gaderlegen before anyone realised what had happened.

We eventually crossed the Rhine and entered a town on its western bank as dusk descended. The station seemed to have taken a direct hit, for working parties were busily clearing away rubble and collecting twisted pieces of wrought iron which had once formed part of the station roof. The line must also have been damaged because gangs of labourers under the watchful eye of armed guards lined the track; using shovels and wheelbarrows, they were rough looking fellows wearing long brown coats.

"Russians" said Rudi, studying them from the carriage window.

As the train ground to a halt, the hollow-cheeked men leaned on their shovels and looked up at us. I had never seen prisoners this close before and wondered how long they must have been here, forced to work in labour gangs far from their homes. I leaned out of the window, glanced around to see that no one was looking and tossed a cigarette towards the prisoner closest to me. The unshaven man with sunken eyes seemed surprised, but grabbed it and swiftly thrust it into his pocket before anyone noticed. He acknowledged me with a faint nod; for a moment the two of us acted simply as one human being to another, each complicit in a small way for breaking rules that forbade such a simple act of humanity between men wearing different uniforms. In response to the blow of a whistle from one of the guards, he turned and trudged away with the rest of the prisoners.

"What did you do that for?" demanded Rudi who had watched the transaction.

"I don't know!" I replied lamely

That hairy Russian bastard would slit your throat and rape your sister given half a chance," he said.

Rudi was probably right, but it had seemed a harmless enough gesture. I wondered how I would feel if I were a prisoner and how well or badly I would be treated; after all, he was just a young soldier like me who had been fighting for his country. In different circumstances I might have had a lot more in common with the hollow-cheeked Russian than some of my comrades-in-arms.

It took six days to reach the border and even then I wouldn't have noticed had Rudi not pointed out that the signposts were in French. I hadn't a clue where we were, though Rudi said that he thought it was probably Belgium and not France. The train continued its pattern of moving slowly through the night and then shunting off into a siding where we usually remained throughout the hours of daylight. I was beginning to get tired of all this inactivity; at least in the training camp we had been given days or evenings off, but here on the train in our cramped compartment, I was growing tired of the interminable games of cards, the countless cigarettes and the same old meals. I could tell that Rudi was itching to do a little exploration in the towns and villages we passed through and which he reckoned might contain an open bar and perhaps a couple of mademoiselles to while away the hours of boredom.

For the last few days of our journey, the train increasingly travelled during daylight hours, passing through pleasant farming country where the small towns and neat villages seemed untouched by war. It seemed that the further we travelled away from our own country, the more normality prevailed. There was a complete absence of ruined buildings, farmers were going about their business in the fields and occasionally we would see groups of children playing near the line. On the nineteenth day of our journey, the fields and woodlands gradually gave way to houses, at first just one or two dotted here and there, then larger groups which eventually gave way to continuous rows of houses and streets. It was clear that we were approaching a large city and, having been told nothing of our destination, Rudi and I craned our necks out of the window in an attempt to find out where we were.

Suddenly Rudi bellowed, "Sheise! I can see the Eiffel Tower! We're in Paris."

Paris! Things were certainly looking up. I had heard all about Paris from the soldiers in the camp at Garderlegen, the bars, the restaurants ………and of course the girls. Now here we were, but the big question was…. would we be allowed to get off this damned train which had been our home for almost two weeks?

25

The Strategist

The Leader had led the country to the brink of the abyss, yet conceded no error, still believing that the tide could be turned. When he spoke of this, his cronies and the generals who should have known better would shuffle their feet and cough nervously instead of confronting him with reality. Cravenly they agreed to his demands, obeyed his strictures to hold this line or seize that objective and never questioned his orders to bring up non-existent divisions that would deliver tons of non-existent munitions to breach the gaps and plug the holes. The huge maps spread out on the table in the briefing room had long been immense works of fiction. Created in the days when everything had seemed possible, when any target on any horizon was both legitimate and achievable, they were faithful in every topographical detail yet filled with armies and divisions long since dead or marched into captivity.

The coloured, wooden blocks that lay scattered upon the surface of the map indicated the position of divisions and entire armies, black to denote the Axis forces and red to denote those of the enemy. During their discussions, these blocks would be pushed here and there to various points across the map, gliding over the smooth surface with great facility. A gentle shove with a field marshal's baton was enough to send perhaps fifty thousand men into a new position from which they could better counter the thrusts of the enemy. The effortless progress of these wooden blocks was never hampered by the shortage of serviceable vehicles or lack of fuel. Wooden blocks never required food and ammunition; they were never damaged or reduced in size by casualties, malnutrition or frostbite.

The blocks could be moved easily at the Leader's whim and no one dared to tell him that they could not so easily be moved on the battlefield. Had they summoned up the resolve to tell him the truth he would not have believed them, for he had been in this situation before. In the early years when those around him were full of doubt and confusion, he alone had the clarity of purpose to seize the opportunities that presented themselves. If he had listened to his generals then, they would not have beaten France so swiftly or been able to advance so far in the east. He knew in his heart that he was the superior strategist whether in the realm of politics or on the battlefield. His generals may have attended the finest military academies in the land, but in the final analysis they were merely men who must be led.

The Leader's strategic decisions bore the hallmark of genius and true genius was beyond the capability and comprehension of men cut from more ordinary cloth. Even after all the successes, he knew they still doubted him, still thought him merely lucky, and this stiffened his resolve to overrule their feeble objections. He recognised that it was the fate of genius to be misunderstood and that weaker men would inevitably fail to comprehend his powers. Ever since the early days in Vienna he had known that he was different. He knew that the people who shunned and despised him then were the same as those who surrounded him now, the only difference was that now they had to listen, now they were within his power and it was a power he would never relinquish.

Because of this omnipotence, a conspiracy of silence and acquiescence enveloped him; he could not read the writing on the wall for he was not permitted by those around him even to see the wall. A man with total power over those around him is a lonely man, for none will speak the truth, especially when the truth is distasteful. So the men of high command, the field marshals and the generals continued to demur to his demands, his impossible orders would be carried out with a curt nod and a snap of heels and none dare tell him that they would not and could not work.

But there were some who had tired of this. There were some who could clearly see the wall and they could read the writing upon it.

26

To my great joy we were ordered to gather up all our belongings and assemble on the platform under the cavernous glass arch of the Gare de L'Est. The fifty other paratroopers and I formed up in two columns behind Feldwebel Braun and a junior officer who had been waiting at the station. We then marched out of the station and through the cobbled streets of the great city to our billet in a nearby hotel. The walls of the entrance lobby were covered in rich, but faded fabric and immense crystal chandeliers hung from the gilt moulded ceiling. I gazed open-mouthed at the opulence of my surroundings, I had never been in a hotel in my life, not a real hotel, the small one in Lippstadt was functional and plain with just a few rooms for travelling businessmen, but it was nothing like this. Any thoughts of a comfortable four-poster bed with soft feather pillows, however, were soon shattered when we were shown to our rooms. The faded wallpaper and crystal chandelier were present, but whatever elegant furniture it must once have contained was long gone, replaced by two standard army issue bunk beds identical to the ones we had left behind in the barracks at Gaderlegen.

I was assigned a room with Rudi and two others, Waldhof and Meise who had joined the train in Hannover. I consoled myself with the thought that it was nevertheless a huge improvement on the railway carriage that had been my home for the past three weeks. The room was situated on the third floor at the front of the hotel and from the window there was a view of the elegant tree-lined boulevard below. There was clearly no bomb damage here, no boarded-up windows or sand-bagged anti-aircraft gun emplacements on street corners; had it not been for the groups of soldiers standing outside the hotel entrance it would have been easy to forget that we were at war at all. The citizens of Paris, dressed in civilian clothes, were going about their daily business, walking their dogs, visiting the shops and reading newspapers in the cafés.

No-one in command thought it necessary to tell us how long we would be staying, but it was clear from the constant comings and goings that the hotel was being used as a staging point for troops arriving or departing from the nearby station. I could only hope that we might be allowed to stay long enough to enjoy some of the pleasures the city had to offer. Rudi and I went down to the lobby where we found Sergeant Braun. We asked him if he knew what our orders were, but it turned out that he knew little more than we did, either about how long we might remain here or the whereabouts of our ultimate destination.

"You can be sure the bastards will have some plans for us to be sent to the back of beyond," said Rudi. "Come on Theo, we'd better take our chance to have some fun before it's too late."

I was feeling rather weary after the endless nights on the train and even the uninviting bunks in the hotel room seemed heaven sent, but I could sense that Rudi wasn't going to allow me to sleep when there was a rare opportunity to have some fun. As we hurried out through the front door we heard Braun shout: "The brothel's on the corner at the end of the street."

A brothel! I wasn't too sure about this, but I could see that Rudi's mind was already made up, his jaw set with the same determined look that I had seen before. He was heading straight down the road for the building that the sergeant had mentioned. I swallowed hard; like most teenagers I'd had the usual fumblings with some of the girls in the village, but like all good girls they had only allowed me to go so far, allowing me to place a hand up their skirt to touch their soft thighs, or if I was lucky, they might permit a hand inside their blouses for a fondle of breast. Nothing went further than that, but now here I was in Paris, legendary city of pleasurable excess and striding up to a brothel where, despite all my brave talk, my inexperience with the opposite sex would surely be discovered.

Knots of soldiers were loitering on the corner as we went up the steps. As with the hotel which had been turned into our temporary barracks, this building was also elegant, but worn. The rich, embossed wallpaper of red and gold must have looked magnificent in its day, but along with everything else it was now dusty and faded. Rudi strode purposefully up to the desk where a middle-aged woman sat smoking a cigarette in a silver holder. If the establishment's decoration was well past its prime then this lady certainly fell into the same category. Her hair was blonde and unnaturally shiny which only served to make her face, smothered as it was with pancake makeup, appear like a white mask punctuated only by two black eyes and the hideous red gash of her mouth.

The feelings of misapprehension I already had were heightened by this apparition and for a moment I wondered whether all the women in the establishment looked so awful; if they did I had a feeling that my manhood might completely shrivel up in disgust. In a room which led off the entrance hall a number of women were lounging on sofas, glasses in their hands and talking to soldiers. I was relieved to see that they looked considerably younger than the harpy at the desk.

"Twenty minutes, ten marks,' she said in a businesslike tone.

Rudi slammed his money down on the counter. She counted it and nodded in the direction of the stairs.

"Room 14" she said, and then turned to me, looking me up and down.

She smiled, her red-coated lips parting to reveal a set of yellowing teeth.

"Sending us boys now are they?" she said, licking her lips suggestively.

I was well aware that I didn't look my age, though I liked to believe that when I was in uniform I looked like a man of experience. This old hag had, however, seen right through my disguise.

"First time?" she asked as I blushed furiously.

"N..nn.....no!" I stammered.

From her knowing smile it was clear that she didn't believe me. Thankfully, Rudi had already disappeared upstairs, but as I looked around three other paratroopers had gathered behind me to witness my discomfort. Now that the old hag had an audience, she was clearly beginning to enjoy herself.

"I think I'll send you to Michelle," she said. "She will be gentle with you, unless................" she paused for a moment, winking at the older men standing behind me. "Unless perhaps you might like someone with a little more experience.............." She unclipped the front of her blouse, allowing her enormous breasts to cascade out. She took hold of my hand to place it on them, but I pulled away.

"I'll take good care of you," she cackled, gathering up her breasts and replacing them inside her blouse before adding, "I will only charge you five marks for the privilege, it's been a long time since I had a virgin."

As the men behind roared with laughter, I turned and ran out into the street, my humiliation complete. I strode down the streets and boulevards as my face burnt with a mixture of fury and embarrassment. I walked until my cheeks began to cool. I knew that there were standing orders not to venture out alone and that I risked being picked up by the military police, but I continued my furious march until I reached the river. I leant on the parapet for half an hour, smoking one cigarette after the other, gazing at the magnificent sweep of the river and the grand buildings that lined its banks. When I had finished my last cigarette, I decided I had better return to the hotel, which I eventually found more than an hour later. Relived that Braun was nowhere to be seen, I went straight up to the room and found Rudi lying on his bunk.

He sat up when I entered.

"Theo! Where the hell have you been?"

"Walking," I replied.

"Christ! She couldn't have been much good," he laughed.

I realised that he couldn't have known about my embarrassing retreat from the brothel.

"She was alright, I just needed some fresh air," I answered in what I hoped was an off-hand matter-of-fact kind of way.

If he knew I was lying, he didn't say, merely recounting in great detail the intimacies of his adventure with the prostitute. I fell asleep, thankful that my embarrassment had not been witnessed other than by a few paratroopers and the old hag herself, none of whom, with luck, I would ever see again. Rudi paid two more visits to the brothel during the next two days, as did Waldhof and Meise, but I feigned an upset stomach or found some other excuse when they asked me to join them.

Rainer Waldhof was a slightly built fellow, not much older than I. The only son of a baker from Cologne, he had completed his training at Gaderlegen just a few months before me, but for reasons best known to the Luftwaffe, had not received a foreign posting until now. He had been returning from leave to Gaderlegen when he was stopped at Hannover and re-directed to join our train bound for France. He told us that whatever dangers we might face, anything was preferable to sitting in the cellar of his parents' house in Cologne as he had done night after night during his leave while British and American bombers gradually demolished the city above their heads.

He told us how the inhabitants would emerge each morning from their hiding places, still shaking from the incessant explosions, to find a little less of their city remained standing. In the centre of the destruction, however, the cathedral alone remained unscathed, standing proudly amid the rubble of the buildings that had once crowded around it. Some of the citizens had taken this as a sign that God was on our side, but others had said that it merely demonstrated the accuracy of the enemy bombers. Whatever the truth of the matter, listening to his stories of the nightmare of life in a big city made me thankful that my family lived in a village small and insignificant enough to escape such attention.

27

The dubious delights of Paris were soon nothing more than a memory, for our stay there proved to be merely a short interlude in our seemingly endless journey westward. Three days after our arrival in the capital, we were assembled in front of the hotel and taken by lorry across the city where we boarded another train. Naturally we were not informed of our destination and I found myself sharing a compartment with Rudi, Waldof and Meise in a carriage even more ancient than the one in which we had arrived.

As the suburbs of Paris slipped away, the others bemoaned the fact that we were leaving the big city, but I couldn't wait to see the green fields and open countryside once again. The train journey was slow and frequently interrupted by long periods when we remained at a standstill, usually for no apparent reason. Sometimes we were told that there was the possibility of an air raid, but although we were ordered to disembark, we were not allowed to venture far away from the carriages, waiting like sitting ducks, so Rudi said, a perfect target for an enemy pilot. The more likely danger was not an air raid however, but an attack by the French Resistance. The increasing frequency of such attacks was the reason that armed guards had been placed on the roof of the carriages and in the wagons at either end of the train. Many of the delays were due to the fact that the tracks at bridges, embankments and other vulnerable places had to be checked for explosives or other types of ambush before the train could pass.

We had heard rumours of recent incidents where railway tracks had been blown up in this part of France, which had resulted in many casualties. The attacks were becoming more frequent and audacious, because the Resistance had been emboldened by talk of an impending American and British invasion. No mercy was shown to those who engaged in these acts of sabotage, with reprisals being taken against whole families and occasionally entire villages where the saboteurs had lived. I didn't know whether these stories were true or not, but Rudi reckoned that the SS wouldn't hesitate to kill the innocent along with the guilty. We were told repeatedly that we were to be constantly on our guard, never to travel alone and under no circumstances were we to go anywhere unarmed.

The four of us swapped stories as rural France slipped past the carriage windows. Rolf Meise was tall, lean and fair. He was everyone's idea of what a paratrooper should look like, but his strong, handsome physique masked a nervous disposition. He told us that he had received his call-up papers on the same day as a black-edged card arrived informing his mother that his father had been killed in a U-boat. He came from Flensburg, a small port on the Baltic coast in the far north of Germany near the border with Denmark. The sea was a way of life up there and there was never really any question of which service men joined when they were called up. His father had been in the navy since before the war and his elder brother had joined in 1940 and, as far as he was aware, was still serving on a U-boat somewhere in the cold darkness of the ocean. Meise suffered from claustrophobia which prevented him from becoming a submariner and after the death of his father, his mother was keen that he should avoid the sea altogether. He had therefore opted to become a paratrooper, forgetting that he might occasionally be required to climb into the narrow confines of an aeroplane fuselage.

There was little to do on the train except eat, drink and sleep. I fell asleep many times and each time awoke to the same monotonous clanking noise of the ancient carriage wheels. On the second day of our journey I had woken to this familiar noise, but instead of rumbling on, this time the train slowly ground to a halt. It was mid afternoon. Most of us got off to relieve ourselves, standing in a line as we pissed against the rusting carriage wheels. I lit a cigarette. The first cracks seemed far off and unthreatening, but I looked around to see men throwing themselves to the ground. I instinctively followed suit; there was a scream of pain from somewhere towards the front of the train and three of the guards from the front wagon scrambled down the grassy embankment and ran towards a small hut in a field some fifty yards away.

Suddenly Braun was at my side.

"Terhorst! Meise! Follow me." We grabbed our rifles and followed him as he slid down the embankment. There was another crackle of gunfire and I saw a puff of white smoke at one of the hut windows. The three guards, who were rapidly approaching the building from the first carriage, returned fire. I followed Braun and Meise as we worked our way around to the other side of the hut. My heart was beating furiously as more shots rang out and I wondered why Braun had selected me for this little adventure. I concluded that it was merely because I had been standing next to him when we had been having a piss and I made a mental note to keep as far away from him as possible in future. More shots were exchanged as the guards got closer, but then it fell silent.

I thought that whoever was in the hut was probably dead as we crept closer, but when we were ten yards away, the door of the hut suddenly flew open and two figures dashed out into the open, guns blazing. Meise and I instinctively crouched low and fired of a couple of rounds, but Braun calmly stood up, carefully took aim and fired twice. The two figures instantly dropped to the ground.

The guards checked the hut to make sure there was no one left inside while we approached the fallen figures lying face down in the grass, our guns at the ready. Braun put his boot under one of the bodies and rolled it over. A trickle of blood ran from the open mouth of a young man who appeared little older than me. The other figure wore a beret. Rifle pointing, Braun rolled it over with his boot and as he did so the beret fell off and a cascade of auburn curls fell down around the pale face of a beautiful girl of similar age to the man. A spreading patch of blood from the bullet hole in her forehead rapidly soaked the curls. Her staring, unseeing eyes reflected the colour of the sky. I felt sick.

Braun quickly went through their pockets, but found nothing. We returned to the train while a working party went ahead down the line, checking to see whether explosives had been planted by the couple we had killed. Nothing was found and we boarded the train once more. The two bodies were left in the long grass where they fell. No doubt the local Gestapo would be informed and an investigation held. That wasn't our problem, Braun would file a report, but nothing would be allowed to interrupt the movement of soldiers to the front. Nevertheless I wondered what had possessed the two young people to open fire on a train full of armed soldiers, with such predictable and terrible results.

At dawn the next day, the train pulled into the station at

Rennes in Britanny where we were to finally join up with our unit. The weather had turned quite mild and the greatcoat I had gratefully wrapped around myself when we left Gaderlegen, now made me sweat profusely as we marched away from the station. Rudi, Waldhof, Meise and I, together with the other paratroopers who had travelled from Germany, were assigned to the 2nd 'Troges' regiment of the 5th Paratroop Division. The Division had made its headquarters on the outskirts of the city in an old factory which had once produced agricultural feedstuffs.

Our sleeping quarters were in one of the storage sheds that was now home to one hundred men. I didn't have a clue where we were and if someone had shown me a map, I would have been hard-pressed to find Rennes upon it. It soon became clear that we were not very far from the coast and the reason we were there was to defend that sector against possible attack. I soon discovered that the talk among men who had been there for some time was about one thing – the invasion. I was shocked to discover that the general mood among the men was one of pessimism, with many of the men believing that it was no longer a question of if the invasion would come, but only of when.

I didn't dwell too long upon such weighty matters for as Rudi said, "there's fuck all you or I can do about it, just make sure you keep your belly full and your head down". It was sound advice and as we settled down to routine I tried to put thoughts of any impending action out of my mind. Because I had been assigned cookhouse duties at Gaderlegen, I was assigned to the butchery unit, responsible for feeding the paratroopers billeted at the base. The work suited me, though quite how risking life and limb learning how to jump out of aeroplanes suited me for the cutting up of animal carcasses I'll never know.

Occasional drills and training exercises were the only things to break the otherwise humdrum routine of the barracks. We were allowed out of barracks, but not permitted to go into the town and at all times we had to carry our weapons. There weren't too many distractions in the area around the base, but sometimes if the weather was fine, we would go for walks in the country. One day I went on such a walk alone, it was a warm spring day and I felt a need to get out of the camp for a short while. I was strolling along a narrow lane just a mile from the base when a young girl aged about sixteen came around the bend on a bicycle. She stopped when she saw me, clearly uncertain whether to continue or turn around and go back the way she had come. Before she could make a decision I had reached her.

I looked at the bicycle admiringly, running my fingers gently along the tubular metal. It was quite an old bicycle, but they were in short supply and would be a real asset to any common soldier who had to walk or march everywhere. The girl gave me a nervous smile, suspecting that I might take her bicycle away for my own use. We were forbidden to molest the local civilian population or steal their possessions, but no one would ask too many questions about where I had obtained a humble bicycle. She dismounted, propped the bicycle against the wall and came closer, swinging her hips, and indicating in no uncertain manner that her favours might be available if I would allow her to keep the bicycle. She rubbed my thigh then caressed my cheek with the back of her hand, offering no resistance when I kissed her fully on the mouth and ran my hands up her legs and beneath her skirt.

I looked around to ensure that no-one was around then

climbed over a fence into the field where we undressed. She may only have been young, but she was clearly not inexperienced and we urgently and excitedly coupled until we lay, spent and exhausted, on the damp grass. I lay on my back looking up at the clouds as the girl stirred and began to get dressed. When she had finished, she kissed me on the cheek and made to go, but I caught hold of her arm. The least I could do was let her continue on her way without stealing from her, but the attraction of the bicycle was too strong. As I hastily pulled on my trousers the girl clearly read my intention and began to cry. As I vaulted the gate and mounted the bike, her crying ceased and she uttered a torrent of abuse as I pedalled off in the direction of the camp.

My feelings of guilt grew as I approached the camp. I had always been brought up to distinguish between right and wrong and had never stolen anything from anyone in my entire life, but I had changed. I was now a man with a rifle, I had had power over an innocent girl and I had abused the power. I thought about the incident late into the night, wondering what sort of person I was turning into. As I fell asleep I cursed my uniform and cursed the war, for it was turning men into beasts.

I had been in Rennes for almost a month when it was announced that we were to be inspected by a visiting General. Officers were despised by the common soldier at the best of times, but the more senior the officer the more they were despised. A visit by such a senior officer could mean only one thing – a great deal of hard work. Our quarters were made to look as though they had just been purpose built, gallons of paint were requisitioned to spruce up the buildings, roofs were mended and new uniforms were issued to some personnel. It didn't seem to matter that half of our ammunition was of the wrong calibre or that many of our vehicles were unusable due to lack of spare parts or the shortage of fuel. As long as the General thought that our barracks were neat and tidy then apparently we were assured of victory.

"Bastards!" spat Rudi, getting to his feet after we had finished painting another set of fresh lines on the floor of the barracks building, "These markings will certainly put the fear of god into the Americans when they get here".

The day of the visit duly arrived and we all stood to attention as the General's car swept into the compound. The medals on his jacket glinted in the sun as he saluted the commanding officer before commencing his walk along the lines of assembled troops. He stopped here and there to have a word with individual soldiers and I had an awful feeling as he made his way down my column that he might stop and talk to me. Rudi maintained that when an officer spoke to you it always meant trouble, and so it proved on this occasion when, as I feared, the General came to a halt directly in front of me.

"Name?"

"Terhorst, Sir!"

"How old are you?"

"Nineteen, Sir!"

After answering his questions about where and when I had completed my training, he asked me about my current duties. When I informed him that for the past three weeks I had been assigned to the cookhouse and had been doing nothing more dangerous than preparing joints of meat, he became quite agitated and even though I was standing rigidly at attention and staring straight ahead I could see him glaring at the CO.

"The cookhouse is for old men, not for a fit, young boy just out of training camp," he shouted. The Colonel clicked his heels and nodded curtly and the General moved on down the line.

Within minutes of the General's departure I was summoned to the CO's office and handed orders to leave immediately for the coast. So much for keeping my head down as Rudi had advised me. It was hardly my fault that the General had singled me out and certainly not my fault if he felt that my skills were not being adequately utilised. I was beginning to learn that to survive this war you not only needed to keep your head down, the thing you needed above all else was luck.

28

The last and only time I had seen the sea was at Heiligenhafen on the edge of the grey Baltic on a cold February day the previous year. My second view was of the English Channel on a bright blue April morning in 1944 and it looked a far more inviting prospect. Cottonwool clouds scudded along on a fresh southwesterly breeze and the thought of what lay just over the distant horizon was the only thing to cloud my thoughts.

The Cherbourg peninsula sticks out like a thumb from the Normandy coast, making a defiant jabbing gesture towards the south coast of England. Cherbourg was situated on the northernmost tip of the thumb and I had been assigned to an anti-aircraft battery on the low hills which rose up behind the town. The huge stone breakwaters of the harbour stretched out below me, embracing the calm stretch of water in which dozens of grey patrol boats rode at anchor. Behind the town and all along the coast as far as the eye could see, dozens of gun emplacements and concrete pillboxes dotted the cliff tops and hills. Mile upon mile of barbed wire, tank traps and minefields stretched along the beaches, completing the defensive barrier of the famous Atlantic Wall.

Everyone had heard of this impregnable chain of fortified positions that had been constructed and continually re-inforced over the past four years. It extended along the entire length of the Channel coast all the way from Brittany in the west to the wide estuaries of Holland in the east, built to keep out any invader and defend the gains of the Fatherland. As I touched the thick concrete which housed the battery to which I had been assigned, I could almost feel the strength of these fortifications soaking into my body and giving me a feeling of reassurance. Despite the comments and doubts of some soldiers, I felt that it was impossible, for the Tommies and Amis to land an invasion force beneath these guns. If they tried they would surely be hurled back into the sea.

I put thoughts of any battles that might lie ahead to the back of my mind and settled down to the routine of life in the gun battery. Manned by a mixture of Wehrmacht and Luftwaffe, the men seemed to regard each other as bitter foes rather than comrades fighting a common enemy. There was always rivalry between the different services and in the normal way of things there were no major problems apart from the odd fight, but here with the two services working so closely together things were a little different. Perhaps it was the situation of living together in cramped quarters, staring out over the empty sea day after day, expecting an enemy to appear at any moment; that played upon soldiers' nerves. Whatever the reason, I sensed immediately upon arrival that the atmosphere in Battery 109 – Cherbourg Command was poisonous.

Most of the men had been stationed there for more than six months and had been placed on a state of high alert since the end of February. This meant that they'd had hardly any time off for relaxation, nerves were stretched to breaking point and amid the tedium of a typical day, arguments and fights erupted over the most trivial of things. Card schools provided virtually the only form of relaxation, but also led to the greatest number of fights. Soldiers would bet with anything, cigarettes, money, IOU's and virtually everything they had among their scant possessions; they would have wagered their rifles and ammunition if they had been allowed.

Needless to say, I was the youngest in the detachment of ten men assigned to the battery and had to endure the jibes of those who said that things must be bad if they were sending schoolboys to the front. After a few days, the tension of sitting and waiting for something to happen began to affect me as it had already affected the others. Officers and men continually scanned the horizon with binoculars and telescopes, searching for any sign of the ships that may one day come. Men looked so intently and for so long that they imagined a ship in every smudge on the horizon, a fleet in every grey cloud and the sound of distant gunfire in every gust of wind.

It was little wonder that nerves were at breaking point. Some of the men had already seen action, but on those occasions they had been on the offensive, the element of surprise had been with them. Now they were confined to watching and waiting while the enemy prepared and would decide when and where to strike. Every day the Commandant of the Cherbourg district toured the defences and occasionally some of the batteries would fire off a few rounds to ensure that everything was in full working order. A few enemy reconnaissance planes had been sighted in the area the month previously, but since then there had been no sign of the enemy. This could mean one of two things: either they were performing reconnaissance elsewhere for an attack in another sector or they were lulling us into a false sense of security, waiting for the opportunity to strike.

For eight weeks I suffered the tedium of life at

Cherbourg; rarely permitted to leave the battery I contented myself with walks along the cliff tops studying the effect of the weather upon the sea. When there were clear blue skies, the sea would be an even brighter blue and when the skies were grey and overcast, the colour was mirrored in the even darker surface of the sea. Rain clouds moving on the horizon would sometimes pass on up the channel while others would sweep onto the land, drenching the town and countryside. There was no need of a weather forecast in this place, we could see with our own eyes the weather approaching from the west, its changing patterns reflected in the turbulent and ever changing surface of the sea.

In June I received orders to return to Rennes and rejoin my old unit. I was overjoyed, chiefly to get away from the monotony and the tense atmosphere that prevailed along the coast, but also because I hoped that I would meet up once again with Rudi, Waldhof and Meise. The sea was slate grey and there was a hint of rain in the air as I climbed aboard a truck at the Luftwaffe barracks in Cherbourg to begin the trip back to Rennes. It was the fifth of June 1944.

29

"Raus! .... Raus!"

I stirred dreamily for a few seconds, but Feldwebel Braun soon shook me awake.

"Be quiet! Can't you see we're trying to sleep in here?" someone shouted. Rough hands threw back my bedroll.

"Get up and fall in immediately."

I rubbed my eyes and saw that nearly all the men in the barracks hut were now out of bed. The sound of boots and clothes being hastily pulled on mingled with the shouts of both the non-coms and the men. Meise, who was still somehow asleep, soon felt the attentions of Braun who grabbed his feet and dragged him out of his bunk so violently that he fell heavily on the floor. Meise, shocked into wakefulness, began to rise with his fists clenched and murder in his eye, a look that only disappeared when he realised that it was Braun who had perpetrated the crime.

"You're a lucky little bastard, Theo!" Rudi shouted above the din. "You only returned from Cherbourg yesterday and all hell's broken loose this morning. The invasion's started."

My head was spinning as I hastily pulled on my trousers and boots. Braun continued his way down the hut, pushing and occasionally giving his charges a kick if he felt they were making insufficient haste. It was hard to believe that only yesterday I had been at the coast, everything had been so quiet and peaceful and now the Amis and Tommies had finally come. Even as I had boarded the truck at the barracks in Cherbourg yesterday, the invasion fleet must have been steaming towards the coast, hidden just over the horizon. I thought briefly of those I'd left behind in the battery, wondering if they had already seen any action, whether they had managed to bring down any aircraft with their huge guns, whether they were still alive. More important than any of these concerns, however, was my concern about where I was being sent.

We formed up outside with some of the men still struggling to put on their uniforms, but this was no pointless drill to satisfy Braun, it was the real thing. If any of us remained in any doubt about this, those doubts evaporated when we were issued with armfuls of cartridge bags and grenades. We were told to climb aboard one of the convoy of trucks that had pulled up outside the perimeter fence. Above us in the cloudy, summer sky an occasional plane flew high overhead, so high that I could not distinguish whether it was one of our own or one of the enemy.

Feld told us that we were heading north to Dinan, a small town which lay halfway between Rennes and the coast, where we were to await further orders. Some of the men were saying that the plan was to let the enemy come ashore and then to smash them with our reserves held inland. I did not believe this as to me it seemed incredible that anyone would have been able to land on the beach at Cherbourg, so immense were the defences, and I imagined that this must have been true of the remainder of the coast. If the plan was to let them land then hit them with our reserves, I wondered why the coastal defences had been constructed in the first place. If the Americans and the British had managed to gain a foothold ashore, then they must have arrived in massive numbers for they would surely have taken huge casualties.

The men were clearly talking through their arses and I felt afraid; they had probably never been to the coast and seen the defences. I was filled with foreboding, but said nothing to the others.

As the trucks lurched forward, I looked around at my comrades who were to 'smash' this enemy. Many, like me, had never fired a shot in anger; they were men who had spent their entire military career in sleepy backwaters like Rennes, peeling potatoes, repairing vehicles and playing cards and every day thanking God that Hitler had not seen fit to send them to the frozen steppes of Russia. I fervently hoped that somewhere in northern France there really were seasoned professionals, experienced soldiers with good equipment, tanks and guns with lots of ammunition who might indeed be able to drive the invaders back into the sea.

Rudi saw the concern on my face and started to laugh.

"Hitler's last hope! That's us, Theo my boy." He slapped me hard on the back with his meaty hand and laughed again. The anxious expressions on the faces of the others indicated that they didn't find his jest very funny and had they not been afraid of feeling his fist in their faces, would undoubtedly have told him so.

"Anyway I'm sticking with you, Theo." Rudi continued, oblivious to the others. "Any bastard who's lucky enough to get pulled back from the landing beaches the day before an invasion has got to be a lucky mascot. You'd be mincemeat by now if you'd stayed in Cherbourg."

I consoled myself with the thought that if the enemy had made it ashore, they would surely have been few in number, probably just a few poorly supplied stragglers who could easily be mopped up, and with a bit of luck it would probably all be over before we even got there. As the trucks trundled steadily along the road towards Dinan, army motorcyclists constantly passed us, roaring up alongside the convoy with messages for our commanding officer who was travelling in an armoured car at the head of the column. We would halt for ten minutes or so during these visits, sometimes getting out of the trucks and scattering in the ditches and hedgerows at either side of the road in case of an attack by enemy aircraft. There were certainly more planes in the skies as we moved further north, but they seemed a long way off and either they were our own planes or those of an enemy who didn't consider our convoy a worthwhile target.

Although our destination was Dinan, few of us believed that we would stay there long before we were sent up to the coast or maybe in quite a different direction to intercept the enemy. The only thing of which we could be certain was that, in all the confusion, no-one was telling us anything. We reached Dinan just before nightfall and looked at each other in amazement when we were driven through impressive iron gates into the grounds of a grand chateau not far from the centre of town. What once must have been elegantly manicured lawns were now overgrown, and the evergreen bushes which looked as though they had once been clipped into a variety of geometric shapes were now grotesquely misshapen. The chateau itself was magnificent, turrets with conical tops sprouting at each corner of the steeply sloping roof. Stone steps led up to the enormous front door while along either side, huge windows gave out onto a paved promenade contained within stone balustrades.

We were allocated to rooms that, like the grand hotel in which we had stayed while in Paris, contained only standard bunk beds, the original furniture having been removed long ago. Crudely carved names and other graffiti on the walls had been left by its previous occupants, a panzer division who had already left for the front. On the opposite side of the road a municipal building was the headquarters of the military police, a body that ordinary soldiers hated far more than the enemy. Braun told us that we would be staying there until further notice and to unpack our things. Relieved that, at least for now, we were not to be sent directly to the coast, the 2nd Troges regiment made the most of its new surroundings. There was little hard news filtering down to the common soldier, but we did eventually discover that the bulk of the enemy landings had been made further east in Normandy. There were also rumours that the Tommies and the Amis had been forced back into the sea, some said they'd heard the enemy had surrendered, while others said that they were headed our way and that we had better be ready to leave at any moment.

We only believed what we could see with our own eyes and they told us that increasing numbers of enemy aircraft were now flying overhead. Occasionally we would see one of our fighters intercept one of them and cheer as it was sent plummeting to earth in a trail of smoke, but worryingly we saw that many more enemy planes were flying above us unchallenged. Although none attacked any targets in our immediate vicinity, there was clearly a huge battle going on further away to the north and east. In a climate of constantly changing rumours, we remained in Dinan for eleven tense days as the battle raged. These days were filled with endless drills, equipment maintenance, packing up our gear and then unpacking it once again.

We lived as normally as we could, training, exercising and eating and every evening we climbed back into our bunks thinking that it would be our last night in the comfort of a bed, in the old chateau. We became careless of the daily sight of enemy planes in the skies above; strangely, it seemed that the war was in another time and place; as if somehow it was none of our concern. It seemed for a short while that we had been reduced to being mere onlookers to an event in which we were to play no part. Stranded on the periphery of momentous events, the long June days passed in this way, and just when we thought we had been forgotten by the high command, we received the order to move out.

On a warm, but drizzly grey morning we were assembled in front of the chateau for the distribution of iron rations and ammunition. Each man was given one hundred cartridges and five grenades before we were divided into groups of ten, each of which was an assault group. Rudi, Meise and I were given rifles, but Waldhof's face dropped when he was handed an FM Spandau machine gun, a great weapon for killing the enemy but extremely cumbersome and heavy to carry. Braun told us we were headed for St Lo, a large town at the base of the Cherbourg peninsula about seventy-five miles north east of our present position. We loaded the trucks with our equipment and climbed aboard the lorries that took us eastwards through the Breton countryside before turning north at Avranches.

We reached St Lo at noon and came upon a scene of utter chaos. The sound of gunfire had been growing louder with every passing mile and by the time we reached the outskirts of St Lo, it was clear that the fighting was very close. Trucks, armoured vehicles and motorcycles moved about in every direction as our small convoy came to a halt in the centre of town. We were ordered to climb down from the trucks and we made our way to where the smoke-belching stoves of a field kitchen had been set up on one corner of the square. Hot soup and lumps of black bread were ladled into our mess tins and we spooned the hot liquid gratefully into our mouths. In the haste to leave Dinan and ensure that we had an adequate supply of ammunition, we hadn't had time to pick up our iron rations. Those of us who were still hungry went back for a second bowl of soup and managed to stuff a few crusts of bread into our pockets, for we didn't know when or where we would eat again.

30

The Survivor

Traitors rarely see themselves as such, they see themselves as patriots forced to adopt extreme measures in order to protect their country. In this particular case it was too late to save the country, but things might go easier on its people if there was at least a change of government. Even if the Leader could not see it, the game by now was up. Rome had already fallen, the British and the Americans had consolidated their landings in Normandy, and in the East the unstoppable tide of the Red Army was moving ever closer.

The scion of an old and distinguished family with an impeccable military tradition, Klaus von Stauffenberg, was just the type of natural leader whom the army required and in whose service he had excelled. A combination of intellect and heroism had seen him rise quickly through the hierarchy, gaining medals in Poland and losing an eye and a hand in North Africa. He had fought throughout the war with bravery and distinction, but had become bitterly disillusioned with the atrocities committed against the Jews and the conquered Slavic peoples, which he believed had brought shame upon the nation.

As he surveyed his scarred and broken body, he realised that he had a sacred mission to perform, because he alone would be able to get close enough to perform the deed. He tinkered throughout a convalescent summer with the awkward tongs that had replaced his right hand, working tirelessly to perfect his technique with the explosives and fuses provided by Olbricht's people. There had been attempts before, but all had failed either because of faulty equipment or due to the last minute changes of plan of which the Leader was so fond. Some of those involved had come to believe that his life was charmed and that perhaps his continued survival should be regarded as some kind of sign.

Von Stauffenberg's wife, who had lovingly nursed him back to health, knew better than to try and dissuade her husband from his chosen course of action. She also understood that duty was more important than individual survival and although she had four young children, she knew that hundreds of thousands had already made the ultimate sacrifice for their country during the last five years. It was at this stage unreasonable to expect that she and her family might be spared the loss of a husband and father.

Both knew that if this mission were to have any chance of success, then it would have to be carried out by someone with access to the Leader and von Stauffenberg, as chief of staff to the commander in chief of the Home Army, was one of the very few with such access. When he had resumed his duties he was often summoned into the Leader's presence, usually in order to be asked to provide replacements for the decimated divisions desperately trying to hold back the Soviets in the East. Twice before he had carried bombs concealed on his person into the presence of the Leader, but because his senior deputies were not present, had not set the fuses. This time there could be no postponement: whether his senior deputies were there or not, he would kill the Leader.

When he was summoned once again to the 'Wolf's Lair' deep in the Prussian forest, he wrapped the device inside a folded shirt and, placing the bundle between a wad of papers, carefully pushed it inside his briefcase. The fuse consisted of a glass capsule containing acid, which when broken would allow the acid to gradually dissolve a small wire and release the firing pin against a percussion cap. The thickness of the wire would determine the time required to set off the explosion. This morning, von Stauffenberg had fixed the thinnest wire possible. It would dissolve in just ten minutes.

The flight from Berlin took them over the sombre Prussian landscape in which the Leader had made his headquarters, a dark green blanket of trees covering the flat terrain that stretched away to the horizon. As they approached, he could see that the complex was surrounded by anti-aircraft batteries and alongside the tiny airstrip sandbags indicated the presence of numerous machine gun emplacements. Hidden from his sight among the trees, he knew, was a brigade of SS troops fanatically loyal to the Leader and ready at a moment's notice to spring to his defence.

Clutching his briefcase tightly as the plane hit the runway and rumbled to a halt, his mouth felt dry, but he knew that there could be no turning back. He hoped and prayed that this morning there would only be routine checks and that he would be able to enter the complex without his bag being searched. He was met at the airstrip by a staff car and, although he had to produce his security pass three times before being allowed into the headquarters, there were no other checks. He was ushered in to see Keitel who informed him that he should be ready to brief the Leader in thirty minutes' time. He knew that the Leader often made last minute changes to his schedule, but the glass capsule had to be broken before he went into the briefing room and once it had been broken the die would be cast.

A few minutes before the meeting, Keitel indicated that they should begin walking towards the barracks building where the Leader would be holding his first daily conference. They emerged from Keitel's office and began to walk in the warm summer sun. It was now or never. Von Stauffenberg suddenly stopped, said he had forgotten something and rushed back to Keitel's office where he opened the case and shattered the capsule. He quickly refastened the case, returned to the waiting Keitel and resumed walking the fifty yards to the building where the Leader was waiting.

Inside his case the acid had begun to eat away at the small wire. They entered the building where the conference had already started. Four minutes had ticked by since he had broken the capsule and now he was at last in the Leader's presence. There were six minutes to go. In the middle of the room was a long oblong table at which the Leader was seated. Von Stauffenberg was ushered to a seat a little to his right. He sat down and pushed his briefcase under the table. Five minutes to go.

The previous briefing was continuing, with the Leader and the others carefully studying the large map laid out on the table. Von Stauffenberg arose from his chair and went out of the room. It was highly unusual for anyone to leave the Leader's presence without being dismissed, but so involved was everyone in studying the map that no-one except Colonel Brandt noticed him leave. Brandt immediately took von Stauffenberg's vacant chair to get a better view of the map spread out before the assembled officers. The bulging briefcase was in his way so he reached down, picked it up and moved it to the other side of the heavy table support and away from the Leader. Von Stauffenberg left the complex and hurried back to the airstrip where his plane was waiting. As he boarded the plane at 12:42 pm, the briefing came to a conclusion at precisely the same time as the acid dissolved the last of the thin wire and the detonator came into contact with the explosive.

The Leader looked like a ghost as he crawled from the rubble of the building. Covered in dust, his hair was singed, his legs were burnt and his back was severely lacerated; yet he alone had survived among those standing around him when the bomb had exploded. It was surely another sign that he was indestructible, but his spirit would not allow him to feel gratitude for a miraculous escape, it required vengeance and retribution. The temporary paralysis and his punctured eardrums merely delayed his fury.

Even as von Stauffenberg was flying back to Berlin, the finger of suspicion was pointing firmly in his direction. The others involved in the plot, the generals and field-marshals, seemed unable to shake off the warm sultry embrace which hung heavily over the capital on that summer's day. Instead of moving swiftly to secure buildings and arrest those who would doubtless remain loyal to the Leader, they delayed. Had von Stauffenberg been successful or not? They had neither seized the radio stations nor isolated those in positions of power who remained in Berlin. Their delay was fatal.

While von Stauffenberg returned with news that he had been successful, news began to filter through that the Leader had in fact survived. Those who had orchestrated the attempted coup began to rage at one another for their bungling, while those who had been sympathetic to the conspiracy, but had sat on the fence, now jumped off. Now was the time for damage limitation, a time to profess undying loyalty to the Leader, to distance themselves from those involved. It was also a time to appoint themselves as judge, jury and executioner. Dead conspirators could not point a finger at others who had connived in their treachery; if they acted quickly they would not only be free of guilt, they would be heroes.

Von Stauffenberg, Beck and Hoepner were the first to go, followed by others until the SS restrained the carnage, not to protect those who were suspected, but to ascertain how wide the conspiracy was. The first serious revolt against the Leader in eleven and a half years was over in just eleven and a half hours. Later that evening, the Leader's voice was once again heard on the radio. He spoke of a miraculous escape from death and of his manifest destiny to lead his people until the very end. The criminals and traitors to the nation would be shown no mercy.

The waves of arrests rippled out as surely as if a boulder had been thrown into a placid lake. No means were excluded in the effort to extract information from reluctant witnesses. Not content with punishing those individuals deemed responsible for the treachery, their relatives and friends were arrested and detained. The Leader's thirst for revenge was unquenchable, summary trials were followed hours later by summary executions. Firing squads were for men of honour; these men would dangle from the gallows like common criminals.

Even as the nation's enemies approached and countless soldiers laid down their lives for their country, film of these grisly hangings was rushed to the Leader so that he could enjoy the spectacle in the comfort of his armchair. A warm glow of satisfaction enveloped him as he watched the men who had dared to challenge him dance in their death agonies before hanging lifelessly from meat hooks.

The Leader's fury and thirst for revenge would not be assuaged merely by the deaths of those leaders of the treachery. The tentacles of the police state reached ever outwards, grasping the most tenuous links so that by the end of the summer, almost seven thousand people had died. Word also went out to the front lines in the East, in Italy and in France where the common soldier might also be capable of treachery. The SS and police were instructed to shoot those who had a greater appetite for running than for fighting.

31

We remained in St Lo for three hours, but were not permitted to wander far from the lorries. We smoked cigarettes, put our feet up and passed the time watching the hectic arrival and departure of other groups. The sound of heavy gunfire was almost continuous and from where we were it seemed that our own batteries were answering the fire of what we had now been told was the Americans who had landed in this sector. Although the town itself appeared to be still out of range of the enemy guns, it was clear that shells were falling just a few miles up the road to the east. It also became apparent, during the hours we remained in St Lo, that the majority of men and material were not heading either north or east in the direction of the gunfire, but south and west, the direction from which we had just arrived.

The rumble of artillery crept gradually closer during the afternoon until we were eventually ordered to climb back into the trucks. Our hearts sank as the trucks began moving out of the town towards the east, stopping frequently to allow men and vehicles to pass in the opposite direction, falling back towards St Lo. An hour out of town, with rain starting to fall, a huge explosion a hundred yards up the road shook the ground, violently causing the truck to swerve and shudder to a standstill. To the accompaniment of shouts and the screams of men in the distance, we were ordered out of the trucks, Braun ordering some of us to follow him to see if we could help. I always worried that Braun's attitude might lead us into trouble at some point; he seemed far too eager to assist everyone else while putting his own men at risk. It was blindingly obvious that everyone else in sight was falling back yet, incredibly, we were still moving forward.

At the trot we headed towards the scene of commotion where we discovered that an artillery shell had landed on the road, scoring a direct hit on the armoured car at the head of our column in which the Commanding Officer had been travelling. The vehicle had been turned into a twisted and burning mass of metal. Men wounded by shell fragments streamed down the road clutching at their bloody wounds, while blackened arms and legs in shreds of uniforms protruded from beneath the wrecked vehicle which had taken the hit. The occupants were clearly dead which was perhaps just as well, for we couldn't get near to the furiously burning wreckage to release them, even had they still been alive. Rudi spat, even he was lost for words on this occasion.

We returned to our trucks. The shell had severely cratered the road and there was clearly no possibility of moving forward along the narrow road, so with great difficulty the trucks turned around. We pulled three injured soldiers on board before moving off, anxious to be out of artillery range and back to the relative safety of St Lo. One of the wounded men was delirious, lapsing in and out of consciousness as an ugly red patch spread across his thigh. Some of the men retched as his trousers were cut away to reveal a large hole, the skin at the edges burnt to a crisp. Amid the blood and flux it was difficult to see whether there was anything in the hole or whether the shrapnel had passed straight through. The soldier passed out once again as Braun stuffed some clean rags in the hole to try and staunch the flow of blood.

When we arrived back in St Lo, the scene in the town square was even more confused than it had been when we had left a few hours earlier. The main square was filled with men, some were lost, some wounded, but all were tired and filthy. Men who had become detached from their units during the fighting milled about seeking out their comrades or looking for their non-coms. The field kitchen that had provided us with hot food only hours before had disappeared and an emergency field hospital had been set up in its place. The tureens of boiling water which earlier had provided men with welcome mugs of coffee, now supplied the surgeons who were busily carving up the wounded.

We unloaded the wounded men at the hospital before moving off once again, this time mercifully in a southerly direction. Throughout the late afternoon and early evening our trucks rolled on along roads clogged with retreating men. As night fell, we stopped at a farmhouse which had a large collection of outbuildings grouped around a central cobbled courtyard. It was deserted; the inhabitants had fled and from the state of the house it was clear that we were not the first soldiers to arrive, the contents of cupboards had been strewn across the floor and anything edible had disappeared. Braun and some of the other non-coms grabbed the beds in the farmhouse while others unfurled their bedrolls in the downstairs rooms. The rest of us, instructed to keep our weapons within reach at all times, had to make do with the outbuildings, but we nevertheless managed to make ourselves comfortable. Rudi, Meise and I unfurled our bedrolls in a warm and dry hayloft while Waldhof, who was still carrying the heavy Spandau, slept beside it on the ground floor.

It had been a long, nervous and uncomfortable day. We

had lost our commanding officer, been shaken around in the back of trucks as they travelled over potholed roads, and though none of us had fired a shot, we had at last seen action. We had been able to see for ourselves the confusion, been able to smell the fear and been splashed with the blood of our comrades. If we had not known before, we all now knew that the difference between death and survival was wafer thin, the shell that wiped out the armoured car at the head of the column could just as easily have landed on our truck. We were all exhausted and although the enemy were close, supported by ample quantities of soft, dry hay we soon fell asleep.

The following morning was damp and overcast. We awoke to the yells of the non-coms, hastily packed our belongings, grabbed our weapons and assembled in the courtyard. Some breakfasted on the soup which they had saved in their mess tins from the previous afternoon, while others smoked cigarettes. I had no soup, but remembered that I had stuffed a bread crust in my pocket when we left St Lo. It was now hard and crumbly, but had not yet gone mouldy so I nibbled at it as the drivers went to start the lorries.

The cloud was low and we could hear no planes, but the faint sound of guns could be heard in the distance. Dishevelled groups of infantry passed on the road outside the courtyard, their grim, tired features indicating that they had been involved in the fighting and that it had been hard. As we began boarding the trucks, larger groups of infantry appeared, this time carrying wounded men among them. Their captain, seeing our trucks, immediately requisitioned three of them to take the wounded to a field hospital. The wounded men were duly loaded into the trucks and driven away, leaving us with just three trucks to take eighty men. Some of us would have to walk.

Braun divided us into two groups: those with the heavier equipment, mortars, heavy machine guns and panzerfausts were to go ahead in the trucks, while those of us with rifles and light machine guns would proceed on foot.

"Shit!" said Rudi as we, being more lightly armed, were segregated into the walking group. Those bastards will be drinking champagne in Paris in a couple of days while we'll still be slogging our way down these damned country lanes."

Rudi could never let such a moment pass without griping about it, he always believed that he had been dealt a poor hand even when things were going well. As the others boarded the trucks, we formed up into a column, shouldered our weapons and lined up behind Braun to begin the long walk. The roads in that vicinity were miniature canyons cut deeply into the rich, Normandy soil and lined with thick hedgerows which towered high above the top of steep, grassy banks and permitted no view over the surrounding countryside. As we walked along the shellfire increased in volume and frequency, but lacking a horizon we could not determine from which direction it came.

I had imagined that we had travelled a long way from the front, but even as we retreated, it seemed that the front was edging ever closer. Lucky bastards like Waldhof riding in the trucks were long out of sight, leaving the rest of us to plod along on foot. My FG 42 rifle that normally seemed so light and easy to handle was becoming heavier by the minute and the strap was beginning to cut into my shoulder. Our packs also grew heavy as we trudged along and the cloudy, humid weather was making us sweat like pigs. When we reached the top of a hill, Braun called a halt and we slumped at the side of the road, gratefully laying down our weapons and throwing off our packs. We lay on the grassy bank, those with any remaining food opened their mess tins and scooped out the cold mixture while the rest of us drank water and lit cigarettes.

Some of the men lay snoozing at the side of the road while others relieved themselves in the hedge. I could easily have eaten the entire contents of a mess tin and still been hungry for more, but mine was empty and it was impossible to know when we would get our next meal. Although tired from the morning's march, I wandered a few yards up the road to a gap in the hedge that afforded a good view over the surrounding countryside. Braun and an Obergefreiter were already there, looking intently through their binoculars towards the north and east, the direction from which we had come. The undulating green fields stretched away into the distance, dotted here and there with farmhouses and small copses. I didn't need binoculars to see the clouds of smoke on the horizon or hear the distant rumble of guns indicating that a fierce battle must now be taking place around St Lo. So much for hurling the enemy back into the sea.

After resting for half an hour, we were ordered to fall in once again and moved off down the lane. More aircraft appeared above, but the fighters were swooping much lower across the fields than before, their engines howling as they turned and circled around to select their targets. We looked up, hopeful of seeing the Luftwaffe cross on their wings, but could see only the stars and bars of American planes and we knew that it wouldn't be long before one of them came back to take a closer look. Braun was clearly concerned, ordering us to double our pace and, despite the heat of the day and the sweat pouring from our bodies, we needed no encouragement. Although we could see little of what was happening around us, at least the deep lanes had the advantage of rendering our column less visible from the marauding planes above.

We walked continuously for the next two hours, drinking copiously from our flasks as we went. By a small stream, we stopped briefly to refill them when the gentle sound of rippling water and birdsong was shattered by the howling approach of an aeroplane. This plane was much lower than the others we had seen before and men instinctively threw themselves onto the ground, while some ran into the water. It was just as well, because seconds later heavy calibre bullets tore into the earth on every side. I had lain in a bed of reeds at the water's edge, burying my face in the mud as the ground shook with the roar of engines and the violence of exploding bullets. Like an intense summer storm, the mechanical thunder and lighting passed as quickly as it had arrived. We got slowly to our feet, listening intently for the roar of engines that would signal another attack, ready at any moment to take cover if we heard the dreadful sound.

All was silent except for the gurgling of the stream; even the birds had been silenced. Braun held an impromptu roll call and though no one had been hit, men's faces were ashen and their hands were shaking. I took a gulp of water from my replenished flask and watched Meise do the same, his hands shaking so badly that water spilled down his chin and onto his uniform. We shouldered our rifles once again and rejoined the column. It was the first time I had been shot at and I had an awful feeling that it wouldn't be the last.

32

All the brave claims about driving the enemy back into the sea had proven to be just empty talk. We ourselves had only managed to advance a few miles beyond St Lo before falling back and now it was obvious to even the keenest optimist that we were in retreat, harried by planes and always with the ominous sound of gunfire at our backs. At the many road junctions we reached, we invariably took a southerly direction, hoping to put as much distance as possible between the enemy and ourselves. The plan, if one could describe our shambles of a retreat as any kind of plan, was to try and join up with the rest of the men who had gone on ahead in the lorries with the heavy equipment. Our small column, armed only with light weapons, was a sitting duck for the marauding Ami fighters and would have offered a pitiful resistance had we encountered any enemy armour.

We trudged down the narrow lanes that dissected the undulating Normandy countryside. After many hours of walking, my feet were becoming increasingly sore, the straps on my rifle and backpack had rubbed my shoulders raw, and regardless of how close the enemy were, I prayed that we would soon stop and rest for the evening. We continued in silence, each of us listening attentively for the sound of an aircraft, ready to throw ourselves to the ground or dive headlong into the thick brambles of a hedge. Even after the sun had slid below the horizon we pressed on. The light, warm evenings of summer that would normally be a source of enjoyment, were cursed for delaying the fall of darkness which might hide our retreat from the enemy.

Suddenly the sound of aircraft engines once again split the still air. We needed no instructions to take cover, I scrambled up a bank and wedged myself into the bottom of a thick hawthorn hedge, careless of the sharp thorns which penetrated my uniform and bit into my flesh. Filled with terror, as the plane roared directly overhead, I experienced a strange heightening of the senses, strangely aware of the scent of grass and the texture of soft, brown earth clenched in my fist. The delicate aroma of honeysuckle drifted into my nostrils as first one plane and then a second made a low pass over the road. I held my breath and waited for the explosion of bombs or the staccato sound of bullets ripping into the ground, but the planes continued onwards without releasing their deadly cargo.

As we got to our feet we heard the sound of two distant explosions and shortly afterwards saw two plumes of thick, black smoke rise from the direction in which we were heading. As the two aeroplanes climbed into the evening sky another came into view, but this one was headed straight towards the others. "Messerschmidt!" Meise shouted and we cheered as the pilot bravely gave chase to the Americans who appeared to be fleeing; but as they appeared to climb away from danger, one of the American planes twisted and rolled, coming up behind the Messerschmidt and poured a lethal hail of fire into it. Flame and black smoke instantly trailed out from the stricken plane and it began to plummet headlong towards the ground. We watched in awful silence as our gallant would-be protector smashed into the ground with a sickening explosion. There was no parachute and none of us said a word as we resumed our silent march.

The plumes of smoke we had seen in the distance grew closer as we continued our march. As darkness fell, we rounded a bend in the road and came upon a scene of appalling carnage. The American planes had done their work efficiently, dropping their bombs directly on top of the lorries that we had last seen earlier that morning taking on board our more heavily armed comrades. We had finally caught up with the rest of our regiment. We had cursed them for their good fortune at the time, but as I was fast learning, war is completely random in its selection of victims and what appears to be good or bad fortune can change in an instant.

We ran towards the scene of devastation to see if we could be of any assistance. Two of the trucks were blazing fiercely in the middle of the road while the ground around them was littered with bodies and pieces of bodies. I glanced at one poor wretch; his uniform resembled a sack containing something soggy and bloody. Minus any limbs it was barely recognisable as a human form. Some of the wounded had been blown out of the vehicles, while others had managed to get out of the lorries and drag themselves to the side of the road. The sight of their scorched faces and limbs, together with the acrid smell of those being cremated in the burning trucks, was so overpowering that I thought I was going to be sick.

We did what we could. All of the conscious men begged for water, but for most of them, it was their last ever drink. Many of the horribly disfigured mercifully died soon after they had taken a sip of water from our flasks. Of the forty men who had been travelling in the two destroyed lorries, only ten remained alive. We were too tired and sickened to go any further and when the trucks had finally burned themselves out, we dragged what remained of our charred and blackened comrades from the trucks. The grisly corpses were laid out in a row while Braun went along removing their dog tags. Waldhof was among them. A burial party was detailed to dig a mass grave in a corner of a neighbouring field, and under cover of darkness we gave our fallen comrades a Christian burial. To mark the wretched spot, a few rough crosses fashioned from branches and saplings were pushed into the ground, each with a paratrooper's helmet draped on top.

If Braun survived and managed to get the dog tags back to divisional HQ, then in a few weeks time a black-edged letter would doubtless arrive at the home of Waldhof's parents in Cologne informing them that their only son had 'Fallen like a hero on the field of honour for Germany and the Leader'. It would of course omit to mention that he had been turned into an unrecognisable, burnt carcass which had been hastily buried beneath the Normandy soil while his comrades held their noses and retched.

It began to rain, a soft drizzle at first which then grew heavy, turning the soil around the burial pit into thick, cloying mud. Too sickened and weary to look for a farmhouse or barn in which to rest, we set up camp for the night in the shelter of a small copse next to the field where we had buried the men, well away from the wreckage of the vehicles which still glowed and smouldered, a beacon for any other enemy aircraft. Luckily I wasn't selected for guard duty and, lacking any kind of appetite, rolled out my groundsheet. I was about to take off my sodden boots when Borkenhagen, a veteran of the eastern front shouted to me.

"Don't do that, Theo. You'll never be able to walk in them tomorrow."

I was too weary to argue that my feet would never dry out if I left my boots on, I merely nodded, wrapped my bedroll around my shoulders and fell, exhausted and nauseated, into the deepest of sleeps.

Dawn came all too quickly and I was instantly awake, hoping for a few waking seconds that the events of the previous night had been nothing more than a grotesque nightmare. I sat up and looked around as pale, mottled light filtered through the leafy canopy, eerily illuminating those still lying asleep on the ground, including Rudi and Meise. I could see that Braun was already up and watched him as he went around waking the men. After breakfast, which consisted of a drink of water and a cigarette, we set off once more on the road. We were headed towards Avranches. I took one last look at the mound of fresh earth covering Waldhof and the rest of our comrades and wondered whether there would be the need of any more burial parties before the day was out.

As we marched we encountered other units who were similarly retreating south, using the narrow lanes and side roads as far as possible. We spoke with some who had come all the way down from Cherbourg where their positions had been overrun. They were only just managing to keep ahead of the enemy by dint of a series of punishing forced marches and grabbing the occasional lift on trucks or armoured vehicles.

A few miles north of Avranches we joined the main road where a continuous procession of vehicles, armour and men on foot was moving inexorably towards the town, a weary, grey tide of defeated men. Everyone had the same story. Far from being thrown back into the sea, or even contained at the coast, the Americans had been pouring in men, weapons and ammunition in such unimaginably large quantities that, despite a brave resistance, they had been completely overwhelmed. We had suspected all along that the Amis had more of everything, planes, ships and soldiers, but we had hoped that they could have been prevented from landing. The Atlantic Wall had been an enormous failure and today we were retreating towards Avranches, but what about tomorrow? Rennes perhaps and the day after that…. Paris? Would they chase us all the way back across the Rhine?

Rudi read my thoughts as we trudged along.

"Theo! This war's all crap. There's nothing we can do about it, the only thing that we can do is make sure that we stay alive. Staying alive is the only victory you and I are going to have."

I felt depressed and yet found a strange comfort in his words. After all, what was the meaning of war for the common soldier? Victories and defeats were for generals and politicians to worry about, the only thing the common soldier was concerned about was staying alive. What was the use of victory if you didn't live long enough to see it? I would certainly try to see to it that I did stay alive, but the same thought was probably on the minds of the poor devils yesterday on the truck before the planes came and turned them into a grotesque barbecue. Rudi was right. I made up my mind that come what may, I would stay close to him; if we didn't make it out of this alive, then at least we would die together.

Up ahead, Braun had made contact with a Luftwaffe unit under the command of Hauptmann Buttner to whom our remaining band of fifty paratroopers was promptly attached. Word came through to the ranks that a defensive perimeter was to be established to the north and east of Avranches along a ridge commanding a view towards the north. We were to dig in and make our positions as strong as possible to contain the enemy's thrust until our reserve armoured divisions arrived from the rear. No one knew that our armoured divisions were being kept busy far away to the east at Caen and that they would never arrive to relieve us.

Late in the afternoon, we crossed a small river and turned east. Two hours later we were digging in at the edge of some trees that ran along the crest of the ridge. The small amount of heavy equipment which had escaped the aeroplane attack on our trucks was set up. Mortars and heavy machine guns were placed in trenches and disguised with branches while the rest of us, armed with only light weapons, scooped shallow foxholes in the sandy soil. Along the ridge other units were doing the same thing, although the heavy artillery which had been retreating from the north and which we assumed would be supporting us, continued moving south and out of sight. At least we had now stopped marching and everyone was able to take the weight off their aching feet; some of the men set up a stove and were busily making coffee and some kind of soup. The soup was a watery gruel, but I eagerly scooped it into my mess tin and drank it. It was the first hot food I had eaten for two days and it gave me a wonderful sense of wellbeing, raising my spirits after the long and depressing walk from St Lo.

"Those bastards have left us here like lambs to the slaughter," said Rudi before tipping the last remains of the soup into his mouth. We had been selected for the first watch while the others caught up on their sleep and Rudi had taken the opportunity to refill his mess tin with soup.

"You noticed that all the heavy stuff kept on going when we turned off," he continued. "I reckon they've left us up here to buy a bit of time. They expect us to throw ourselves under the tracks of the Amis' tanks so they can get away. The bastards!"

Rudi always expected our commanders to drop us in it and almost seemed disappointed on those occasions when they didn't.

"How are we supposed to stop the Amis? With these pea-shooters?" He held up his rifle and nodded towards the few mortars that had been set up on the ridge.

"If they come in their tanks, supported by planes we'll be mincemeat in seconds."

I nodded in agreement as we looked out over the sloping terrain in front of the ridge. Although the day had been overcast, the western horizon retained a pale luminescence. The evening was cool and a faint drizzle had begun to fall by the time I reached the end of the watch, during which I'd heard the constant rumble of our retreating trucks and armour. I would happily have fallen asleep, but was kept awake by the pumping of nervous adrenalin through my veins as the men around me snored. There had been no sign of the enemy, but I knew that they were out there. As darkness enveloped the neat green fields stretching across the valley below, I knew that sooner or later they would be coming this way.

33

The sound came on the wind. The rumbling, at first faint, growing gradually louder as we crouched in our foxholes. Our hearts raced as we checked and re-checked our equipment, making sure that we had plenty of ammunition at the ready. We had taken up our positions before first light, waiting for the inevitable onslaught. Fighter planes were nosing through the clouds above, but they were high and flew over us unchallenged, to concentrate on targets further south.

I remembered Rudi's comment the previous day about 'sacrificial lambs' and as I looked around, I began to think that he might be right. The horizon, cloaked in early morning mist, merged seamlessly into sky. The invisible enemy were rumbling ever closer and all we had to repel them were a few mortars and the bullets of our rifles that would bounce harmlessly off their tanks. If we didn't move before they were upon us we would surely be crushed under their tracks.

Hauptmann Buttner and Braun peered through their binoculars. If either of them were frightened they didn't show it, calmly scanning the distance from right to left and back again. The noises grew louder, but still nothing was visible, then a few moments later and slightly to my left, I saw a tank, then another and then half a dozen more. A line of tanks emerged from the early morning mist about a half a mile distant; we were doubtless already within range of their guns, but they had not yet detected our presence.

My mouth was dry as I watched the tanks, more than twenty now, roll across the fields and begin their slow ascent up the gently sloping ground towards us. They cut easily through the hedges which stood in the way of their relentless, upward progress. The Hauptmann moved further along the ridge and out of sight and I prayed that Braun would order us to withdraw while there was still time to get away. Instead he stood up and ordered the panzerfaust and mortars to prepare. Men duly selected their targets and awaited the order to open fire. The ground began to vibrate as the tanks came closer; further in the distance, beyond the leading ones still more appeared, moving slowly across the misty fields towards our position. It was hopeless, even with armour and artillery of our own we would have been hard pressed to contain the advance of such numbers.

I glanced across at Rudi who was lying in his foxhole, his hands clasping his rifle. He looked across and grinned,

"Never mind the Amis, Theo. My first bullet's for Braun."

I wasn't sure whether he was being serious or not, but any speculation was cut short by Braun's shouted order. The panzerfaust erupted in flame and noise as its projectile arced towards the nearest tank. It landed a glancing blow on its left tracks which separated from the wheels causing the tank to spin crazily. It was disabled, but it wasn't knocked out, for I could see its turret turn and the gun barrel trained upon those who had fired upon it. Our mortars promptly opened up, but this was merely the cue for the other tanks to open fire. The first salvo fell fifty yards in front of our positions, but they found their range all too quickly. A deafening roar was followed by an eruption of soil to my left and two paratroopers manning one of the mortars were thrown into the air, landing yards away, broken and bloodied like discarded rag dolls.

The panzerfaust fired once again, this time scoring a direct hit on a tank a hundred yards away. Smoke and flame erupted from the turret while the other tanks manoeuvred past the stricken vehicle, opening up with their main guns and raking the ground around us with heavy machine gun fire. We replied with our rifles, but the effect was as pitiful as it was pointless. The tanks, continuing to pour out their lethal fire, rolled ever closer. Shells ripped the earth apart, uprooting trees and showering us with earth and leaves. I watched Braun jump up out of his hiding place and run over towards the mortar position where the two men had been hit. When he had almost reached the position he suddenly stopped, performed a strange pirouette, almost like a ballet dancer and then fell to the ground.

Suddenly Rudi was grabbing at my shoulder.

"Braun's dead. Come on Theo, we're off."

I needed no further bidding. I stuffed some cartridge pouches into my pockets, scrambled to my feet and followed him. I ran like a madman through the trees, barely feeling the branches and brambles as they cut and slashed my face and hands, expecting at any moment to feel the piercing pain of a bullet as it ripped through my back. We crouched low as we ran in the same manner as someone seeking shelter in a heavy shower. Meise and two others had also fled their positions, catching up with us as we ran across the fields, desperately trying to get away from the fearful noise of the tanks and the hellish sound of shellfire.

The line of trees stretching across the ridge behind us proved a sturdier barrier to the tanks' progress than our futile efforts with rifle and mortar and they were prevented from immediately pursuing us down the reverse slope. I suspected that more men had probably escaped our defensive line than just the five of us, but we could see no-one else and weren't inclined to wait. The only thing we knew for certain was that five of us had made it away from the ridge and that we were running for our lives. After we had covered half a mile, we jumped into a ditch and caught our breath.

"That bastard Braun must have been hoping for a medal," said Rudi, at last. "We're the only ones around here for miles."

He was right, where were the rest of our forces? Apart from Rudi, Meise and myself, Schroeder and Michalak had also made good their escape. The five of us rested in the ditch while we decided what to do next. Schroeder had been able to run, but he was bleeding profusely from a shrapnel wound in his thigh. Rudi and Meise managed to wrap a field dressing on him in an attempt to staunch the flow of blood which had changed the colour of his trousers from green to dark brown. A series of loud explosions somewhere to the east indicated that the enemy were advancing on a wide front. It was quite possible that during our brief and futile stand on the ridge, we had been cut off, and if we were to avoid the soldier's worst nightmare of being surrounded, then we had better keep going. There would be little time to rest.

We followed the lines of hedges and stone walls as we made our way across the fields, our progress slowed by Schroeder who, though trying his best to keep up, was now limping badly and clearly in severe pain. We halted every ten minutes to allow him to rest and to check his dressing, but it soon became apparent that he couldn't go on much further. We took it in turns to support him as he hobbled along, but climbing farm gates and walls was a problem and the increased size of the bloodstain indicated that the dressing had not succeeded in staunching the flow of blood.

We made painfully slow progress, but managed to stay ahead of the enemy. By noon there was still no sign of any friendly forces and we stopped once again to rest. Our mess tins had long been empty, but I had stuffed a few pieces of bread in my tunic pocket the previous evening and I crammed some morsels into my mouth, allowing my saliva to moisten and soften the brittle pieces until I was able to chew and swallow them. Meise was examining Schroeder's wound as he lay on the grass, his face as white as snow and his breathing barely a whisper. Meise raised his head and held a water flask to his blue lips, but the water simply ran down his chin. Schroeder was dead.

There was no time to bury him and in any case we had left our shovels on the ridge. Rudi closed the dead man's eyes and placed his helmet over his face. If it hadn't been for the horrible bloodstain on his thigh, it might have seemed that he was merely taking a nap. As we set off once more, I looked back at Schroeder's body; perhaps some farmer or the Amis would find him before too long and give him a decent burial so that his body would not remain exposed in the open to be torn to pieces by foxes.

Without Schroeder we were able to move much faster. Avoiding the roads, we continued to follow the hedges and used the cover of trees wherever possible. The sound of vehicles not far off raised our spirits, it seemed to be coming from the direction in which we were headed, perhaps we had at last reached our own lines. Emerging from a small wood we came to a road passing through deep embankments below. We crouched down and held our breath; a few jeeps were disappearing in the distance, but walking along the road towards us were two lines of an infantry patrol, about ten yards separating each man. They were Americans.

We crept quietly back into the trees, our escape route was blocked. The Americans had been pushing in from the east far more quickly than we had realised and now it looked as though we were trapped. It was too dangerous to continue during the remaining hours of daylight so we crawled deep into the undergrowth to discuss our next move in hushed whispers. We were tired and footsore having been on the move since early morning and so decided to stay where we were until nightfall, each taking turns to keep watch while the others slept.

It was completely dark when I was shaken from my sleep. Groggy from my recurring nightmare of torn and broken bodies, I stumbled to my feet. Silently we picked up our weapons and crept towards the edge of the wood to peer down onto the road where we had seen the Amis earlier. All was quiet except for a light breeze rustling the leaves above. The sun had gone down a couple of hours earlier, there was no moon, but a faint light was still visible on the western horizon and we used this to navigate. We crossed the road and made our way across still more fields and further stretches of woodland. Our senses, heightened by darkness and fear, gave us the ability to see, hear and smell everything around us. We saw the animals in the fields before they saw us, smelt the smoking chimneys of unseen farmhouses and heard the sound of faraway explosions borne on the breeze.

We hadn't eaten anything except for some pieces of stale bread for more than a day, but our need to make progress was tempered by the pangs of hunger. We had avoided farmhouses thus far, partly because they might have already been taken by the Americans and partly because of the danger that they were in the hands of the Resistance. There were just four of us and we were only lightly armed, we were exposed and vulnerable. The invasion had no doubt emboldened the Resistance who would undoubtedly have emerged from their lairs to attack our troops wherever possible and commit other acts of sabotage. We knew that they often hid in isolated farms and we wanted to avoid them if at all possible.

Members of the Resistance often paid a high price for their audacity, but many seemed determined to exact revenge on the soldiers who had occupied their country for so long and we were taking no chances. We weren't interested in any confrontations, we were driven only by a desire to escape from the clutches of the enemy and get back to our lines. Emerging from the shelter of another copse, we came across a small stone cottage, the glow of an oil lamp in one of the windows indicating that someone might be inside. A few ancient wooden sheds leant against the walls of the cottage, perhaps containing eggs or chickens, but we were in a hurry. There was no time to prepare a meal and raw eggs, even to a hungry man, were not particularly appetising. Rudi decided upon the direct approach.

We crept up to the cottage, guns at the ready. A small tricolour hung above the old oak door, a sure sign that the occupants believed that they had already been liberated. Through the window we could see an elderly man sitting at a table with his wife, a bottle of wine in front of them. It was a scene of peaceful domesticity, an incredible oasis of normality in the middle of a battlefield. There was no sign of anyone else in the cottage or the sound of anyone nearby. Rudi put his foot against the door and kicked it open, Meise and I burst in with our rifles at the ready while Michalak kept watch by the door. The farmer's wife cried out in surprise at the sudden intrusion while the old man attempted to get to his feet. Meise pushed him roughly back down into his chair then shoved the barrel of his rifle into the man's chest.

"Merde! Allemande" the man shouted.

Rudi used his few words of French to tell him that if he knew what was good for him he should remain where he was and be quiet.

The two of them did as they were instructed as Meise pointed his rifle at them. Rudi and I ransacked the kitchen for food, pulling things hurriedly out of cupboards and carelessly spilling the contents on the floor. Half a pot of stew on the stove was quickly poured into my empty mess tin, a couple of French loaves were broken and stuffed into our tunics, while from a wicker basket we grabbed some apples, a few carrots and a small earthenware flagon of liquid which we later discovered to be calvados.

The farmer and his wife sat in silent anger while we helped ourselves to the contents of their kitchen. When we had taken as much as we could carry, we left as swiftly as we had arrived, creeping back out into the night with the sound of the farmer's curses ringing in our ears. We put a mile between ourselves and the cottage before sitting down to sample our feast, enjoying the still warm stew and mopping our mess tins dry with lumps of bread. Apples, raw carrots and a few swigs of Calvados completed our meal; it could not have tasted better if the finest Paris restaurant had prepared it. Full stomachs revived our spirits and increased our sense of optimism; if we could continue to travel by night avoiding the roads and villages wherever possible, then the four of us might still be able to slip unnoticed through the enemy lines.

34

After almost two days of steady progress, it was hard to believe that we had been unable to make contact with any of our units. If there were any in the area, they were well hidden for we saw no sign of them; a retreating army had become a vanishing one. We continued heading south through the night, moving through woodland wherever possible, but otherwise staying close to the hedges and walls, avoiding the roads at all costs. As dawn approached, we once again began to look for a place to hide, but as we moved through a cornfield we heard the sound of vehicles and voices in the distance. In the half-light we crouched in the ripening corn and listened, straining to hear above the beating of our hearts.

"Deutsche!" said Rudi at last, grinning broadly.

At last we had found our lines. We moved closer without revealing ourselves as the last thing we wanted was to be mistaken for the enemy - it would be no less painful to be hit by a German bullet rather than an American one. Crawling along through the waist-high corn, we were finally able to distinguish a column of jeeps and half-tracks which had halted in the road. Although anxious to see a friendly face, my vivid memories of our own company's vehicles ablaze just two days earlier made me nervous of approaching any closer. I listened carefully for the approach of aircraft, but heard nothing.

When we had approached to within fifty yards of the column we stood up, held our rifles high above our heads and shouted frantically for them not to shoot. Walking slowly towards the column, under the watchful eyes and guns of the soldiers suddenly alerted to our presence, we presented ourselves to a Hauptmann. We told him our story and although he listened, he was clearly preoccupied with the constant stream of orders and information that was being passed to him via his radio operator. It was clear that he had more important things to worry about than a few stray paratroopers. He passed us on to a Leutnant who informed us that most units were falling back towards St Malo in order to avoid encirclement. It seemed that as well as rapidly advancing from the north, there were reports that the Americans had also broken through in the east.

He told us to keep on moving and we needed no further encouragement. I for one was desperate to get away from the stationary line of vehicles that would present such an easy target for an enemy plane. Although we had walked all night, we were in no mood to stop and decided to press on in daylight, believing that we were now in a more secure area. We left the bulk of the column behind and moved steadily throughout the morning, once more steering clear of the main roads and avoiding villages, heading in what we hoped was the direction of St Malo.

Tired and hungry, I had an awful feeling that we were caught in a trap and half expected the enemy to fall upon us at any moment. This thought had prompted us to keep walking for most of the day, but we were exhausted and badly in need of sleep. It had started to rain and we decided to find somewhere to shelter, a dry barn or even a farmhouse in which we could spend a few hours. During the late afternoon we reached a small stream running swiftly over rocks and pebbles. We filled our flasks and eagerly drank the cold, refreshing water before wading across to the other side. The sound of rushing water masked the sound of gunfire as we crossed, for it was only when bullets began hitting the water causing it to erupt in small fountains, that we realised we were under attack.

We scrambled for cover in some bushes on the other bank, getting off a few shots in reply, but our shooting was wild for we had little idea from which direction the attack had come. As we crouched in the bushes we saw no sign of anyone and there were no more shots. Whoever had opened fire on us seemed to have disappeared and we concluded that it had probably been some Resistance bastards taking a few pot shots at retreating soldiers then running for cover. We waited in the bushes, listening for any sounds with fingers poised on our triggers. Five minutes elapsed with no sound or further shots so we decided to keep moving. Scrambling once more to our feet we moved quickly, getting as far away as possible from the place of ambush.

I didn't realise that anything was wrong until we stopped for a short rest an hour later. I had been aware of a dull pain in my lower leg since we crossed the river so I took my boot off to see if I could find the cause. It was full of blood. I examined the boot, and found a small hole near the top of the leather just below the knee. I realised that one of the shots fired as we crossed the stream must have passed through the boot and into my calf; I had clearly lost some blood, but the amazing thing was that I hadn't even realised that I had been shot. I emptied the blood from my boot while Meise found a bandage and wrapped it tightly around my calf, then pulled the boot back on. I was determined that nothing would stop me from keeping up with the others, there would be time enough later to get it patched up properly.

Around eight in the evening, as it was growing dark, we clambered over a gate and onto a narrow lane. We usually avoided the roads, but felt that we were now in safer territory and besides, we had seen an old barn in the distance that might offer some protection for the night and perhaps some food. We had walked for a few hundred yards when Rudi suddenly stopped.

'Stille!' he shouted.

Rudi had been the first to hear the sound of the approaching vehicle. We stopped and listened, it was coming our way and quickly. The narrow lane ran between high banks topped by thick thorn hedges; it was impossible to get out of the way, so we quickly took up position, crouching, two of us on either side of the road, rifles at the ready. As the speeding vehicle came around a bend, we could see that it was a jeep, but not until it was less than thirty yards away could we see that it bore not the familiar black cross we had been half expecting, but the white American star.

"Sheise! Amis."

We opened fire and the jeep came to a standstill amid the sound of screeching tyres and breaking glass as our bullets raked the vehicle. We pumped a few more rounds into the jeep then waited, silently crouching in the twilight, listening intently for the sound of other vehicles approaching. Nothing broke the silence except for the sound of a man groaning.

We crept closer to the jeep, hands trembling and rifles at the ready. The driver was draped over the wheel, the exit mark of a bullet in the middle of his back; another soldier in the front passenger seat lay slumped against the door, a large, red blotch spreading across the chest of his jacket. They were both dead; a third soldier was lying in the back, this was the man we could hear groaning. The rest of us covered Rudi while he checked to make sure that the wounded man wasn't holding a weapon. He pulled him upright, but the soldier was clearly incapable of offering any resistance, a bullet had torn through his neck and a combination of blood and phlegm bubbled from his mouth as he struggled to breathe.

A white, rectangular patch above one chest pocket proclaimed US ARMY, while above the other pocket his name was printed: SCHMIDT. We lifted him out of the vehicle and lay him at the side of the road. He looked no older than me. Rudi and Michalak pulled the two dead men from the front of the jeep and lay them next to their wounded comrade while Meise and I lifted the wounded man's head and tried to give him a drink of water, but his wounds were so horrific that he was unable to swallow.

"Let's get out of here," Rudi shouted. "There's bound to be more Amis where these came from."

"What about him?" I shouted, hesitating to use the name emblazoned on his uniform…it seemed too close, too personal, better to refer to the wounded man as 'him'.

"Leave him."

Meise ran towards the jeep while I lay the wounded soldier's head on the bank. I then moved towards the jeep, but stopped short, removed the flask from my belt clip and returned to the man, placing it in his hand and clasping his fingers around it before finally climbing into the jeep.

"Christ! Theo, hurry up! You'll get us all killed," Rudi shouted as he turned over the engine of the stalled vehicle.

I jumped into the back, ignoring the blood on the canvas seat and we roared off into the gathering darkness. Now we could really make progress, the only danger would be if we ran into a roadblock…German or American. The jeep had no windscreen or headlights, but this didn't slow us down even though the last vestiges of light that remained in the sky were barely sufficient to see the road in front. Using the western sky as our compass, we drove in what we hoped was the opposite direction to the enemy and by the time we entered a small town half an hour later it was quite dark. Rudi slowed, following the narrow road that twisted between rows of stone houses before it opened out into a small square in the middle of town. There had been no checkpoints as we entered the town and we were surprised to find the square lined with military vehicles of every conceivable type. At last, it seemed that we had found our missing armoured columns. I was about to shout out a word of greeting when Meise held his hand up to silence me. We stared in horror at the vehicles, tanks, half-tracks, trucks and jeeps for they were not decorated with German black crosses but with white American stars.

The square was in almost complete darkness; the only light came from a few torches and lanterns erected by the crews next to their vehicles.

"Sheise!" said Rudi through gritted teeth as he slowed the jeep to a crawl. "Quick! Take off your helmets and turn up your collars."

We instantly obeyed, while he drove slowly around the square before parking as inconspicuously as possible at the end of a line of half-tracks.

"Don't speak," he hissed.

It was something he hardly needed to say, for we were all too frightened to say a word. Rudi slumped down in the driver's seat and pretended to be asleep and we followed suit. We clearly wouldn't be able to drive off at this time of night without being challenged; our only hope lay in staying where we were, hoping that no one would notice us and praying that somehow we might get away at first light.

It was the longest night of my life, for although all of us feigned sleep, not one of us, exhausted though we were, dropped off for even a second. I sat with my eyes half closed listening to strange voices speaking English all around us; it was the first time I had ever heard the language spoken up close and it was something I will never forget. Some of the American soldiers seemed to be playing cards, one man in the distance played a mournful tune on a mouth organ, but most slept.

Just before dawn, we heard commanders shouting at the tank crews to get ready to move out. Engines were fired up, acrid exhaust fumes mixing with the faint smell of bacon and eggs wafted through the air and I was suddenly reminded that I hadn't eaten for more than twenty-four hours. I glanced over at Rudi in the driver's seat who, although feigning sleep, was alert and scanning the scene around us. Within ten minutes the vehicles had begun moving out of the square. We stayed where we were, watching anxiously and half expecting some over-zealous officer or military policeman to question us or ask to see our papers, but no-one came near.

As the truck beside us pulled out, Rudi started up the jeep and followed closely behind at the rear of the column. With the roar of engines masking our voices to anyone outside the jeep, we talked freely once again. It was quickly decided that we would follow the column out of town, but at the first opportunity we would break away from the column and make good our escape. We were conscious that with the growing light our uniforms would give us away and we looked anxiously for a turn off. Two miles outside the town, with the rising sun illuminating the landscape the column passed through a crossroads; Rudi turned the wheel hard, floored the accelerator and sped off to the right. If the rest of the column noticed our abrupt departure, there was no sign of it and as I looked anxiously from the back of the jeep, I was relieved to see that no one had turned off to follow us. We breathed a collective sigh of relief as we drove westwards in what we hoped was the direction of St Malo and safety.

35

As the sun crested the horizon, enemy planes once more appeared in the sky. This time we were not so afraid of them, trusting that the star on the hood of the jeep would act as our talisman. Rudi as usual wasn't happy, complaining that it would just be our luck for our heroic friends in the Luftwaffe to put in a belated appearance and finish us off.

We eventually reached a crossroads where an ancient signpost indicated that St Malo lay another fifteen kilometres further west. The countryside had changed imperceptibly from the rich, undulating fields of Normandy to the harder, rocky landscape of Brittany. The land was poor and stony, scored with steep valleys and ravines through which fast flowing rivers carved their way to the coast. There was little sign of damage in any of the deserted villages through which we passed and it appeared that the Americans were concentrating on pushing south towards Paris rather than heading for the coast.

On the outskirts of one village we passed an open piece of land containing some huts enclosed by a chain link fence. A small swastika flag hung limply from a flagpole. It was clearly an army depot. The place looked deserted. Rudi stopped. Leaving Meise and Michalak on the road with the jeep's engine running, Rudi and I went to see whether any food or equipment might have been left inside the huts. Rifles at the ready, we entered the largest of the buildings and were surprised to find a Wehrmacht corporal behind the counter of what was obviously the quartermaster's store.

"Hurry, we need food," Rudi shouted.

The corporal looked at him coldly.

"Can I see your requisition?" he replied, bridling at Rudi's apparent lack of respect towards the two stripes on his sleeve.

"Requi....... The fucking Amis are half a mile down the road and you want a fucking requisition?"

He slammed his fist on the counter.

"Give us what we need now and be damned with your stupid pieces of paper."

"Nein!" said the corporal, suddenly reaching beneath the counter.

The discharge of Rudi's rifle next to my ear almost deafened me. I turned and looked at Rudi in horror as the corporal lurched backwards, a blood-red hole in his chest.

"Rudi! What the hell..........?"

Rudi ignored me, leaned over the counter and found what the corporal had been reaching for - a loaded machine pistol. He threw the pistol at the body of the corporal.

"Dumkopf!"

He leapt over the counter, hurriedly helping himself to food and cigarettes. Instead of doing anything practical to assist, I stood motionless, scarcely able to believe that he had shot one of our own soldiers.

In an instant Rudi was back over the counter and we ran for the door. Miese and Michalak had heard the shot and nervously trained their guns on us as we emerged from the store, lowering them only when they were sure who it was. We jumped back into the jeep and Rudi roared off at speed, hurling the jeep around the many bends in the road, pushing it to its limits. After he nearly lost control on a couple of corners, I began to think that we might all soon be killed without the assistance of the enemy, and after the incident at the quartermaster's stores, I was no longer sure whether we were running away from the Americans or from our own side.

We rounded a bend at the top of a hill and began to descend towards a bridge spanning a deep gorge through which a river flowed almost a hundred feet below. We were almost halfway across the bridge, when Rudi suddenly slammed his foot hard on the brakes. The rest of us looked in alarm, thinking that he had seen a roadblock ahead, but there was nothing, not even a road. Rudi had seen, far too late, that the central span of the bridge had been blown out and that directly in front of us there was a gap in the road some thirty feet wide.

The wheels locked and the acrid scent of burning rubber filled my nostrils as the tyres tried vainly to grip the surface of the road, but the speed of the vehicle was too great, we were never going to stop in time. The seconds passed in slow motion as the jeep left the road and sailed through the air, the momentum keeping it airborne for a few moments before beginning its inexorable fall. We fell in eerie silence until at last the rocks and earth rose up to meet the jeep with a sickening bang. Then there was nothing but blackness.

I didn't regain consciousness until I woke in a field dressing station in a cellar on the outskirts of St Malo, and when I did, I wished that I still was unconscious. I screamed with pain. An orderly appeared, stuck a needle into my arm and I re-entered my dream. Falling and tumbling into the ravine, the broken bodies of Meise and Michalak lying in the twisted wreckage of the jeep. Rudi lifting me, hauling me over his shoulder and clambering up the side of the rocky gorge, watching in detached fascination as the stones and pebbles dislodged by his boots, rolled back into the abyss. Dream and reality faded seamlessly into each other. The hum of an engine, the rocking back and forth over the holes in the road. The screaming pain that attended every jolt.

I was lifted once again, hearing Rudi's familiar voice booming out over a babble of other voices, moans and screams, then more darkness. I had no idea how long I had been lying in that cellar; a few hours? A few days? a week ? The chloroform had done its work well.

A shell exploded somewhere nearby causing the ground to shake and showering everyone in the shelter with dust. I was instantly awake, the dreams banished to the farthest recesses of my mind. A captain entered the bunker and shouted above the din.

"We have to move. Everyone must get down to the harbour immediately. I'll return in five minutes and if I find anyone still here who is able to walk, I'll shoot them myself."

He turned on his heel and departed to the accompaniment of the sound of further explosions. I looked down at my arm and saw that it was strapped to my chest with two leather belts. An orderly helped me to my feet.

"You heard the Captain. Let's go."

"Where's Rudi?" I asked, but the medic ignored me and motioned for me to rest my weight on his shoulder. He placed a helmet on my head and helped me make my painful way up the steps and out of the bunker, groaning every time my shoulder was jolted. We emerged into a street and joined a river of wounded men streaming down the hill towards the harbour. Damaged stone buildings lined the street through which the swarm of soldiers limped along, a field-grey tide swept along like a bow wave created by the artillery exploding behind them. I searched the faces for any sign of Rudi, but none of the grim, determined faces around me looked familiar. Suddenly a couple of fighter planes screamed low overhead and everyone scrambled for cover. As they disappeared over the rooftops we once again got to our feet as best we could and continued down the hill.

It took twenty minutes to reach the quayside. Out in the harbour, smoke belched from the funnels of a white ship which had a large red cross painted on the side of its hull. The orderly helped me to sit down next to the other wounded men; some were able to sit up like myself and we were propped up with our backs resting against a stone wall, while others lay on stretchers. I leant back against the wall and surveyed the human wreckage that lay all around. Some of the men had bandages around their heads, some had lost limbs and some appeared not to have any injuries at all. The corporal sprawled on a stretcher next to me had a heavily bandaged right leg.

"The damned ship's been in and out of harbour three times already," he said, nodding towards the vessel with the large Red Cross. "Every time we're ready to board there's another fucking air raid and it steams out into the bay. I've been here since dawn …no one bothers to move us when the planes come over. They leave us out here in the open while they are busy looking after themselves."

As if on cue, the steamer bellowed and waters churned as once more it pulled away from the dock. Belching smoke from its two funnels, it swung wildly around and headed rapidly out into the estuary beyond the breakwater. Moments later the familiar whine of aircraft engines drowned out the sound of everything else. Three American planes swooped low over the bay attracting a salvo of anti-aircraft fire from the gun positions around the town. As the corporal had predicted, the orderlies and anyone else who could move, scurried away to find shelter while we were left where we were. It seemed as though the planes were heading straight for me and, ignoring the pain in my shoulder, I instinctively turned and pressed my face into the wall as they passed overhead. The noise was deafening as they roared past and I waited for the whistles and the inevitable explosions that would follow. I closed my eyes, clenched my fists and flattened myself as best as I could against the wall.

I counted…one…two…three…four…waiting for impact, but there were no explosions, only the receding noise of the aircraft and the repeated crash of the anti-aircraft batteries. I turned and looked up at the china blue sky, filled with puffs of flak smoke drifting above the town, masquerading as innocent white clouds. The sound of barked orders and running boots on the cobblestones resumed, as those who had been able to take shelter returned to tend those they had temporarily deserted.

"Bastards!" hissed the corporal beside me. "They come back out now the danger's over." One of the soldiers who had helped me down from the first-aid bunker emerged from his hiding place and handed us each a cigarette by way of apology.

"Orders," he said as he struck a match. "We don't have time to move all the wounded so we have to just save ourselves."

The corporal took a long pull on his cigarette. "Bastards!" he breathed again as he exhaled smoke into the orderly's face.

Out in the bay the steamer swung around once again and headed back into the harbour.

"How long do you think it will take to get back to Hamburg?" I ventured.

The corporal levered himself up on one elbow and gave me a look of contempt. He looked into my eyes to ascertain whether or not I was joking and when he saw that I was not, threw back his head and bellowed with laughter. He shook with mirth for fully a minute before fixing me with a steely gaze.

"What the fuck are they sending to the front line now. Have you no idea what's going on, boy?"

"They said we were being evacuated," I spat, beginning to find him tiresome.

"Not to fucking Hamburg we aren't, Sonny." He took another pull on his cigarette before exhaling the smoke, this time directly into my face. "That old tub out there wouldn't last five minutes if it started sailing for Hamburg ....no matter how big a red cross they paint on the side.

"Well then, where are we going?"

The corporal lay back on the stretcher and looked skywards as he took another pull on his cigarette. He exhaled a plume of smoke, watching it climb into the air before answering.

"Some say Portugal, others say Spain and some say we're going to a place called Jersey."

"Jersey? Where the hell is that?"

The corporal spat. "In the middle of fucking nowhere and a long way from home. So you can forget about seeing Hamburg for a while, Sonny.... if there's anything left of the place that is."

I turned away from him to see that the ship was once again inching its way back into the harbour. The quayside was still filling with more wounded, while a group of soldiers were preparing to grab the ropes hanging over the sides of the steamer.

"It looks like they're taking us on board," I said.

"I'll believe it when I'm in my hammock," said the corporal.

Orange stripes of rust streaked the white paint of the ship's hull as it towered high above us at the dockside, almost blotting out the sky. The ropes were secured and the gangway was lowered. Stretcher-bearers and medical orderlies began hurrying aboard with their war-damaged cargo, busily working down the line of men assembled on the quay until they reached me.

"Come on son," said a short rotund private, who appeared to be as old as my father, "you can't stay here all day sunning yourself."

He pulled me to my feet and helped me along the dock and up the gangway. At the top of the gangplank an officer checked everyone, satisfying himself that each would-be evacuee's wounds were genuine and announcing as he did so that anyone who was subsequently found to be feigning injury would be shot when we arrived at our destination. I was taken down a series of steps into the lowest, darkest parts of the ship where I was laid on a thin mattress that smelt of stale urine and medical spirit. A few nurses were tending to the wounded who lay on the deck around me. I must have been one of the last to get on board for within a few minutes, the throbbing of the engines echoed the throbbing of my shoulder and signalled that we were underway.

In the end it had all happened so quickly. I had spent six months in France, slow, tedious months, waiting for something to happen before the madness of the past few days broke over me like a storm. Now I was leaving, but as I looked around at all the unfamiliar faces, I could only wonder what had happened to my comrades. Had Rudi survived and if so, where had he gone? Had Meise and Michalak really been killed when the jeep crashed into the ravine? Where were the others, had they all been crushed under the tanks on that godforsaken ridge near Avranches?

As the ship left the coast of France behind, I found myself adrift in a sea of strangers and I knew that I would never find the answers to my questions.

36

I slept only fitfully as the ship sailed. The chloroform in my system made me drowsy and my limbs felt like lead weights that could be moved only with the greatest of effort. Each time I awoke it was to the constant vibration of the engines and the sound of the ship's propellers spinning inches below the metal plates of the deck on which I lay. As the effects of the chloroform wore off, the pain in my shoulder became more severe and caused me to wince even when I moved a fraction, but these were not the only disturbances. All around me lay the other wounded, variously shouting, groaning and screaming as they relived their individual horrors in nightmares that would give them no peace.

I managed to fall asleep once again and didn't wake up until some time later. The engines had ceased their throbbing and an eerie silence had fallen on the lower deck. Lapsing in and out of sleep as I had, it was difficult to tell how long we had been sailing, but I had a vague idea that we had not travelled so very far. For a moment I wondered if for some reason we had been forced to return to France, but an orderly came down and announced that we had arrived. I was helped to my feet and guided painfully up the numerous flights of steps to the deck. As we ascended I thought I heard the sound of music, as if a military band was playing. At first I believed it to be my imagination, but the sound of music grew steadily louder as we ascended. I was helped up the final flight of stairs and a cold blast of fresh air hit me as I arrived on deck to the accompaniment of trombones, trumpets and drums. I descended the gangplank and was placed on a stretcher as the sounds of the welcoming army band filled the air. As I was carried away, it was clear that wherever it was that we had landed, we were being given a heroes' welcome.

The band played a selection of familiar marching tunes, the 'Horst Wessel' Song and "Wir Fahren nach England" which was quite appropriate because, although I didn't realise at the time, I had actually arrived on English soil. The ship had docked in the port of St Helier on the island of Jersey, one of the Channel Islands. I had only vaguely been aware of the existence of these places which belonged to England, but had been occupied by our forces ever since the fall of France some four years earlier.

I was taken by lorry to the Continental Hotel, a large, white three-storey building near the seafront that had been converted into a military hospital. After waiting for more than three hours while the more serious cases were being treated, I was finally examined by a doctor. He first examined the bullet wound in my leg, wiping some of the puss away from the suppurating hole in my leg before applying some stinging antiseptic with a cotton swab, which made me gasp in pain. With a grunt of approval he pronounced himself satisfied, but when he unstrapped my right arm he looked more concerned.

He told me to raise my arm, but I could not. There was no feeling, and no matter how hard I tried, the arm would not move.

"What stupid bastard strapped this up?" he demanded.

"The medical orderly in St Malo," I replied meekly, feeling as though it was somehow my fault.

"The moron!" he exclaimed. "He should have put it in a sling instead of strapping it to your body like this."

"It was difficult in the dressing station. We had to be moved quickly……." I stopped, aware that he wasn't impressed with my story and wondering why I was bothering to make apologies for the medics in St Malo. I tried to raise my arm once again, but to no avail. I tried once more, straining every sinew to force my reluctant arm to move, but then I passed out and when I awoke I found myself lying in a hospital ward with half a dozen other men.

That evening a nurse came round pushing a trolley full of soup bowls. The delicious aroma made me realise that during all the pain and excitement of the evacuation, I hadn't eaten a hot meal for three days. Unable to hold both the bowl and the spoon with my one available hand, I thought I had arrived in heaven when the nurse sat on the edge of the bed and fed me spoonful by spoonful. I gulped down the thin broth as quickly as she could empty the bowl. When it was gone, I asked her if there was any more, but she appeared surprised by my request and informed me that I had already been given my full allowance. I thought this a rather strange reply; we had always been permitted second helpings of food, even when we were away from barracks and being served at field kitchens. I concluded that either the nurse had taken a dislike to me or that it must be some unfathomable hospital regulation, and didn't give the matter much further thought. I went to sleep that night still feeling hungry, but I little suspected that it was a feeling with which I would become very familiar.

I remained in St Helier for two more days before I and ten other patients were given orders to transfer to another hospital elsewhere on the island. Despite the wound in my leg and my incapacitated arm, no transport was provided and I had to join the others on foot. Fortunately my leg wound didn't cause too many difficulties, and anyway I was glad to be out of the hospital ward and in the open air. We followed a non-com for four miles along a road which followed the shore before turning up a narrow wooded valley which led away from the sea. Half an hour later we reached the entrance to a tunnel that had been cut into the natural rock of a thickly wooded hillside.

A red cross painted above the entrance was the only clue that this might be a medical facility. As I entered this strange subterranean world, I saw that it was indeed a hospital and, apart from the absence of windows, could see that it was laid out like any other, with wards, consulting rooms and even an operating theatre. Each of the wards contained a dozen beds and all the wards were connected by a series of smaller access tunnels. Although the curved ceilings and walls had been lined with white painted concrete and illuminated with bright lights, a damp, musty airless smell permeated the place.

I was shown to a waiting room before being once again examined by a doctor. He referred to the notes I had brought with me from St Helier and examined my arm, which had now been placed into a proper sling. Removing the sling carefully, he asked me to try and lift my arm, but I still could not. My shoulder was causing me great discomfort, but I had every reason to suppose that the pain would soon pass. Nothing had apparently been broken, but my arm was a worry - it didn't hurt, but just hung limp and useless by my side. At the end of the examination the doctor informed me that he couldn't guarantee that he would be able to save my arm. The news hit me as hard as a bullet for I thought that I had survived the worst of it. I believed that I had escaped the fighting with nothing more than a minor bullet wound, slight concussion and a dislocated shoulder, yet the doctor was now telling me that I might lose my right arm. I prayed that the doctor was mistaken and cursed the medical orderlies in St Malo just as the doctor in St Helier had done.

Many of the patients in this strange subterranean hospital had, like me, been evacuated from St Malo during the past week, but some had been evacuated to Jersey soon after the allied invasion in June. I saw a range of horrific injuries: bullet and shrapnel wounds, some soldiers were missing limbs while others had been blinded, their heads swathed in yards of white bandages. All had a ghastly translucent pallor, which was probably due as much to the lack of natural light in the place as to their injuries. Whatever the reason, a look at some of the men made my own difficulties seem minor by comparison. I would often lie awake at night in the dark, dank ward, listening to the whimpers of those in pain and the occasional soldier who cried out for his mother. The eerie echoes emanating from the various tunnels and chambers gave me nightmares; it was like a vision from hell where we had descended into the underworld and I sometimes awoke in the night with the notion that I had been killed and then buried in some vast tomb.

Desperate to avoid the spectre of amputation, I removed my arm from the sling as often as possible and tried to move it, but although I was unable to lift it, I found that I was gradually able to make slight movements with my hand and fingers. The doctor said this was a good sign and advised me to continue with these exercises as often as possible. I constantly moved them, clenching and unclenching my fist, playing an imaginary piano with my fingers, endlessly making sure that the nerves and the blood supply continued to work. I was damned if I was going to lose my arm. Every day I was given thirty minutes formal physiotherapy by a nurse and despite the agony of straining every sinew, my arm gradually began to respond and after a week of this therapy I was able to raise it a few inches from my side.

The pain in my shoulder was beginning to lessen and although I still could not lift my right arm more than a few inches, after a week in the underground hospital, I was pronounced fit enough to leave. I couldn't wait to leave the strange underground world of pale ghosts who seemed to inhabit neither this world nor the next. Some of the other wounded men in the hospital were fellow paratroopers and four of us were discharged on the same day with instructions to report to the Luftwaffe HQ in St Helier.

Once again we were expected to walk because of some unaccountable lack of transport. The three other men and I emerged from the hospital's main entrance, blinking in the unaccustomed brightness of a cool autumn morning. The days spent in the hospital with only dim light bulbs for illumination had made my eyes sensitive to the light and even though it was not an especially bright day, it was a considerable time before my eyes became adjusted.

A Wehrmacht corporal met us at the entrance, ordered us to follow him and we began the long walk back to St Helier, down the narrow wooded valley away from the hospital until we reached the sea. We turned left and followed the road back towards the island's capital. It may have been a reaction to being kept underground for a week, but the sound of seagulls, the crash of waves upon the shore and the vivid colours of green, blue and gold, seemed brighter and louder than ever before. I was already beginning to feel better as we followed the line of a great sweeping bay towards the great castle which stood watch over the towns' harbour.

Concrete gun emplacements and watchtowers stood sentinel every few hundred yards while scattered across the golden sand, triangular metal tank traps with barbed wire stretched between them were lapped by the waves. Signs bearing skull and crossbone motifs announced that the beach was mined, dangerous and off-limits. I had seen coastal defences like these at Cherbourg, the seashore filled with similar devices which at the time I had naively believed would be able to hold back an invading army. For all their apparent strength, I doubted whether these fortifications would prove any more effective.

We arrived at last in the town and halted outside a large stone building near the harbour. In the Commandant's office we were given instructions to join up with a company of paratroopers who were based on the nearby island of Guernsey. We were told that it would mean a short sea journey, but the sergeant assured us that the crossing would be safe and uneventful. I had learned by now that when anyone in authority used words like 'safe' and 'uneventful' they were usually lying so I prepared for the worst as we marched down to the harbour. A small, grey motor vessel was tied up at one of the jetties and a dozen soldiers, some of whom were paratroopers, were already on board. We were evidently the last group to join the boat, for the crew cast off as soon as we clambered over the rail.

There was no room available in the cramped spaces below deck so I found myself a vacant spot close to the bow. Although it wasn't a particularly warm day, I wasn't too concerned about being out in the open; the dark subterranean world of the hospital was a too recent memory to wish for a return to stale air and darkness. Sitting on the deck with the wind ruffling my hair, I enjoyed the sense of freedom as the small boat sped out of harbour and headed westwards. I gripped the rail with my good arm and watched the island of Jersey slip slowly behind and I wondered whether on this other island called Guernsey I might be reunited with any of my old comrades.

37

Despite the clear weather, the safe and uneventful three hour crossing promised by the sergeant in Jersey turned out to be quite rough, and many of the men had been sick over the side. We had been lucky, said one of the crew as we neared our destination, proceeding to tell us that on one such crossing the previous week, one of the boats had been so badly strafed by an enemy fighter that it had gone to the bottom taking eighteen men with it. I was glad he had kept this information to himself until we were in sight of our destination.

It was early evening by the time we approached the rocky island of Guernsey, its steep cliffs silhouetted against the pale light in the western sky. The boat slowed as it entered the calm embrace of the stone breakwaters that enclosed the inner harbour. Behind the harbour, grey stone houses and churches clung tightly to the steep slopes rising behind the waterfront. I was told that the name of the town was St Peter Port, the main town of the island and although it appeared to be considerably smaller than St Helier, it seemed to be even more heavily defended. Ancient stone forts and modern concrete gun emplacements were visible everywhere around the harbour, along the esplanade beyond the harbour wall and high on the cliff tops beyond the town as far as the eye could see.

We jumped down onto the quayside where our papers

were checked by a corporal. He had a cursory glance at each one, then motioned the three other paratroopers and me towards a Luftwaffe sergeant who was waiting further along the quayside. As we approached, everyone saluted except me because I was still unable to lift my right arm more than a few inches. I wondered how long it would be before my failure to salute would land me in trouble with an officer or the military police. I needn't have worried on this occasion for the sergeant barely acknowledged the salutes of my comrades.

I couldn't help but notice the sergeant's untidy appearance; the top button of his tunic was undone and the stubble on his face showed that it hadn't seen a razor for at least two days. Even in Normandy, fighting and living rough in the fields and hedgerows, I had seen officers and non-coms looking smarter, yet here in the middle of a town likely to be swarming with officers and military police, the sergeant looked as if he had just got out of his bunk. He informed us that we would be rejoining some other paratroopers who had already transferred from Jersey and were now stationed at the island's airfield some five miles out of town. Unsure of how long we would be here and of what this island of Guernsey might have in store for us, I was nevertheless pleased to be rejoining the paratroopers. I would not have relished the prospect of being attached to the regular Luftwaffe and certainly not to the Wehrmacht who would doubtless have conspired to make the life of a paratrooper as miserable as possible.

I slung my pack onto my one good shoulder and looked around expecting to see a truck or a jeep. There were none, in fact there were no vehicles in the streets at all, apart from a few bicycles and a horse-drawn cart. The reasons for this, and the sergeant's untidy appearance, would soon become clear, but for now we fell in behind the sergeant and headed up the steep hill away from the harbour. As we passed through the narrow streets of the town, soldiers were everywhere, strolling around, smoking in groups on street corners and idly peering into shop windows, although it appeared that these shops were completely devoid of anything to buy.

By the time we left the town behind and emerged into open countryside, it became clear that there would be no transport and that we were going to have to walk the entire distance. Although I had walked to and from the hospital in Jersey, it had been relatively flat, but the torn calf muscles in my leg soon began to ache in protest at the uphill slog. Fortunately the road eventually levelled out once we had climbed above the town and then twisted through more undulating country. My leg was still sore, but it was bearable and in the darkness I limped along, keeping up with the others who, fortunately for me, merely followed the sergeant as he led us at a leisurely pace towards the airfield.

As we approached our destination the sergeant, who thus far had walked along in silence, began to question us about the nature of our various injuries. He wanted to know where and how they had been sustained, how the situation in Normandy had been after the invasion and he was particularly interested in whether we had received any recent news from home. He was a good deal older than I was and it occurred to me that, apart from those who had been evacuated from Normandy, he and probably most of the men on the island had never fired a shot in anger. Their only contact with the enemy had perhaps been the sight of a naval vessel on the distant horizon or a fleeting glimpse of a reconnaissance aeroplane high overhead. It had not been their misfortune to pick up the charred and stinking remains of their comrades and bury them in a hastily dug pit in some godforsaken field.

It was quite dark by the time we turned off the road and approached a guardhouse manned by two sentries. We produced our *soldbuchs* for inspection.

"Just what we need, more mouths to feed," the surly guard muttered as he examined our papers. When he had scrutinised every one he announced:

"The paratroopers are over there in the hotel, but you've arrived too late for the evening meal."

Our spirits fell; we had been travelling all day and we were tired and hungry. Considering we had not been provided with any food since a snatched breakfast at the underground hospital in Jersey, we had been expecting something to eat, even if it wasn't a hot meal. He pointed to a large building, completely in darkness on the other side of the road from the airfield's main gate. It certainly looked like a hotel, but any joy at the appearance of our quarters was tempered by our hunger. The disappointment must have registered in our faces for, as we trudged away, the sentry shouted after us:

"Welcome to Guernsey – home of Hitler's leanest and meanest."

The other sentry laughed at his joke, but his laugh had a hollow ring.

In the old hotel we were re-united with our fellow paratroopers; some like me had escaped on the last ship out of St Malo, others had been there much longer, but there were none that I recognised. There were no officers, the most senior rank was a sergeant major named Kolze who welcomed us, apologised for the lack of a meal and promised that we would be the first in the line when breakfast was served the following morning. Our quarters were more comfortable than I had expected, even though the old furniture had been removed and instead of soft feather beds the rooms now contained only standard issue bunk beds, four to a room.

I lay in my bunk that first night with my blanket pulled around me, but sleep would not come. I wondered about the sort of place I now found myself in; the groups of soldiers idling in the town, the empty shops and the untidy appearance of the soldiers and even the non-coms. These strange little islands – I had heard that there were also others, even smaller than Jersey and Guernsey which made up the Kanalinseln – they all belonged to England yet had been occupied by us for years. We still occupied them, but things had changed, Normandy, if not the whole of France, had now fallen and instead of being impregnable outer bastions of the Atlantic Wall, the islands were now effectively cut off. Thousands of German fighting men were floating offshore like shipwrecked sailors aboard gigantic lifeboats, but these lifeboats would never be able to carry us to safety.

I stared at the ceiling with such thoughts running through my mind, but my chief concern was the emptiness of my stomach. I suddenly remembered that in my breast pocket there was a small piece of chocolate which I had been given when I arrived at the hospital in St Helier. I looked around to make sure that no-one was watching before pulling the blanket over my head and nibbling hungrily on the sweet, dark chocolate just like a little boy enjoying a midnight feast. Chocolate had never tasted so good and that night I dreamt not of home, but of food. It would not be the last time.

The next morning, I awoke with light from the autumn sun streaming through the window. The sun was already well above the horizon and I was surprised that we had not been turned out of our beds at first light as was the normal custom. I looked around the room and saw that the others were still asleep in their bunks. I got up and went down the corridor to the toilet. I noticed that in the other rooms, men were either still asleep or lying in their bunks smoking cigarettes. I had never seen anything like this before; from the time I had been called up into the Arbeitsdienst there had always been an early morning reveille and parade, the only exception was when I was in the hospital and those crazy days of combat in August. Here everything seemed different; had it not been for the fact that everyone was in uniform, anyone would have thought that this was some place of recreation or a convalescence camp for the wounded rather than an operational base.

I returned to my room, dressed, and leaving the others still sleeping went off in search of breakfast, quickly locating the kitchen in the basement of the building. From the doorway I could see that something was warming in a large cauldron on top of the stove, but as I entered I was shooed away by the cook:

"Breakfast is at nine and there's only one bowl each!" he shouted, without specifying what the bowl might contain.

I returned upstairs and went outside to take a look around and attempt to take my mind off food. I lit a cigarette. It had been dark when I arrived the previous evening, but now in the daylight I could see the open grassy expanse of the airfield, divided by a single concrete runway upon which a number of tractors, old agricultural implements and other obstacles had been randomly placed to prevent anything from landing or taking off. The concrete control tower from which a flag was flying stood on the far side; next to it there was a large hangar with a curving roof and a number of anti-aircraft guns were placed at intervals around the perimeter. There wasn't a single aircraft anywhere to be seen.

In addition to ourselves and the Luftwaffe across the road at the airfield, I discovered that Guernsey was home to over fifteen thousand German soldiers plus five thousand Organisation Todt labourers recruited from every corner of Europe, as well as a civilian population of almost twenty-five thousand. It didn't take a genius to calculate that such a large population on a relatively small island could not exist solely on locally produced food. I had believed that when I left St Malo I had escaped from the enemy's trap, but I now realised that despite the fact that I still wore uniform and carried a rifle, I was caught just as securely as if I had been taken prisoner at the point of a gun.

38

I gradually settled into the languid, predictable routine of life at the airfield. There were almost a hundred paratroopers billeted in the hotel, most of whom had arrived within the past few weeks, escaping with various wounds just as I had from Normandy. I shared a room with two others - Michael Lenz, a wiry youth from Mannheim and Karl Riedle, a tall Bavarian from a small village near Augsburg. They had arrived on Guernsey a month before after collecting a series of minor wounds and injuries. Lenz had a bullet wound in his thigh while Riedle had lost a finger courtesy of some flying shrapnel. Out of the entire complement of ninety-five men, I had never come across any of them before. While I had been based in Rennes before the invasion, most of the others had been stationed further east in Laval and Coutances.

Paratroopers always had a feeling of superiority towards other branches of the military, but the fact that we alone of all the troops on the island had been involved in fighting, and had wounds to show for it, gave us an even greater sense of superiority. This may have explained why we were so unpopular with the other services, for there was little camaraderie between the various service branches present on the island and even within the same service, jealousy and rivalry were the order of the day.

There was a complete absence of the daily duties that

soldiers are usually required to perform and it soon became clear that the overriding task was not to defend the island against attack, much less to launch some kind of offensive, but merely to ensure that we had enough to eat. Rations had been cut the week before I arrived and there were murmurings that they were to be cut once again so that the remaining stocks of food on the island could be eked out for as long as necessary. The only problem was that no-one knew exactly how long this might be.

We had no way of knowing how the war was going and although we suspected that those in command were aware of the situation, they chose not to confide in us. I had discovered that it was the lot of the common soldier to be told lies by those in command - the officer class believed that enlisted men are incapable of intelligent thought and would be unable to maintain discipline if told any unpalatable truths. Many of us suspected that, despite the occasional messages of encouragement emanating from the office of the Island Commandant, the truth was indeed unpalatable. Those who, like I, had escaped from Normandy and St Malo by the skin of our teeth, had witnessed the enormous firepower that had been ranged against us. It was inconceivable that the British and American invasion could have been turned back and even the most stupid soldier or fanatical Nazi realised by now that we were fighting an enemy who had more men, more guns, more tanks, more aeroplanes, more ships……. more everything.

The progress of the war may have been on our minds, but our most urgent priority was to stay alive and in this regard, we paratroopers who had recently arrived were at a disadvantage. Soldiers who had been on the island for a considerable time, aware that rations only went so far, had made some provision for supplementing their diet. Small plots of land, unused by the civilian population, had been cultivated to produce a few potatoes, cabbages or leeks. Some units had even acquired a few chickens to provide fresh eggs and there were some stationed not far from the airfield who had managed to procure a goat to provide them with fresh milk. None of these agricultural projects had been carried out on a grand scale; most had been undertaken merely as a hobby to pass the interminable hours of watching and waiting. Anything which could not be produced on the island could easily be shipped across from France so there had been no need for self-sufficiency, but June 6th had changed all that.

Supplies of food, fuel and ammunition had abruptly ceased when control of the channel ports was lost and the already large population of the islands, swollen by wounded evacuees like myself, had been rapidly forced to learn the art of self-sufficiency. The knowledge that we were now cut off, and that everything would henceforth be in short supply, had naturally sapped morale and made the high command nervous. Everything now became clear to me: the lack of transport, the meagre rations and the lax discipline were just an outward manifestation of a situation that many believed would lead either to an early surrender or a lingering death.

Sgt Major Horst Kolze was a large man with fair hair and a ruddy complexion. A scarred veteran of campaigns in Greece and North Africa, he had received a bullet wound in his arm while fighting in Normandy and had been evacuated to Guernsey back in July. He had scant respect for officers and the rules and regulations that governed military life, but he had the highest regard for the men serving beneath him. He held the highest rank of all the paratroopers on the island and was therefore in command of the ninety-five men billeted in the hotel at the airfield. He nominally reported to the colonel in charge of all Luftwaffe forces on Guernsey, but we were largely left alone with little interference.

When Kolze had arrived on the island with the initial group of paratroopers he had gone to see the Luftwaffe quartermaster to organise the distribution of food and equipment and had been appalled at the meagre rations on which his men were expected to live. They had been steadily reduced since then and one week after my arrival, Sgt Major Kolze addressed the whole company and told us they were to be cut again. The simple truth was that our rations were insufficient for survival and that if we wished to live, we would have to supplement them by other means. It was no wonder that the sentry we encountered upon our arrival had complained of 'more mouths to feed'.

Although Kolze never said what these 'other means' might involve, he told us in no uncertain terms that the local civilian population were not to be molested and that anyone caught stealing food, or acting in any way which might bring dishonour on the military, would be dealt with severely. I had already heard stories of soldiers being shot for such breaches of discipline and knew that this was no bluff. Such pronouncements had been fairly commonplace in France, but food had been plentiful and it remained to be seen whether threats of dire punishment would prove a deterrent to hungry men.

Kolze went on to inform us that we were nominally charged with airfield defence, but that henceforth there were to be no work details or any kind of formal exercises. We were not encouraged to get up early as breakfast would be served late and we were instructed to rest after our main meal of the day in order to conserve our energies. He told us frankly that things didn't look too good, but promised us that he would do everything in his power to ensure that we received no less than anyone else on the island. From that day on we began to hatch plots and devise schemes to supplement our rations.

After Normandy fell, everyone was sure that the enemy would launch an attack on the islands, but weeks passed by and apart from a few half-hearted raids by lone aircraft, nothing much happened at all and with every passing week the chances of an attack seemed less and less likely. So much time and effort had gone into constructing the islands' defences that the enemy would undoubtedly have taken severe casualties had they attempted to land, and for what? Soldiers more concerned with filling their empty stomachs hardly represented a threat to the enemy and there was a growing suspicion among all ranks that they were content to starve us into surrender.

The fine, dry weather of October turned into a wet and cold November. The stunted, misshapen trees that grew along the exposed cliff tops lost their leaves and the first winter storms further out in the Atlantic churned the grey waters around the island. My injured arm had only slightly improved since my arrival and I was required to visit the hospital in St Peter Port three times a week for physiotherapy sessions. With no available transport it was a five-mile walk in each direction, and although my leg wound had all but healed, I was tired and sore by the time I returned to the airfield. For these sessions, an Army medic would usually treat me, but occasionally I would get to see a doctor. To my relief he told me that there was now little danger that I would lose my arm, but there was a distinct possibility that I might never regain the full use of it again.

I found the prospect of being crippled at the age of nineteen less than appealing and so, in addition to the physiotherapy I received at the hospital, I devised a contraption involving some string and the wooden slat of an upper bunk bed. Tying one end of the string around my wrist and the other end around my foot after passing it first around the wooden slat, I found that by pressing down with my foot, the improvised pulley would raise and lower my right arm; I would do this repeatedly for an hour or so at a time, desperate to strengthen the withered muscles which were still too weak to lift my arm unaided by more than a few inches.

Predictably, a week before Christmas our rations were cut once again. Apart from the high command that kept in radio contact with Berlin, we were still told nothing of what was going on in the outside world. In the absence of hard fact, conversations consisted of rumour, half-truths and fantasy, but the eternal topic for most of us was when the war would end and when would we be able to go home.

39

When you can eat as much as you like, food is taken for granted. A fine meal is something to be enjoyed, anticipated even, but roast meat, fresh vegetables and delicious gravy are not normally the stuff of dreams. I had never before been deprived of food; at home my mother had always provided hearty, nutritious meals and throughout my years of service, first in the Arbeitsdienst and later in the Paratroopers, I had always eaten well, with an appetite as healthy as any normal teenager.

This happy state of affairs changed abruptly when I arrived in the Channel Islands. When I had left St Malo, apart from my injured right arm and my leg wound, I was in generally good health, but good health depends upon an adequate, healthy and varied diet and our recently reduced rations were none of those. Initially we were not unduly concerned and though we would all have welcomed a hearty meal, we thought that the situation would be only temporary, but imperceptibly my health and that of my comrades began to slowly deteriorate. As Christmas and the end of the year approached, there was still no word of surrender and even less sign of an attack. We were in a strange kind of limbo, living on a fortress island, bristling with weapons and thousands of men to defend it, which had been completely by-passed by the war. The men had nothing to do except watch, wait and worry about losing weight and what might be happening at home.

The island had been partitioned between the various branches of the military and the Todt Organisation. Most areas were out of bounds to everyone except those assigned to them and this rule was applied everywhere apart from St Peter Port which was considered an 'open' town. As a result of this situation we hardly ever came into contact with other groups, even in the areas immediately surrounding our base at the airfield. The high command had done this for a good reason: if men were separated and isolated from each other there was less chance of gossip and complaint, for an island crammed with idle and frustrated young men was potentially volatile. Thousands of disillusioned men, tired of being marooned on this isolated piece of rock, unaware of what was happening at home and now hungry, made their commanders increasingly nervous. They realised that with many of the men convinced that the war was already lost, they had good reason to fear a mutiny.

One day late in December, Sgt Major Kolze told us simply that we should redouble our efforts and devise new ways of supplementing our diet. Men had already begun to indulge in a little foraging, usually under cover of night, but as the weeks passed, this became more organised and widespread. We knew that every other soldier on the island was in the same predicament as ourselves, but we were relative newcomers and didn't know the lie of the land as well as those who had been here much longer. We didn't know where the orchards were located, where there might be the possibility of catching rabbits or where we might find a good place to fish.

Those who had been on the island for years had been able to survey the land at their leisure, they knew where to find all these things and they weren't about to tell anyone else. Each battalion or platoon jealously guarded whatever knowledge and privileges it had gained for itself. Priceless intelligence might consist merely of knowing the whereabouts of an apple tree, the likely spot where wild mushrooms grew or the best place to shoot a seagull.

Hunger will drive men to do whatever is necessary to stay alive, it matters not whether it is illegal or immoral or whether it involves taking huge risks. Men didn't care what it was or where it was found, if it was remotely edible then it would be picked, dug up, shot or taken. To conserve energy, men would laze around during the day, lying in their beds or playing interminable games of cards, but at night these idlers were transformed into nocturnal hunters. Stealing out of their lairs, creeping through the fences and hedgerows, and roaming the moonlit lanes of the island, they were armed and dangerous men in relentless pursuit of their quarry. The enemy was anyone who stood in their way.

Although my arm was gradually getting stronger and I was able to raise it a little more with each passing week, boils would sometimes form in my armpit because it hung limply down by my side for long periods of the day, with no air circulating, and also due to the lack of vitamins in my diet. Although the visits to the hospital in St Peter Port were helpful, it was my improvised pulley system which had the greatest effect, and I continued to use it religiously for an hour every evening before I went to sleep, pressing down with the foot and raising my arm repeatedly until both my arm and leg ached.

Occasionally, to relieve the boredom of life at the airfield, Lenz, Riedle and some of the others would walk with me into the town. After my physiotherapy session we would stroll around the harbour and then through the streets, looking in the empty shop windows and hoping to see a pretty girl. The local girls never returned our glances, but it was fun to watch them. We knew that some of the senior officers had local girlfriends, but there was no chance for the ordinary soldier. Apart from eying up the local girls, the only form of entertainment in the town was the cinema. I was told that at one time it showed a number of popular films, but now it only had one that was shown every day of the week. The film was a romance called *The White Dream* which, through utter boredom and lack of anything else to do, I saw more than a dozen times until I had eventually memorised almost all the words. After watching the film we would talk with other groups of soldiers and always there would be three topics of conversation: news from home, the possibility of surrender and what new rumours were circulating about the food situation.

On one of my visits to the clinic the medics were busy treating some sailors who had been injured when a patrol boat had inadvertently struck one of our own mines placed near the entrance to the harbour. While I waited to be seen, I wandered into the courtyard at the back of the building and lit a cigarette. Although I had visited the clinic many times I had never before been into the courtyard and I saw that along one of the walls there were rows of small wooden boxes, each with a wire mesh door. I looked inside one of them and was surprised to find that it contained a small rabbit. I looked in the others and discovered that there was a rabbit inside each one. I noted that the courtyard was only separated from the narrow lane that ran behind the clinic by a stone wall just over eight feet high.

"We caught them in the summer."

I spun round to see who had spoken. It was one of the medics who, like me, had come out into the yard for a smoke.

He continued, after taking a long draw on his cigarette,

"I doubt you'll find a wild one anywhere on the island now. Fifteen thousand hungry soldiers each armed with a rifle will soon get rid of such a pest. The farmers should be thanking us."

"What do you feed them on?" I enquired.

"Certainly not with carrots and lettuce," the orderly replied. "They have to make do with grass, leaves and potato peelings and we don't throw so many of those away these days. That's why they're such scrawny little things, there's not much meat on them. Still, they'll make a good stew if cooked for long enough."

As I inspected the creatures in their tiny hutches, the orderly continued,

"We thought we could get them to breed, we put them together, but they don't seem too keen on it when they're in captivity."

I hadn't tasted fresh meat for almost a month and the thought of a delicious rabbit stew with some potatoes and maybe some cabbage or parsnips would preoccupy my mind for the remainder of the day.

The medic and I finished our cigarettes and went back inside for my session. Later that night I mentioned the rabbits to Lenz and Riedle, their eyes lighting up as I described the row of hutches in the courtyard at the back of the clinic. A plan to get into the yard and steal the animals was quickly hatched and the following night as soon as it was dark, armed with knives and sacks, we took the familiar road into St Peter Port. Lenz was from the city and knew nothing about the land or about animals except that he enjoyed eating them, while Reidle was a country boy like myself and had done a fair bit of poaching in his time on the farms and estates around his home in Bavaria. Well over six feet tall and powerfully built, he was a useful man to have on your side in an argument and he would easily be able to scale the courtyard wall behind the clinic.

The night of our mission was cold and blustery with rain blowing in off the sea which suited our purpose ideally as we were less likely to run into any police patrols. We reached the town around eight in the evening finding, as expected, that the clinic was quiet and with any luck very few, if any, of the medical staff would be in the building. We made our way along the narrow lane running at the rear and I pointed out the walled courtyard at the back of the clinic. Checking to make sure that no-one was watching, Reidle lifted Lenz onto his shoulders and he peered over the top of the wall. He quickly ducked back down, whispering that there were a couple of men in the yard. We looked around, praying that no one would come along the road and see three suspicious looking characters. A few minutes later Lenz was hoisted up on Riedle's shoulders again, but once more he found that someone was in the yard. We hastily conferred before it was decided that I would go around to the entrance at the front of the building and try to distract the medics while Lenz and Riedle climbed over the wall and grabbed the rabbits.

I was a familiar face to most of the medics and I would easily be able to make up some story about my arm being in pain. The only thing that concerned me was if Reidle and Lenz successfully grabbed the rabbits then they might put two and two together and work out that they had gone missing while I was there and that I might have been involved. If they tied me in to the crime, then at the very least my next physiotherapy session might prove more painful than usual, but I could hardly back down now after bringing Lenz and Riedle all the way into town from the airfield.

I went around to the main road and up to the front door of the clinic. I hammered on the door and after a few moments it was opened by the same man I had spoken to earlier in the day. I told him that my arm was giving me a lot of pain and asked whether I could have anything to ease the discomfort. He informed me that the clinic was closed to all but the most urgent cases and said I should return first thing in the morning. I protested that I had walked all the way into town from the airfield and only wanted a little something for the pain. He sighed;

"Klaus!"

His colleague came in from the back. He scribbled something on a piece of paper and handed it to Klaus who went off to the pharmacy, returning shortly with a small bottle of pills.

"Take two of these now and two in the morning," he said, handing me the small bottle and writing something in a notebook.

I thanked him and left. I had kept them occupied for just a few minutes, but it had been long enough for Lenz and Riedle to empty the hutches and fill their sacks with the rabbits, Riedle having swiftly despatched them first with a quick pull of the neck. Within ten minutes the three of us, sticking to the narrow lanes and alleyways which we had come to know so well, had made it safely out of town and were on our way silently back along the country lanes towards the airfield, carrying our precious cargo. We remained vigilant for police patrols or any one else who might try to deprive us of our booty, but fortunately the roads were deserted. Out there, unseen in the darkness, doubtless other small bands of hungry, desperate soldiers were involved in similar felonious acts.

Safely back in our quarters, we went straight down to the

kitchen, tipped out the contents of the sacks, then skinned, gutted and removed the heads of the small creatures. There wasn't a great deal of meat on any of them so we dropped them, bones and all into a large cauldron. We already had a bag containing a few potato peelings and withered cabbage leaves and these we added, along with some seasoning. It was an unwritten law that no-one ever asked about how or where food had been obtained and it was also the rule that those who provided food would be the first to partake of it, provided that the other men were allowed to share if any was left over. To hide any evidence of the crime, the fur, skulls and entrails were buried in a pit at the back of the building.

The smell of stewing rabbit flesh was soon permeating the kitchen while Lenz, Reidle and I sat and salivated, eagerly watching the cauldron bubble, occasionally giving it a stir with a large wooden spoon. After two hours, the meat had completely separated from the bones and we could hold back no longer, eagerly spooning the stew into our bowls. Although the pains in my stomach insisted that I bolt down the meal as quickly as possible, I deliberately ate slowly, savouring the taste for as long as possible. There was another good reason for this. I had seen what happened to men, their bodies grown unused to meat, writhing on the ground in agony as their stomachs protested at the unaccustomed richness of their diet. Often they had gained relief only after they had been sick and this had left them feeling even emptier and more miserable than they had before.

It was well after midnight by the time we finished our magnificent feast and by then others, drawn by the smell of cooking, had appeared. There was no way of preserving that which we could not eat, so they were able to help themselves to some of the remains of the stew although Lenz, Reidle and I had long since eaten the tastiest portions of rabbit meat.

I seriously considered missing my next appointment at the clinic, but decided that this would only point to my guilt. I did however feel a little apprehensive as I walked into St Peter Port. Fortunately I was attended by a medical orderly that I had not seen before. He cleaned and put a new dressing on the boils in my armpit after my physiotherapy session, and it was while replacing the dressing that he related the story of the stolen rabbits.

"We were saving them for Christmas, been fattening them up for months," he confided bitterly, "then some swine broke in and stole them. Can you imagine? Stealing like that from their comrades. What kind of people could do that? I hope they choked to death on them."

I couldn't of course tell him that not one of us had choked to death, but I expressed sympathy at his grievous loss and added that it was probably the work of those Kriegsmarine bastards who were forever causing trouble around the town.

40

Sgt Major Kolze made it abundantly clear that he didn't give a damn about anyone except the men under his command. Like most paratroopers, he believed that we were superior to everyone else in uniform and like the rest of us, he despised officers and was especially scathing of the high command, particularly those who made the rules regarding the distribution of rations. As far as he was concerned, if there was no longer sufficient food for men to live on, then it was pointless holding out any longer, it only subjected men to unnecessary hardship and suffering. He was particularly bitter that, as newcomers to the island, the paratroopers were denied access to many other areas of the island and were consequently unable to take advantage of some of the privileges enjoyed by those who had been on the island for some time.

He winked at the nightly forays of his men, he had only one rule and that was that we must not get caught. As our commanding officer, Kolze never joined in these illegal food gathering expeditions, but the men knew that he would do all he could to protect them and we always made sure that he was included in the distribution of any available food. The searches for food were often unsuccessful, and it was not unusual to see men returning to their beds just before dawn, tired, hungry and dejected having fruitlessly expended their energies searching throughout the night.

They would invariably spend most of the following day sleeping, finally getting up in the late afternoon to eat their meagre rations before once again they would begin plotting and scheming.

Food was our prime concern, but not our only one. As the weather grew colder we also had to devise ways of keeping warm, for in addition to a shortage of food, there was also a severe shortage of fuel. Coal and oil shipped to the Channel Islands before the Normandy invasions had long since been used up, so wood was the only available material. Some time ago a small stove had been installed in each of the rooms with pipes rigged up and passed through the windows to allow the smoke to escape. The stoves could make the room very cosy provided they had sufficient wood to burn, but that was the problem. Many of the island's trees had already been felled despite orders expressly forbidding it, and anything that might have been used to provide heat or fuel for cooking became a precious commodity. Nothing was wasted, grass was cut and dried, even the sawdust created by the sawing of wood was carefully collected and stored to be added to fires.

Some years earlier, a small air-raid shelter had been built next to our quarters. Half underground and built in regulation style, the entrance and roof were supported by large pieces of timber. One particularly cold night when the flames in our stove had finally flickered out, Lenz, Riedle and I crept outside with some hatchets and set to work cutting up some of the larger pieces of the support timbers. The shelter had never been used and as far as we were concerned, was never likely to be, so we thought that we might as well make some use of it. Unfortunately Sgt Major Kolze was also outside that night and had seen us disappearing into the shelter. He came over to find out what we were up to and when we explained that we were collecting firewood, he went crazy.

"Don't you realise this building is here to protect us in case we're attacked?" he stormed.

The look on our faces must have told him that this tiny dugout with a wooden roof covered in earth and grass, right next to the largest building for a half a mile, was the last place any sane individual would go if we were ever attacked. There was far greater risk in being buried alive and in any case it was only large enough to hold a dozen men at the most; where the other seventy men were supposed to shelter in the event of an attack wasn't clear.

Kolze looked at us for a few moments as we stood, axes in hand, awaiting our inevitable punishment.

"So you think it's a good idea to deprive the men of their shelter?"

We made no answer, but I could see from his expression that he wasn't really upset, but it was also clear that he wasn't going to allow us to get away with such a gross breach of discipline.

"Very well, you have my permission to demolish the shelter. You will recover all the wood, chop it into logs and sticks, divide it up equally then distribute it to all the rooms."

With that he turned on his heel. I swear I saw a smile flicker on his lips as he did so.

I looked at Lenz.

"Bastard!" he said, grinning. It was difficult to get upset with Kolze for he wasn't one to stick rigidly to orders when they made no sense.

"We'd better get started then," I said, "there's a lot of timber to get through."

The men held Kolze in the highest regard, but bridled at the stream of orders issuing from the commandant's headquarters that always seemed to have the intention of making our lives even more miserable. The only directive that we truly longed for never came: the order that we should lay down our arms and be allowed to go home.

The day before Christmas, news came through that three paratroopers who had been captured by the Americans in France had not only managed to escape, but had stolen a boat and sailed to Guernsey. They were treated like heroes and granted an audience with the island commandant who personally bestowed the iron cross on each of them. After they had been fêted for two days in St Peter Port, they were sent to join us at the airfield. We were only too glad to hear the story of their daring escape, but not so pleased that we would have to share our food with them. At meal times, while the rest of us chewed slowly, savouring every mouthful before finally allowing it to drop into our craving stomachs, they ate like pigs, gulping down their food as if it arrived in unlimited quantities.

On Christmas Day we were permitted double our normal daily ration and many of the men had saved something extra from their raids in the previous few days, a cabbage here, some potatoes there and best and most generous of all, one man donated a chicken which he had stolen at great personal risk from a group of Luftwaffe ant-aircraft gunners on the other side of the airfield. Although the chicken was too small to be divided up between the men, it made an excellent and most welcome addition to the large stew which cook had prepared. Sgt Major Kolze managed to obtain a bottle of brandy and a small cask of calvados which he had 'liberated' from the quartermaster and hidden away weeks earlier so that at least we would have something with which to celebrate this day.

Toasts were drunk to Sgt Major Kolze and to the newly arrived escapees, who in turn toasted the rest of us and spoke enthusiastically of their joy at being re-united with their comrades. They appeared less enthusiastic when the meal arrived, for while the rest of us eagerly filled our dishes from the large cauldron which arrived from the kitchen, they ate sparingly, drinking the liquid, but examining every solid piece they found with the greatest suspicion. I had long ago given up worrying about what such dishes contained; it was better not to know as long as it filled my belly and removed the gnawing hunger pains for a few hours.

That night we sang songs and told jokes and for one night tried to make light of our situation. Schultz played requests on his harmonica while Frick and Breitner performed a song and dance act, but as the evening wore on men grew quiet as thoughts inevitably turned to home. My last letter had arrived two months ago and even that had been written back in July. None of us really knew what was happening back in Germany, the official news spoke of 'heroic resistance' on all fronts, but we knew it was a lie. For all we knew the English and the Americans might even now be marching down Unter den Linden and right into the Chancellery Building. Thoughts like these made our predicament all the harder to bear; the war had passed us by, we had been rendered completely useless and we were gradually starving to death.

The following day, the three heroes who had escaped from France realised just how bad things were and how much worse they were likely to become. Despite the risks of being shot as deserters, they stole the boat in which they had recently arrived and returned from whence they came, their apparent joy at being re-united with the rest of us evaporating as quickly as morning mist hanging over the sea. The appeal of wholesome food in an American prisoner-of-war camp was ultimately greater than the shared misery of a slow starvation with their comrades in arms. There were many of us who wished that we had gone with them.

Our misery was compounded a day later when the *Vega,* a Red Cross ship bringing food and medicine to the islanders was allowed into the harbour. The supplies were destined only for the civilian population and Red Cross observers came ashore to ensure that none of it was diverted for military use. There was near mutiny among the soldiers who were detailed to unload the ship when they discovered that they would be receiving no extra rations for their labours; in fact the port commander was so concerned with the possibility of a breakdown of order that he had to station armed men along the route to the warehouse with orders to shoot any soldier who might be tempted to steal some of the provisions.

Hundreds of crates containing condensed milk, wheels of cheese, barrels of flour and cans of preserved meats, the stuff of a starving man's dreams, were unloaded onto the quayside and then taken to a heavily guarded warehouse for division into food parcels which civilians could claim using an identity card. While the islanders queued for their parcels, soldiers with loaded guns and empty stomachs stood guard and silently cursed their luck.

The cinema in St Peter Port finally closed at the end of January when the electricity supply was cut to all non-essential facilities. I had no wish to go and see 'The White Dream' ever again, but a walk into St Peter Port sometimes relieved the monotony of life at the airfield. In order to conserve our energy, we rarely exercised or played football, which left only card schools and conversation that often led to fights, usually over money, but sometimes over politics.

Fink was an Austrian and a keen Nazi. He was also a cheat and a liar and was only rarely permitted to join a card school. One night however he was involved in a game of poker when talk got around to the hopelessness of our situation. Lenz and Reidle weren't slow to complain aloud that the sooner we gave up, the better off we all would be. Fink was quiet initially, but when Reidle described the Leader as a carpet chewer he took exception and proclaimed loudly that the Leader would ultimately lead us to triumph. In response to the general derisory laughter he threw down his cards, leapt to his feet and pulled a knife out of his boot. Suddenly there was silence, no one moved as Fink's blade flashed in the light.

Reidle slowly got to his feet and circled slowly around. He told Fink to drop the knife, but the Austrian refused unless Reidle first apologised. When Reidle laughed in his face, Fink lunged at him. The struggle was brief, it was an uneven match between the giant Reidle and the slightly built man, but both men were cut before Fink was eventually overpowered. When Sgt Major Kolze found out what had happened he had Fink locked up for five days and upon his release refused to allow him to carry any weapons. Although Fink was unusual in his unswerving loyalty, he was by no means unique. It was amazing how some of the men refused to believe the evidence before their eyes; they could see men reduced to eating grass and catching mice, yet they still insisted that victory would be ours.

In February Admiral Huffmeier replaced General Von Smettow, the commandant of the Channel Islands for the past three years. Any hopes that this might signal an improvement in our situation was dashed when he addressed all the occupying forces at a series of large parades held on each of the islands. I stood out on the airfield to hear him proclaim to the two thousand men assembled that he would share our pain and suffering, but that we all owed it to our Leader to maintain our discipline and hold out, even if we only had one can of sardines a day.

"Bastard!" muttered Lenz who was standing next to me.

"I bet he's never eaten a can of sardines in his life. He'll be off back to his headquarters this evening for a five-course meal washed down with a couple of bottles of chilled Mosel."

If our new commandant was expecting a rousing response to his patriotic speech he was sorely disappointed. Apart from idiots like Fink who gave the party salute and shouted 'Sieg Heil!', the rest of us merely gave the military salute and cursed him beneath our breath. We trooped away wondering what we had done to deserve such a fate. Reidle even suggested that if we had been sent to the Eastern front, at least our end might have been swifter and would have been preferable to this lingering torture inflicted upon us not by the enemy, but by the pig-headed stubbornness of our own commanders.

With our rations cut once more, it was clear that our continued survival would depend increasingly upon obtaining food from other sources and this we did without compunction. By now there were few feelings of guilt in the stealing from our fellow soldiers, or indeed from civilians, it made no difference to us. The only two rules we observed were that we would never steal from our fellow paratroopers and that we should never get caught. In February another Red Cross ship arrived with more supplies for the civilian population. This was another severe drain on morale as once again hungry soldiers were forced to watch as food they would never taste was unloaded and piled high in the warehouses of St Peter Port.

If these warehouses were the focus of our envy, rage and frustration, it was as nothing compared to our fury at the heavily guarded military quartermaster's stores located throughout the island. Everyone knew that they contained an abundance of food, but because our commanders insanely believed that they might have to hold out for much longer, many years if necessary, they permitted the distribution of such paltry rations that men began to die. When I had been evacuated from St Malo, I had weighed one hundred and fifty pounds, four months later I weighed a mere eighty pounds and had cut five extra holes in my belt in order for it to hold up my trousers. My uniform hung loosely over my frame, giving me the appearance of a scarecrow, and every day I would look at my body and see the ribs and shoulder blades protruding further through the flesh. All around me, young men who should have been in the peak of physical condition were wasting away. Strength and vigour were replaced by lethargy and lassitude, vitality and potency by weakness and infirmity and, most importantly of all, hope was being replaced by hopelessness.

41

Nettle soup can be quite tasty, especially if other ingredients are added, and although nettles grew in relative profusion throughout the island, we rarely had much in the way of other ingredients. A man familiar with the ways of the country, a farmer perhaps, can tell the difference between those plants which will provide nourishment and those which will not, those plants which contain vitamins and protein and those which contain poison. Hunger is democratic; it affects everyone in equal measure and is blind to the subtle differences between men. It does not discern between those who are cautious and those who are foolhardy, between those from the country and those from the city. Hunger does not discriminate between those who know that a plant is poisonous and those who do not.

Alongside the nettles grew hemlock, and men driven crazy by hunger might collect these along with the nettles and other grasses which might keep a man alive; such ingredients might even prove tasty if prepared well and seasoned. At the beginning of March, three men, all from the city, prepared themselves such a feast, adding rather more of the hemlock and less of the nettles. Once the cauldron had been bubbling for half an hour they ladled the soup into their mess tins and began to spoon it into their mouths. The liquid quieted the pain of their hunger for a short time before they became aware of another pain spreading slowly from their stomachs, into their chests and then into their limbs. This was a pain that could not be stilled by food or drink, a pain that produced sweating, vomiting and eventually paralysis.

Their howls and frantic convulsions were heard by all of us throughout the night, and only with the dawn when they drew their last agonised breaths was there peace in the barracks again. The three men were buried with full military honours in a small plot at the perimeter of the airfield, their caps and badges retained by Sgt Major Kolze who promised to return them, if at all possible, to the men's families. The Sergeant Major had one of the men make a drawing of the hemlock plant and hung it in a prominent place on the wall of the kitchen so that none of the other men would make the same fatal mistake.

The sad end of our three comrades left a bitter taste in all our mouths. We knew that they had died because of the stubborn stupidity of the high command and wondered how many others on the island had met a similar fate as a result of being driven half mad with hunger. Men had not only died of poison as these had, some had been blown up by our own mines as they tried to collect seaweed and mussels on the seashore, or been killed by grenades suspended on cliff faces as they attempted to collect seagulls' eggs. Gradually our anger at such deaths turned into hate, hatred of the war, hatred of our officers, and hatred of the island, until finally we even began to hate each other.

Every other man on the island was seen as a competitor, another mouth to feed, someone else to consume the finite amount of food available, someone who was taking the food out of one's own mouth. The enemy had long since ceased to be the British or the Americans, the enemy was now much closer, it was anyone who stood in the way of us being able to fill our bellies.

A dozen armoured vehicles had been parked a mile down the road which ran past the airfield for at least a year. Their rust streaked sides and corroded tracks gave them the appearance of a strange metallic protrusion thrown up from the underlying geological formations. Their idle crews were quartered in a collection of wooden huts standing in a nearby field that had once been home to a herd of pigs long since slaughtered. This area was out of bounds to us, but we had observed on some of our walks as far as we were permitted to go, that in one corner of their field, the crews kept a nanny goat which provided them with a regular supply of milk. The goat was contained within a complex system of wires and bells that had been set up with the dual purpose of preventing the animal from straying and to warn the men of intruders.

On the pretext of taking evening strolls we had carried out a detailed survey of the area and put a plan into action to steal the animal from right under their noses. The major snag was the system of wires and bells, because if these went off, the men would more than likely open fire first and ask questions later. To solve this problem we recruited Johann Korff, who before the war had worked as an engineer in a car factory in Stuttgart. He calculated that with care, the wires could be cut and tensioned in such a way so as not to trigger any of the alarm bells. Armed with wire cutters, a sharp knife and a large sack, Lenz, Reidle, Korff and I set out one night to 'liberate' the goat from its captivity. Creeping across the fields until we arrived at the enclosure, Lenz took up station near the huts to warn us if anyone appeared and if necessary create a diversion. Korff crept closer to the goat's enclosure to cut the wires while Reidle and I waited with baited breath, listening for the ringing of a bell which would be the signal to scatter and run.

The only sound we could hear was the faint murmur of voices coming from the huts. As soon as Korff gave us the signal, Reidle and I crept forward with the knife and sack at the ready. Slipping through the gap in the wires, we could just make out the black and white shape of the goat munching contentedly on the grass. We crept up behind it and I grabbed hold of it while Reidle expertly slit its throat before it could utter a single bleat. We held it firmly to the ground as its life poured away in a spurt of blood. It kicked a few times, but after a minute it lay still and dead. Stuffing the lifeless body into the large sack, we dragged it away, taking care not to touch any of the wires on the way out. Within half an hour we were back at the airfield skinning the unfortunate animal. It was vitally important to dispose of the evidence, so the skin and bones were promptly buried in a trench behind our building in time honoured fashion alongside the residue of countless other operations carried out by the men during the past year.

We feasted well that evening, but two days later we received a visit from the military police. The vehicle crews had screamed blue murder when they had discovered the theft of their goat the following morning and had called in the police. As usual the finger of suspicion had pointed towards the nearby barracks of the paratroopers. Sgt Major Kolze's distaste for the high command was exceeded only by his hatred of the military police, but he managed to hide it as they questioned him about the nocturnal expeditions of his men. He was affable but firm, telling them he was convinced that none of his men could have been responsible for the crime, but promised that they could take a look around if they chose and that if they could find any evidence he would be the first to make an example of the culprits. They had a cursory look around, inspecting the kitchen and some of our rooms, but there was no possibility of their finding any evidence, we had made sure of that. The police went away disappointed; they probably knew full well that we paratroopers had been responsible, but were unable to prove it.

We thought that we had heard the last of the matter, but they had duly made their report to the Luftwaffe commander at the airfield. No doubt the report was heavily flavoured with suspicion and conjecture, but to the commandant it was as good as a signed confession and it presented him with an opportunity to get rid of the troublesome band of paratroopers with their arrogant ways who had difficulty acknowledging any authority beyond their own Sergeant Major. The following week orders came for half of our number to leave the airfield. We were to be split up and despatched to various Luftwaffe anti-aircraft installations around the island; the excuse was operational reasons, but we knew that it was a form of punishment.

We were not pleased, but there was nothing we could do. Lenz and I were ordered to report to one of the gun batteries at the harbour in St Peter Port which didn't seem such a bad posting, but some of the men were sent to the farthest, rockiest extremities of the island where they would have only crashing waves and screeching seagulls for company. I knew from my time at Cherbourg the previous year that we were unlikely to get a warm reception from the Luftwaffe crews, but on a more optimistic note I wondered whether the food situation might be any better in the town than it was at the airfield. My optimism was tempered by the realisation that, even if these crews had organised some illegal supplement to their diet, they were unlikely to share it with any newcomers, much less a couple of paratroopers.

Beneath the ancient stone fortress guarding the harbour, stone breakwaters enclosed the calm water within. A concrete battery had been built at the end of each of these breakwaters and each of them contained an anti-aircraft gun. Crews of six men were responsible for maintaining them in a constant state of readiness to open fire should enemy planes be sighted. Lenz and I reported to the battery Obergefreiter. He seemed affable enough, but our hearts sank when he asked if we knew where they might be able to get their hands on some more food. The situation was clearly no better here in the town than it was at the airfield, the only benefit was the fact that we were able to hang fishing lines out along the breakwater to catch the occasional fish.

The men manning the batteries located around the harbour fished religiously, either holding a rod and line for hours, waiting patiently for a bite, or rigging up multiple lines which were left hanging over the side. They had also fashioned a number of lobster pots that were dropped into the water from a small rowing boat. Although it was strictly against orders, it wasn't unusual for hand grenades to be thrown into the water at night to kill a few fish and send them floating to the surface to be scooped up with nets. Another source of food were the seabirds that had once flocked around the harbour in great numbers, but which now survived in smaller numbers due to the curtailment of the domestic fishing industry and, not least, because many had already been shot for food.

I had never tasted seagull before, but one of the men had managed to bring one down the day that Lenz and I arrived and it had been prepared for a meal. The smell of the cooked bird was awful, but we were invited to try some of the meat. I had never tasted anything so disgusting in my life and, hungry though I was, I managed only a few chewy mouthfuls of flesh before I gave up. The other men continued to eat heartily. They told me that when they had first cooked a seagull they too had been unable to eat it. It was then that they discovered that seabirds have glands beneath their wings that secrete an oil to prevent their feathers from becoming waterlogged. These secretions are extremely bitter to the taste and they had learned to remove these first before cooking, to make the flesh more edible; nonetheless it had proved impossible to get rid of the taste completely. Although I ate it a number of times, I never did come to enjoy it during the time I was there and concluded that it was a taste that could only be acquired over an extended period of time.

Lenz and I remained at the anti-aircraft battery for three weeks before I and all the other paratroopers were recalled to our old base at the airfield. The Luftwaffe commandant had apparently decided that we had served our punishment, but had one last trick up his sleeve. When we returned, we found that a lieutenant by the name of Speier had been put in charge and that Sgt Major Kolze would henceforth have to report to him. To put an ordinary Luftwaffe officer in command of paratroopers was bad enough, but the fact that he was also young and inexperienced and had only been promoted to an officer while on the island, ensured that he got little respect and even less cooperation from the men. We had been punished and were clearly on notice that theft on the scale in which we had previously been involved would no longer be tolerated. The appointment of Speier was meant to put us in our place.

Spring was now well advanced, the islands had been cut

off for more than eight months and the situation was growing more desperate by the day. With no likelihood of attack and still no word of surrender, we remained trapped and until our commanders gave us sufficient rations on which we might survive, we and every other man on the island would continue to beg, forage or steal and do whatever was necessary to stay alive.

42

The Bridegroom

It had been a difficult journey for the bride, but it was a journey she had insisted on making. The small plane had flown low, running the gauntlet of enemy planes which flew at will above the land and eventually landed in the beleaguered capital. The young woman made her way down the steps; she had arrived to join her betrothed.

In the end the Leader had not failed, his people had failed him. The German people had ultimately failed the greatest leader they had ever known and proved themselves unworthy of his greatness. They had failed to prove their mettle and were therefore destined to destruction. History would record that they were weak and would therefore be dominated by those who were stronger; it was the eternal law of nature and the law of politics.

He gave orders to destroy everything in the land which had not already been destroyed by the enemy. Everything: all the factories, electrical facilities, water works, gas works, food stores, clothing stores, all the bridges, railway installations, locomotives, ships and boats, anything which might be of value to the enemy. It did not matter that the nation would be turned into a wasteland, for if the people were to be destroyed, they would have no need of anything that might sustain them afterwards.

He waived away all arguments that he should leave the people the bare minimum for survival, with which they might, at some distant point in the future, need to reconstruct their lives. The pleas fell upon deaf ears; if the war was lost then the people would perish. It was not necessary to take into consideration what the people might need to continue even a primitive existence. On the contrary, he argued that it would be better to destroy these things ourselves because this nation will have proved itself to be the weaker one. Those who remained after the battle would be only the inferior ones, for the good ones would all have been killed.

The time was now at hand for him to make the ultimate sacrifice, as so many had done before, but first there were certain matters to be attended to. Even at this late hour, the bridegroom insisted upon the observance of etiquette and despite the fact that the enemy were close at hand, the ceremony would be performed correctly. A municipal councillor fighting in the nearby streets was summoned to the bunker to officiate, the witnesses were assembled and the bride and groom made a declaration that they were both of pure Aryan descent and had no hereditary disease to exclude their marriage.

In the dead of night, they were pronounced man and wife and the certificate was signed. The party retired to the bridegroom's private rooms for a wedding breakfast of champagne and delicacies provided by his personal chef. As shells crashed and exploded outside, the guests reminisced about the good old days and the bridegroom reviewed the high points in his dramatic life. Time was short, however. He left the festivities briefly to sign his last will and testament and once again went over the arrangements. He had decreed that nothing must remain of him and all that was his. While his faithful dog was being poisoned, the Leader and his bride retired to their rooms while the guests waited outside. The bridegroom had one last gift for his bride.

He ensured that she was comfortable and then presented her with the small glass phial which he pressed, into her hand. He gently kissed her for a final time before she placed it in her mouth. She looked once more at the man she loved. He nodded and she bit down. As she slumped backwards on the sofa he removed his revolver from the leather holster, placed the barrel in his mouth and pulled the trigger.

43

It is difficult to describe the gnawing, empty pain in the pit of the stomach to someone who has never known the slow horror of malnutrition. Our pitiful rations, combined with any other scraps of food we were able to find, were never enough to rid us of the perpetual feeling of hunger that haunted our lives like a ghost. Even when we had just eaten, our minds were consumed with thoughts of what we might be eating in a few hours' time or the fear that we would have nothing to eat at all.

Men driven mad by hunger are not easy to control. Rumours of imminent surrender, or that the war had already ended, only served to fuel the instability of the men that the officers most feared. There were persistent stories that Huffmeier had already turned down a number of chances to surrender and this made men angry. Apart from a few idiots like Fink, we had long ago given up the notion that we were going to win the war and we wanted it now to end as soon as possible. We were certainly in no mood to lay down our lives in some futile attempt by Huffmeier to repel an enemy attack on these god-forsaken bits of rock. As far as we were concerned the British were welcome to them and good riddance.

Men were desperate to return to what was left of their homes and families, but more pressingly, they wanted an end to the living nightmare of slow starvation. Anything that might delay either of these things would incur the wrath of the men and it was clear that the officers were becoming increasingly nervous. They worried that men already at the end of their tether might rise up in mutiny if sufficiently provoked. They were right to worry. Raids on the heavily guarded quartermaster stores, or even the warehouses in St Peter Port, groaning with the weight of Red Cross aid delivered for the civilian population, were openly discussed. If we were to die anyway then what difference would it make? But the men held back as the rumours proliferated; they had already suffered a great deal, they had survived six years of war and no-one wanted to die at this stage, much less at the hands of a comrade. The rumours continued: Hitler was dead......Germany had surrendered....... the Russians were in Berlin. Stories such as these were on everyone's lips, we desperately wanted to know what was happening; yet from the lips of our own commanders there was only a deafening silence.

May 7th dawned bright and clear. High white clouds streamed in off the Atlantic and some of the men said that down in the port they had seen some British flags flying. We realised then that the time had finally come. We were ordered not to leave the airfield and we watched as the obstacles that had been placed on the runway for the past nine months were hauled to one side. We waited expectantly all day, yet still nothing happened – nothing landed and nothing took off. It was not until the following day that we were instructed to assemble on the airfield where the commander of Luftwaffe forces on the island told us that Germany had signed the surrender and that the war was over. I looked around at the faces of the men nearby and, apart from Fink's tear-filled eyes, I could discern neither joy nor sadness, only relief. The following day Churchill made a radio broadcast to the Islanders telling them that they were free, and while they celebrated their deliverance we awaited ours.

On the surface little had changed. We still held our weapons and still wore our uniforms, but as the black and scarlet flags that had flown over the island for over five years were finally hauled down, we knew that nothing would be the same again. As stories spread that the British were on their way and that we would soon be taken off the island, the men questioned the fact that the food stores were still operating a strict regime of rationing. We complained that if we were to be taken off any day, then there was little point in conserving food, we might as well fill our bellies before the British came and helped themselves.

The atmosphere was tense, word came that the commandant was still refusing to open up the stores. We were told that no-one knew know how much longer we would remain on the island, it could be a matter of hours or we might remain marooned for weeks. We had heard that one of the stores on the other side of the island had already been broken into and that soldiers were helping themselves. A group of paratroopers went to see Sgt Major Kolze to inform him that they intended to break into the stores at the airfield that night.

He had made no protest, merely sighed and nodded. The men made plans, loaded their rifles and prepared to attack the store that very night and release the food or die in the attempt. Some of the men eagerly volunteered to join the expedition while others held back. Reidle, Lenz and I sympathised with the plotters, but felt that this was the wrong time to take such drastic action – we might be leaving the island within days and would surely be able to survive a little longer.

An hour before sundown, Kolze summoned us all together. He told us that it had been a privilege to be our commanding officer for the past nine months and praised us for maintaining our discipline in the highest traditions of the Parachute Regiment under often intolerable conditions. He declared that whatever fate had in store for us, we had done nothing of which to be ashamed; Germany had been defeated, but we should still hold our heads high. Then he announced that the next morning we were to march down to St Peter Port to form part of an honour guard as the commandant formally surrendered the island. There was not a word about the proposed attack on the quartermaster's stores, not a word of criticism for any of the men, only words of praise and the statement that tomorrow, finally, the British would be coming.

There was no raid on the store that night. The following morning, for the first time in nine months, we formed up in the road in front the old hotel, shouldered our rifles and stood to attention. Kolze performed an inspection, walking up and down our lines checking that everything was in order. Despite the fact that our uniforms hung scarecrow-like from our emaciated bodies, we looked smarter than we had done since our arrival on the island. I had lost seventy pounds in weight during my time on the island, making further notches in my belt in an ongoing attempt to keep my trousers from falling dawn. Satisfied that we at least superficially looked the part, Kolze saluted and took his place at the head of the column as we marched away from the airfield.

Crowds of locals lined the streets as we entered St Peter Port. My mouth was dry as we marched between them, nervously trying to gauge the mood of the people. Many were waving British flags, but the mood seemed celebratory rather than revengeful. We kept our eyes forward, continuing to follow Kolze as he led us to a halt on the esplanade in front of the church. We stood smartly to attention before standing at ease. Detachments from the Navy and the Army were also drawn up in ranks as part of the honour guard.

As we waited I recalled the day I had arrived almost nine months earlier with my arm in a sling and limping from the wound in my leg. It seemed as though it had happened years ago. In the harbour stood the anti-aircraft battery on the breakwater where I had spent three weeks in January, the concrete walls shining white in the sun. We waited for an hour until a grey motorboat entered the harbour, slowly nosing between the ends of the breakwaters. The islanders cheered and waved their flags as the vessel flying the British flag approached the quayside.

At that moment a large, black car swept onto the esplanade in front of us. Admiral Huffmeier got out to receive his visitors and each one of us silently cursed him. The ten khaki-clad soldiers and an officer who had disembarked from the boat walked towards him and we stood to attention as the commandant and the British officer saluted each other. It seemed strange to watch enemy soldiers marching calmly towards us. A few weeks ago we would have been shooting at one another, now we merely stood to attention and eyed each other warily.

We had been fighting the British for more than five years, but in all that time I had never seen a single one of them. They had always been there of course, a barely visible presence, a plane high overhead or a ship no more than a smudge on the horizon, but now the British Tommies were standing right in front of us, fewer than twenty yards away. We were soldiers of two armies, both armed and dressed in our uniforms, but the differences were clear to see. Our enemy was ruddy-cheeked and robust, filling their tunics with healthy nourished bodies, while we stood in our rags, pale skeletal shadows of the men we had once been. There could not have been a more visible contrast between victor and vanquished.

The two men spoke briefly through an interpreter and then saluted one another again. Logic had been turned on its head, five hundred armed soldiers standing to attention by the harbour, not to mention the thousands more scattered across the island, were surrendering to a dozen men who had just disembarked from a small boat. As if that were not strange enough, when the formalities were over, we marched back out of town and returned to our barracks still carrying our weapons.

This oversight was rectified the following afternoon when two British officers came up to the airfield and instructed us to hand in all our weapons: heavy guns, rifles, pistols and even knives which were locked away in one of the Luftwaffe storerooms, which had to be emptied of the remaining food rations which had hitherto been stored there. It was a popular transaction with the men because that evening the quartermaster announced a doubling of our rations. I didn't see the contents of the quartermaster's stores myself, but the men who had, spoke of barrels of dried meats by the hundred, huge vats of sugar and lard, sacks of flour by the dozen, enormous mountains of food which might have relieved the misery of the past months and allowed those who had died, to live.

The next day we filled our packs with our few possessions and as much food as we were able to stuff into our pockets and packs and departed the airfield for the last time. We walked the six miles to the designated assembly point for prisoners that lay in open country on the opposite side of the island, to the north of St Peter Port. We arrived to discover the entire island garrison of ten thousand men scattered over half a dozen fields. Some had erected tents, but most were sitting or lying sprawled on their bedrolls. Rumours of our likely fate spread among the men like wildfire: some said that Germany had not been defeated, but had merely signed a truce and that we would be going home to fight on with the British and Americans against the Russians, others said that we would be sent to some neutral country and then home a few weeks later. I gave them little credence as I recalled that similar wild rumours, when I had been evacuated from St Malo a year earlier, had proven to be false.

Despite the optimism of some, most of us knew in our bones that there had been a calamitous end to the war and that we were nothing more than prisoners with whom the victors could do as they wished. On the second day out in the open at the assembly point, we were informed that we were to be taken to England and would be treated as prisoners of war in accordance with the terms of the Geneva Convention. The announcement put an end to the foolish talk of truces and uniting with our erstwhile enemies to fight the Russians. We had lost the war, it was the end and I for one was glad of it.

Throughout the following days, groups of men, three or four hundred men at a time, would leave the assembly point at intervals throughout the day. We spent a further two nights sleeping out in the open before our own turn came to form up and march down to the harbour in St Peter Port. I walked with Lenz and Reidle, relieved to be out of our misery yet apprehensive about where we were going and when, if ever, we would see our homes again. None of us had received any letters from home for more than six months; we didn't know whether our families were dead or alive or if they knew of our fate.

As we were marched away, Guernsey had its final jest at our expense - the vessel that would take us into captivity, was called a Liberty Ship. The ship, which had clearly seen better days, was docked at the quayside while out beyond the stone breakwaters others were riding at anchor waiting their turn to enter harbour. We filed on board and were directed down to a dark, cavernous hold containing the stale smell of sacking and grain. The ship had clearly been used for transporting grain or flour for rats, grown enormous on their rich diet, scampered across the decks as we unfurled our bedrolls. By the time the boat was ready to depart there were about five hundred of us aboard. Ignoring Fink who sat dejectedly nearby, Lenz, Reidle and I sat at one side of the hold so that we could at least rest our backs against the sides of the ship and make ourselves as comfortable as possible for the voyage. We sat in almost complete darkness, were given no food and the only place to relieve ourselves was in a few large oil drums placed at one end of the hold. An hour after we came aboard, the sides of the ship began to vibrate as it got under way. Men fortunate enough to have some cigarettes smoked, while those with food in their packs ate. There was little conversation in the hold - only the soft, mournful sound of a harmonica drifted through the darkness while men slept or sat in silence, each lost in their own thoughts.

Many nationalities had fought for Germany during the war; there were Austrians of course, but also Poles, Romanians, Bulgarians, Ukrainians and Georgians. A company of twenty Georgians who had served on the island as part of the Wehrmacht were sitting on the other side of the hold and they were all unwell. It was difficult to imagine the various twists of fate which had led to them being sent to Guernsey, many thousands of miles from their homeland. The reason they were unwell was because they had broken into a Red Cross food store shortly before being moved to the assembly point, and helped themselves to the contents that consisted chiefly of tubs of pigs' lard. They must have been suffering from hunger more than we were, because in their desperation they had proceeded to eat the stuff, spooning it hungrily into their mouths to sate their hunger until their stomachs could take no more.

Their bodies, emaciated and weakened through many months of malnutrition, were not able to tolerate the sudden injection of rich animal fat and shortly after they boarded, they began to collapse one by one, moaning and rubbing their stomachs as their bodies began to reject the lard. They eventually went into spasms and began rolling around in agony. Shortly afterwards they began to vomit and void their bowels, some made it to the oil drums and some did not. They retched and vomited until there was nothing left to bring up, the stench of vomit and diarrhoea was awful and they received little sympathy from those around them who had to sit in the fetid pools they had made. One by one the Georgians lapsed into unconsciousness, lying in the vomit, faeces and blood that surrounded them. None could or would help them, while those sitting nearby tried to move away, suffering the curses of their comrades upon whom they trampled as they sought to escape. By the time we reached England only one of the Georgians was still alive.

44

The vibrations stopped. In the stifling, foul darkness of the hold, it was the only way of telling that we had probably arrived at our destination. The dead and dying Georgians were sprawled across the deck, while the rest of us, unwilling to go anywhere near the befouled drums, had relieved ourselves where we were. The stench must have been appalling for the guards held pieces of cloth to their noses and mouths as they shouted for us to get to our feet and make our way on deck. We were only too glad to oblige.

It was dark as we disembarked amid the din of shouts and whistles. I followed Lenz and Reidle down the gangway, but watched in horror as Lenz and Reidle were pushed away towards a different group of about thirty men while I was pushed towards another group. I shouted to get their attention and made towards them, but got a firm push in the chest from a guard's rifle. I could only watch as my two friends disappeared amid the chaos on the dockside. I joined the other group, frantically searching for a familiar face, but saw none. It became obvious that the guards had orders to divide the men in a random manner so that men were separated from their platoons, units or battalions.

With a blast of a whistle my group was led away from the quayside. Under the watchful eyes of our guards, we were shepherded a few hundred yards to a waiting train. As we neared the carriages I became aware of some shouting and commotion on one of the other platforms. Behind a cordon of soldiers an angry crowd of civilians, men and women, gesticulated towards us, waving their fists and shouting. I wasn't able to understand what they were saying, but you didn't need any knowledge of English to know that it wasn't a friendly greeting. Our guards appeared nervous and with good reason, for a few moments later we found ourselves the target of a hail of stones and bottles. The guards urged us to hurry aboard the train, and as we climbed aboard the carriages the sound of stones hitting the windows and the sides of the carriages reverberated along the length of the train. As we began to move off, I watched as the guards pushed back the crowd who continued to throw objects at the carriages, and it was a relief when the train finally left the station leaving the angry crowd behind.

The carriages were so full that men who couldn't find seats sat on the floor or stood in the corridor. I wondered if Lenz and Reidle might be in another carriage, but such was the crush of men that it was impossible to move around. I was squashed into the corner of a compartment with two bench seats facing one another. I had no clue where we were being taken and though surrounded by dozens of other men, I had never felt so alone in all my life.

The train rumbled on through the night, rain streaking the carriage windows. I had no idea in which direction we were travelling, knowing only that each mile was another mile further from home. I closed my eyes to try and shut out the world. Lulled by the steady clatter of the train I fell asleep, waking only when it stopped at a station, the sign on the platform indicating that it was a place called Devizes. There were more whistles and shouts as the guards ordered us out of the carriage. We joined the men already standing on the station platform and once more I looked in vain to see if I could see Lenz or Riedle. The only other paratrooper I spotted was Korff, though the sight of his familiar face made me feel little better. Carriage doors were slammed shut, the engine belched steam and the train once again shuddered into life, pulling slowly away from the platform, taking the prisoners still on board to other destinations. Following the guards, we walked out of the station through the small town and a couple of miles out into the country to what looked like a large army camp, surrounded by a wire mesh fence topped with barbed wire. Inside the wire perimeter were row upon row of identical wooden huts.

We were led in through the gates and on to a large parade ground where we were split into smaller groups. This seemed to be done on a completely arbitrary basis so that I was again separated into a different group from those who had been in the same carriage on the train. It was growing light as my group of around twenty were ushered towards a concrete building on the other side of the parade ground. As we entered the block in single file, a man wearing a large rubber mask and wielding a long, rubber tube sprayed us with a foul smelling mist. Each man was sprayed from head to toe before the nozzle was stuck inside our tunics and down our trousers. Clouds of the noxious mist hung in the air causing us to cough and our eyes to water. After each man had been subjected to this treatment we were moved on through the building and then told to strip. Quickly undressing and gathering up our clothes in piles, we walked naked towards some trestle tables where the guards went through our clothes, looking in every pocket and checking that nothing had been concealed in the linings of our coats or trousers.

It was clear to see from the skeletal frames and gaunt faces that all the men arriving at the camp had been brought from the Channel Islands. Many of the guards were Polish and they took great delight in finding some item in the pockets and linings of our clothing which they would remove and put into their own pockets, smiling and laughing as they did so. Hardly any of us had anything of value, perhaps the odd keepsake we had been given by loved ones, a photograph, a small locket containing a lock of hair or a ring, but the Poles took delight in removing even these small mementoes. One soldier next to me watched in tears as one of the Poles removed a crumpled photograph of what appeared to be his wife and two little children from his tunic pocket and tore it into pieces.

"Tot," he said with a laugh, dropping the fragmented picture onto the ground and grinding the pieces beneath his heel.

After our clothes had been inspected we placed them in piles on the ground before being led into the showers. I expected the icy cold douche beloved of the military everywhere, but was pleasantly surprised to find that the water was hot. The warm water felt good upon my body. I was tired and hungry, but the warm water flowing over my skin was rejuvenating. I hadn't been able to wash since leaving the airfield in Guernsey four days earlier, so I scrubbed the accumulated filth and memories of the ship from my body. After the showers we were allowed to put on our dirty uniforms and were then required to turn in our *soldbuchs,* the only item that the guards had left in our pockets. These small books not only contained our home addresses and service numbers which might allow them to make contact with our families via the Red Cross, but also contained records of our military service. It was this information that interested our captors, for they were anxious to verify whether we were merely ordinary soldiers or whether we had been members of any units which might warrant further investigation.

I had heard talk among the men that the British and Americans might put people on trial for what they called 'war crimes', including the German leaders, if any had survived. It was common knowledge throughout the military that certain regiments, particularly the SS, had been involved in some atrocities such as the shooting of civilians, and now that the war was over it seemed certain that there was to be a reckoning. I knew that I had done nothing wrong, but if they were to punish our leaders then what hope was there for the ordinary soldier like myself? Perhaps we would all be given some kind of collective punishment. I recalled the ambush on the train in France when we had shot the young boy and girl who had shot at us. Could they possibly know about that? Would I be able to prove that it was self-defence?

At last we were given something to eat. We queued for bowls of soup and a plate of floury, boiled potatoes; amazingly we were even allowed to go back for more. Some men ate too much and were sick, their distended stomachs unable to cope with a sudden intake of nourishment in anything but the most meagre quantities. Despite the indignities we had suffered since we arrived, the undisguised glee of the Polish guards at our humiliation and their casual disregard for men's personal possessions, there was not a man among us who was not eternally grateful for the fact that now we were in England we were given food in ample quantity.

We were each assigned to a hut containing thirty bunks, but no-one told us how long we were to be held at the camp or what would happen to us next. It appeared to be a transit camp rather than a permanent one, as new groups of prisoners were constantly arriving while others were leaving. The new arrivals went through the procedure of stripping and showering as I had done the day before. There were no officers among the prisoners and this appeared to be no accident. I had noticed when we got off the ship that the officers had been quickly separated from the other ranks. The men in my hut reckoned that once the British had satisfied themselves that there were no officers or SS hiding among us then we would be sent somewhere else. An interrogation hut had been established where, as a result of examining our *soldbuchs,* men might be summoned to account for their deeds. All the men in my hut had been on the Channel Islands for three years or more and none of them had been interrogated, so I was surprised to be summoned to the interrogation hut on the second day after my arrival.

I was ushered towards one of a dozen tables where interrogations were in progress. The interrogators wore British army uniforms, but spoke fluent German. I was told to sit. The lieutenant was English, but his German was faultless, in fact it was better than mine, he was clearly an educated man. He began by asking me how I was being treated and asked me a few general questions regarding my well-being before picking up my *soldbuch* which lay on the table in front of him. He casually leafed through it, asking me to confirm one or two details, then folded it open at a place where a stamp had been made in a section marked *Special Remarks*. He asked me what it meant, but I couldn't remember. Clearly unimpressed with my answer, he spun the booklet around on the table so that I could see exactly what he was referring to and it was then that I remembered.

It referred to the incident a year earlier when Renschler's Bar in Gaderlegen had been wrecked and Leutnant Heller, in his anger, had put the stamp in our books then sent us away before the police arrived. It seemed a lifetime ago, no wonder I had forgotten about it. This was the mark in my *soldbuch* to which the Lieutenant was referring. I explained what had happened in Gaderlegen and though he appeared sceptical, my answer seemed to satisfy him for the moment. I was asked no more about the incident or any other aspect of my military service, but instead of being allowed to return to my hut in the general camp, I was placed in an area fenced off from the rest of the camp with others who, like myself, were clearly not free from the suspicion of having done something wrong. I was now confined in a prison within a prison and wondered just how much worse things could get.

The following morning I expected another interrogation session, but instead I was merely released back into the general camp. My explanation of the mysterious mark in my *soldbuch* had obviously been accepted and I was no longer considered to be a danger to anyone. Later that day, groups of fifty or so prisoners were summoned to one of the larger huts for a 'talk'. We entered the hut and found rows of chairs laid out the length of the hut with a screen at the far end. A film projector was mounted on a table at the back and all the windows were covered with heavy, black material. When we were all seated, the lights were turned off and a film began to roll.

As the black and white images flickered on the screen a German narrative began. The scene that unfolded was one of complete devastation. What seemed to be a large city was now just a collection of ruined buildings, the streets filled with rubble and burned out vehicles. A large building came into view, I had seen it somewhere before…we had all seen it before. There was a collective intake of breath. Everyone recognised the Reichstag. It was still standing, but it was now just a shell, the roof was missing and the façade was pockmarked by artillery fire. What appeared to be a Soviet flag hung limply from the pediment. The chaos of rubble and craters on the screen was Berlin. The scene changed to a nondescript piece of waste ground on which barely a wall survived. The commentary stated that this was the site of the Reich Chancellery where our Leader had committed suicide rather than be captured by the advancing Russians.

So it was true, there could be no remaining doubt in anyones' mind. The rumours I had heard in Guernsey and on the ship about Hitler being dead and the war being lost were all terribly true. There had been no truce, no cease-fire and no joining together with the British and Americans to fight the Russians. The war had been lost, completely and utterly. It was over. Many of us had suspected it all along, but in ignorance there was always hope, now there was none. There wasn't a man in the room who had any illusions now about the fate that had befallen our country and ourselves. As the film continued rolling, showing more scenes of ruined cities, I thought of my own home. If this awful destruction had happened in Berlin then what must have happened to the rest of the country? What must have happened to my parents, my brothers and my sister?

The scene in the film changed abruptly from the ruins of Berlin to a kind of camp not unlike the one we were in, but this one was strangely different. This camp didn't contain soldiers; instead there were images of men, women and children dressed in a uniform that resembled striped pyjamas. Those of us who had endured the misery of the Channel Islands were emaciated, but our condition was nothing compared to the people shown in the film. The commentator stated that these people were Jews, Gypsies or political opponents that our Leader had considered undesirable. The film cut away from the pathetic figures in the striped clothes and the screen was filled with hundreds of naked corpses piled in mounds, barely recognisable as human beings, they were little more than skeletons covered by a thin layer of translucent skin.

The silence in the hut was total. Some of the men held their heads in their hands while others bit their lips. The film continued, only the sound of the whirring projector disturbing the silence. The narrative said that the scenes we were witnessing were the work of the leaders for whom we had fought and for whom our comrades had sacrificed their lives. The Leader himself had committed crimes beyond human understanding and the narrator warned that any one of us who still harboured favourable sentiments towards him and his regime should remember these images.

45

Everyone in the camp received a full medical examination, but despite a special diet for the severely malnourished, many of the men became ill. Their bodies, fragile from months of starvation, were unable to tolerate rich and plentiful food. Men whose hearts and lungs had grown dangerously weak were treated in the camp hospital, but despite medicines and dietary supplements, many died during those first weeks of captivity. Almost every day there was a death, quickly followed by a funeral with full military honours and burial in a special plot in a corner of the local cemetery. The war was over, there was no longer any shooting or bombing, but men were still dying just as surely as if they had been killed in battle.

I soon began to gain weight and was at last free of the gnawing hunger which had been my constant companion for almost a year. I noticed that I had far more energy and was no longer content to lie on my bunk for hours staring at the ceiling. My arm had been improving, even while I had been on Guernsey, and the painful boils in my armpit soon disappeared thanks to my nutritious diet. I was now able, with some effort, to lift my arm level with my shoulder, but determined to make a complete recovery I once more rigged up a pulley system with which to exercise my arm.

When the mind is no longer pre-occupied with hunger and the urgent business of finding food, it concerns itself with other matters. I began to think more about my family, particularly after seeing the destruction of Berlin shown in the film. I worried increasingly about Bernie who had been fighting in the East, my parents at home in Beckum and my sister and younger brothers, wondering if they were alright or even if they were still alive. We had been denied any true information while stationed on Guernsey, and even now that it was all over the only information we received was that which was allowed by the British authorities. We had been told only that Germany had been defeated and that it was now occupied by the Russians, Americans and British who had divided the country into three zones. We had been told that Hitler was dead and the country was in ruins, but beyond that we knew nothing. We didn't know whether there had been any great battles fought on German soil, whether all the cities had been destroyed or what conditions were like for the survivors now that the shooting was over. Cooped up in the camp with nothing else to do, I had plenty of time to dwell upon such matters, and in the absence of hard news, rumours inevitably abounded.

I was held for two weeks in the camp in Devizes, long enough for my captors to satisfy themselves that I wasn't a war criminal and could be safely sent elsewhere. I had no idea where I was to be taken when I and all the men in my hut were one day ordered to gather up our belongings, in readiness to march to the railway station at six o'clock that evening. A roll call was held on the parade ground, after which we walked the short distance to the railway station to board a train. Part of our route passed through the town and I was apprehensive about the reaction of the local people when they saw us, but unlike the scenes when we came ashore at what I now knew to be Southampton, those we did encounter just stared or ignored us completely.

I had spent enough time on railway trains to know that wherever we were going, the journey was likely to be long, uncomfortable and punctuated by frequent stops. I wasn't to be disappointed. We weren't informed of our destination, but as the train rumbled slowly on, I instinctively knew that it was taking me away from the coast and even further away from home. The sun was high in the eastern sky by the time the train stopped; a sign hanging on the station platform proclaimed the name of Oswestry. To the accompaniment of shrill whistles, the men gathered up their belongings and we disembarked. There was another roll call and then we marched for half an hour to Prison Camp No 8 at a place called Mile End which lay in open country just beyond the outskirts of the town.

Upon arrival we underwent the same routine of stripping, searching and showering, although the guards at this camp were British and didn't seem to take the same pleasure in our predicament as the Poles had done at the previous camp. I'd had more showers during the few days I'd been in captivity than I'd had in the previous six months, I had never been so clean. Camp No 8 looked much the same as any other, the layout was a familiar one, rows of dormitory huts situated around a central open space, but this one looked older than others I had seen. Someone told me that it had been built for prisoners during the Great War which must have been true, for on close inspection one could see names and dates carved on timbers within the huts: there was a Willi dated 1917 and a Karl dated 1919.

There were almost two thousand prisoners in the camp; all were German and many had been captured in the Channel Islands. Men arriving from a dozen different transit camps spent the first few days looking for friends from whom they had become separated. I searched high and low for any sign of Lenz or Riedle, but there was no sign of either. Resigned to probably never seeing them again, I continued to search for any familiar face wearing the distinctive paratroopers' uniform. I had almost given up any hope when I caught sight of Korff. Although we had not been the closest of friends while on Guernsey, we embraced each other like long lost brothers, each glad to find at least one person we knew in this sea of strangers. We joyfully recounted our experiences since we had landed in England and each of us bemoaned the fact that our closest comrades appeared to have been scattered to the four winds.

Another series of interrogations was arranged for the new arrivals, or debriefings as the guards liked to call them. I had naively believed that my previous interrogation at Devizes had concluded the interest of the authorities in me, but I was wrong. My debriefing was set for eleven o' clock. Some of the men had already been interviewed and reckoned that it hadn't been too bad, however, it seemed that the experience very much depended upon the interrogator. One of these interrogators was a German Jew by the name of Sternberg and some of the men who'd had the pleasure of an interview with him said that he had been particularly harsh. On the morning of my interview, I was escorted to the main building and shown down the corridor, at the end of which was a closed door.

The guard knocked.

"Komm."

I entered while the guard remained outside. Sitting behind a desk was a middle-aged man in British army uniform with sergeant's stripes on his sleeve. The room was small with walls of plain white in which a solitary window, set high up just below the ceiling, allowed light in, but no view out. The only furniture was the desk and chair occupied by the sergeant and one other simple stool on the other side.

"Sitzen," he said, motioning me towards the stool.

"Mein name ist Sternberg," he said and my heart sank. I had got the German Jew. He studied my face for a reaction, but I was determined to show no fear. I had done nothing wrong and had certainly not been involved in any of the scenes we had witnessed in the films. I had only done my duty like thousands of other soldiers, but still...........

"Ich war in Frankfurt geboren,". he announced as I sat down.

He watched me intently as I digested this piece of information. I said nothing.

"Do you want to know why I am wearing this uniform?" he asked, tapping the stripes on his sleeve.

I had been in the military long enough to know that it didn't pay to ask too many questions, especially of superiors and certainly not of anyone wearing a foreign uniform. I merely shrugged.

"I left Germany in 1934. Have you any idea why?"

I shook my head, but I knew the answer.

"I had to leave because your Leader, the one for whom you have been fighting for the past five years, didn't care too much for me and my...kind."

I recalled the film we had been shown at the camp in Devizes. The piles of bodies and the skeletal figures dressed in striped clothes.

He jabbed his finger towards me.

"How could you wear that uniform and serve that...that ...criminal?"

Sternberg had a habit of pausing before finishing his sentences, as if he was searching for the correct word or perhaps to deliberately emphasise the one he had already chosen.

"I was called up," I replied simply.

A smile passed momentarily over his features, a brief sunny interval before the dark clouds returned. He glowered.

"Have you seen the film?"

There was no need to ask which film. All the prisoners had seen it. I nodded.

"Did you know that people were being murdered?"

"Nein!"

"That's what every one of you prisoners says," he replied dismissively.

I knew that some of the men hadn't been sure whether the film we had seen was genuine. Some thought that it was a piece of propaganda which had been fabricated to further sap our morale and get us to admit to doing things we had not done. I wasn't so sure, there had been many stories before and during the war about strange goings on, whispers and rumours, but as with so much else, there were things that it was best not to enquire about. As far as the Jews were concerned I, like many others, believed that they had been re-settled somewhere in the East, not starved to death in hideous death camps like the one shown in the film.

I cast my mind back to the day, many years before, when I had gone to visit the Weissmanns with my mother. They had clearly been upset and had left suddenly, leaving many of their possessions behind, and I remembered that, even as a boy, I had thought it strange. We had been told that they were being resettled in a place of their own where they would not be a danger to the rest of us and people accepted this as the truth. Now I realised that they had instead probably ended up like the other tortured souls I had seen in the film.

Sternberg continued:

"Why didn't you try to kill this Leader of yours instead of fighting for him?"

The question was so ludicrous that it took me by surprise and I was unable to answer. How on earth could I, Theodor Terhorst from a small village in Westphalia, have been able to even contemplate such a thing, let alone carry it out?

"Well?" he persisted, annoyed at my silence.

Perhaps this man had conducted too many interviews; perhaps his experiences and those of his family had affected him in some deep, unfathomable way. Whatever it was, I decided that he was clearly insane so I decided to humour him.

I was never in Berlin," I ventured, "and of course he was always very well protected."

A grim smile crossed Sternberg's face and I realised that he hadn't been entirely serious about my failure to kill the Leader. He was merely toying with me, going through the motions of interviewing men who, like him, were merely victims of circumstance.

He abruptly changed the subject.

"Your name?" he said, "Terhorst doesn't sound German to me. Where did you get it from?"

"My father," I replied flippantly.

Sternberg's frown at my answer prompted a fuller explanation.

"It's Dutch" I said, briefly relating the story of how my grandfather settled in Germany and that both my father and I had been Dutch citizens until 1938.

He leafed through the pages of my *soldbuch* as he listened to my story.

"Have you any living relatives in Holland?"

"An aunt in Deventer and some cousins, but I'm not sure where they are now."

Sternberg leaned back in his chair.

"How would you like to have your old nationality back?"

I was caught off guard by the question. I wondered what he was getting at, suspecting a trap. At that moment I heard Rudi's voice in my head saying *don't volunteer for anything.*

"Well," I said, "I've been told that once you're a German, you're always a bloody German."

Sternberg jumped up from his chair. "Raus!" he shouted as he flung my *soldbuch* back onto the desk.

The interview was clearly at an end so I got up and left the room. I lit a cigarette to calm my nerves when I got outside and strolled back to my hut, wondering whether it had been wise to answer his question the way I had. Perhaps the offer of Dutch nationality hadn't been a trap at all. Time would tell whether or not I had made a big mistake in turning it down. There were no further interviews and I was left at leisure to consider the fact that I would be treated just like any other German prisoner and was therefore likely to be kept as a prisoner of war for the foreseeable future.

Conditions at the Mile End camp were reasonably good, food was plentiful and nutritious and the guards for the most part treated us with respect, some of them being quite friendly. We were allowed to keep our uniforms, but were issued with camp clothing which consisted of surplus British Army tunics, dyed a lighter colour with a large black diamond sewn on the back and smaller black diamond patches sewn on the trousers. For the first time since we had been taken prisoner we were allowed to send letters home telling our families where we were and giving them a return address to which they could reply. The initial letters had been pre-printed and stated that we were in good health, were being treated well and were being held as prisoners of war in England. We were allowed to add some personal words in the margins before placing them in unsealed envelopes in case the censor wished to read them.

The letters were duly sent and we all waited anxiously for replies, but any hopes that we might receive a quick response were dashed. It had been more than a year since I had received any word from my family and that had been while I was still in Normandy. Now, as the months passed by with still no word from home, my concern grew with each passing day and I became more convinced that my family had perished and that I might have been the only survivor of a family of eight. Dark thoughts took hold in my mind; perhaps they had not been killed, maybe they had been left homeless and were wandering the land, desperately seeking shelter at the mercy of the elements and occupying Russian soldiers. And what had happened to Bernie? Had he been killed on the eastern front or, like me, had he been taken prisoner? I was not alone in harbouring such fears, for none of the men had received word from home and a veil of despondency gradually fell over the men.

Prisoners who had been resident at Camp No 8 for some time were permitted to work outside, receiving their pay in the form of vouchers which could be redeemed at the camp shop. More recent arrivals were not permitted to perform work of any kind until passed fit to do so by a doctor and, until they had also proved themselves to be of good behaviour and unlikely to abscond. Most of the prisoners who had arrived during the past week had either been injured or were suffering from malnourishment like myself, and were not in any case considered fit enough to carry out even the lightest manual work. We were put on a special diet chiefly consisting of a milk soup and white bread, but supplemented by the normal prison camp food should we desire it.

I had weighed 140 pounds before I was sent to Guernsey, but had lost half of that during the nine months I was there. With the help of the special diet, I soon began to regain weight and felt my natural strength slowly returning. My skeletal figure gradually filled out and the chronic fatigue which had plagued me for months, and which had caused me to spend so many hours lying in my bunk, was finally banished. My arm was also getting stronger, due in part to my improved diet, but also because I continued to use my pulley system to strengthen it, obsessively pumping away for hours so that I was now able to raise it level with my shoulder and lift heavier objects.

At the end of my first month at the camp, my weight had climbed to more than one hundred pounds and the camp doctor pronounced me fit enough to perform light manual work. I was not, however, permitted to apply for a place on one of the work gangs for a further two weeks as punishment for my lapse during the interview with Sternberg. As a result, I spent the next two weeks kicking my heels around the camp and watching enviously while my newly employed comrades used their pay tokens to buy luxuries like chocolate and cigarettes at the camp shop.

Life wasn't particularly onerous and we amused ourselves in a variety of ways. To relieve the monotony of our existence and take our minds off the situation at home, endless games of football were organised, with huts competing against each other, or Luftwaffe taking on the Army. Card schools were always a popular way of passing the time and occasionally there were films to watch, or theatrical performances put on by some of the prisoners who had somehow managed to borrow costumes and musical instruments. Domestic duties continued just as they had throughout my military service. We were still in uniform and although we were now prisoners, we were not allowed to forget that we were still serving men. Each hut had a leader who was either the highest-ranking or longest-serving soldier and he was responsible for the duties to be performed by the men under him.

The highest-ranking soldier in my hut was Sergeant Kranz who organised our duties on a roster basis. Each occupant was required to take turns in sweeping the hut floor, but the military pecking order was still alive and well. A group of corporals who occupied the far end of the hut felt that they were above such menial tasks, and insisted that the privates be solely responsible for this work. Some of the men put up with this state of affairs, but when it was my turn to sweep the floor I refused, telling Sgt Kranz that if everyone else performed this task then so would I, but that if the corporals refused then I too would refuse. The war was over as far as I was concerned, we were all stuck in this camp for God only knew how long and I believed that everyone should have to do it. The sergeant, who only wanted a quiet life, listened to what I had to say and the following morning instructed one of the corporals to clean the hut, and gave orders that henceforth everyone would take their turn regardless of rank - everyone except Sgt Kranz of course.

In any military organisation it's inevitable that there will be a clearly defined pecking order running all the way down from a field-marshal to the common private, and while this is accepted during time of war, I felt that the privileges of rank should no longer apply when all men were prisoners regardless of the number of stripes they had on their sleeves. I had always been a bit of a rebel and wasn't afraid to speak out, especially when I felt that someone was being treated unfairly, and especially so if that someone was me. This tendency to speak my mind didn't always make me the most popular person and it was clear that I had upset the corporals.

It was shortly after the confrontation over the cleaning roster that I played in my last ever game of football. I had never been a particularly good player, but ever since I was a schoolboy eager to impress the schoolmaster, I had always relished the opportunity for a run out on the playing field. One Sunday afternoon an informal game was organised in the camp; one of the corporals in my hut was playing on the opposing side and during the first half, when I went for a ball, he came charging across the pitch like a lunatic. He raised his boot and raked his studs down the back of my leg, making absolutely no effort to make contact with the ball. I cursed him loudly as I lay writhing on the ground, but he merely smiled. He was clearly enjoying his revenge for the cleaning incident. Ten minutes later I exacted my own revenge, my right boot connecting sweetly with his groin as I pretended to make a tackle. It was effective, but not very subtle for I had committed the foul right under the referee's nose and he had no hesitation in sending me off. I never bothered playing football after that, for me the fun had gone.

46

Summer was almost over by the time I was at last allowed to join an outside working party, and able to earn the vouchers with which to buy a few extra luxuries. Korff had already been working in a gang of men assigned to a local building company that was repairing roads in the area. He reckoned that it wasn't such hard work and that the foreman treated them fairly, so I decided to join him, even though it meant starting very early in the morning. The company would send a lorry to the camp at six in the morning to pick us up and take us to wherever the work was to be carried out that day. The work itself consisted of mixing and spreading asphalt to repair potholes or repair the edges of road surfaces where they had crumbled away. We would have a break for a cigarette or a cup of tea every hour. I had never drunk tea until I arrived in England and although it took some getting used to, any hot drink on a cold autumn day was welcome. The great thing from my point of view was that we worked in a different location each day and after the monotonous confines of the prison camps in which I had lived for the past five months, this gave me a wonderful sense of freedom.

At last I began to get a sense of the area in which I had been living. I was surprised to discover that the nearest town, Oswestry was only just located in England and that a couple of miles to the west lay the Welsh border. Frankly, I had never heard of Wales before, and although it wasn't a completely separate country, it had its own distinct and unusual language which was clearly visible on the road signs which contained names even stranger and more unpronounceable than the English ones. As we journeyed by lorry to repair the roads, we would pass by signs indicating places like Llansantffraid, Llanymynech and Rhydycroesau. I still found the English language baffling, but I decided that this strange tongue which I sometimes heard people speaking, and which appeared to contain no vowels, would be quite impossible for any foreigner to learn.

The terrain was rural and hilly, the narrow roads twisted through pleasant, green pastureland punctuated with small market towns where farmers from the surrounding area and the hill farms over the border in Wales came to trade livestock and buy supplies. The region wasn't entirely rural, however, there was some coal mining and I heard that many mines were located just to the north around the larger town of Wrexham. One day I happened to pick up a road map that was lying in the lorry cab and studied it while I was having a cigarette break. When I discovered the exact location of Oswestry relative to the rest of the country, it became clear that the British had deliberately dispersed prisoners to places like Wales and Shropshire in order that they were as far away as possible from the shores of the North Sea to discourage potential escapees.

It wasn't long after I had started on the road gang that the camp commandant asked for volunteers who had experience of working on the railways. He gave no further information, but some of the men came forward to give details of their work experience. Although I had no direct experience with railways, as a bricklayer I probably could have turned my hand to most things, but I never came forward, adhering to the principle that it was dangerous to volunteer for anything in the army. It was only later that we discovered that those who had volunteered, and had provided evidence that they might perform this type of work, were to be released early and allowed home. The occupying powers in Germany urgently required men to repair a railway system which had been shattered by five years of relentless bombing. By the time we discovered that this was an opportunity to end our captivity and return home, they had obtained enough volunteers and I, together with many others, was left to rue another missed opportunity. Korff and I complained about the injustice of the situation and both decided that we would break the habit of our service careers and volunteer next time – if there was a next time.

Many of the prisoners at Camp No 8 - Mile End who were allowed to work outside were often assigned to agricultural work. There was great demand for labour by local farmers whose own labourers over the past few years had either been killed, were still in uniform or had been attracted away to the cities with the promise of better pay. Many of the prisoners working on local farms said that they were treated well, but others complained that some farmers treated them as little more than slaves. My aversion to working on the land might have been a throwback to my schooldays when Hans and I had been duped into working on Karl Muller's farm in Beckum and had received no payment, but listening to some of the men's complaints confirmed that, for once, my decision to join Korff in the road gangs had been a wise one.

The months passed and there was still no word about when we would be released. I had now been a prisoner for three months and increasingly there were rumblings among the men. Many were saying that if a state of war no longer existed, then we should be repatriated according to something I had never heard of called the Geneva Convention. What we did not know at the time was that a deal had been worked out between Attlee, the British prime minister, and the provisional German government led by Adenauer, whereby prisoners would have to remain in England for up to three years to work off some of the war reparations which the shattered German economy was unable to pay in the form of hard currency.

No doubt the German government were also mindful of the unrest fomented by returning troops after the Great War, and so the men in uniform who had paid the price of war under the old government were now obliged the pay the price of peace under the new one. There would have been a mutiny if we had known about it at the time, but the authorities decided to keep it secret. Hitler had betrayed us in our millions and now it seemed that Adenauer was doing the same thing. If anyone deserved any reparations for the war then surely it was the poor soldiers who had suffered so much for the folly of their leaders, and especially the families of those in uniform who had paid the ultimate price.

47

Georg Segerer was in a bad way. Before the war he had been a carpenter in a small town near Chemnitz on the Czech border. He was older than most of the other men in my hut, old enough to remember the Great War though not quite old enough to have fought in it. He was married with three young children, two girls and a boy who was only three years old when he'd last seen him four years earlier. Like many of us in Camp No 8, he'd spent time in the Channel Islands, in his case Alderney where he had suffered the effects of malnutrition along with the rest of us. The one photograph of his wife and children, that he had kept safely in his pocket throughout the war, had been torn into pieces by the guards upon his arrival at the transit camp in England. Starved of any communication for more than a year, the photograph had been his last tangible link with his family and his previous life.

Throughout the war it had always been difficult to tell the difference between rumour and truth, but stories were nevertheless traded like precious currency between all the men. Camp talk invariably revolved around what might be happening at home and when we might finally be repatriated. The fortunate ones who had at last received a letter from home were able to relate with some authority what the situation in Germany was like, while those of us who had still received no word hung on their words as though they were dispensing some indisputable truth.

By the middle of November more of the men began receiving letters and every evening, when I returned from working with the road gang, I would go straightaway and ask Sgt Kranz if a letter had arrived for me. It seemed that hardly a day passed without someone in my hut receiving a letter from home, but always Sgt Kranz shook his head whenever I asked. I had begun to fear the worst when one day Kranz handed me a slim, brown envelope. I sat on my bunk and, with trembling hands, slit it open. Instantly recognising my father's handwriting, I read and re-read the contents contained on the single flimsy piece of paper. Thank God! They were alive and well, there had been difficulties for a time, but they had survived. He reported that everyone was as well as could be expected and that they had been overjoyed to hear that I was alive and looked forward eagerly to my return, but he added that there had been no word at all from Bernie. My relief was immense. I had been able to think of little else for the past few months, so I smoothed the slip of paper as if it were a valuable historical parchment and carefully placed it in my bedside cabinet. Now I had some positive news of my own to share with the others over the evening meal.

The cold, damp days of November came to an end and our working day was cut a little shorter because of the fading light in the late afternoon. Soon it would be Christmas, but there was little festive colour to lift men's spirits and the drabness of the weather matched the drabness of the camp. Some of the men tried to relieve the gloom by putting up some bunting which they had fashioned out of old newspapers. A small fir tree, cut down in a nearby wood, was placed near the hut entrance so that men might place some small bright or coloured object in the branches, a bit of ribbon or a screwed up ball of coloured paper.

Georg Segerer was not noted for his lively conversation. When he did speak it was in slow, measured sentences seemingly tailored to economise on the number of words he used. He spoke only to impart or to request information, never in idle gossip, and spent most of his evenings silently carving a Madonna and child out of a piece of wood. Everyone in the hut had now received word from home except Georg and while the rest of us sat and talked or played cards, he sat alone on his bunk, slicing and cutting, smoothing rough edges and polishing his creation with chisel, file and cloth. When after many weeks it was completed, he stood it on the small cabinet next to his bed. Word of the wondrous carving went through the camp and men from other huts in the camp came to marvel at his creation. The figures were perfectly formed and well proportioned. The face of the infant was angelic, but men recoiled at the face of the Madonna for its features were anguished rather than serene. The eyes were tightly shut as if in pain and the mouth was twisted into a silent scream. Perhaps it was a knot in the wood that gave her features such a distressed appearance, but I suspected that it was no accident, merely a reflection of Georg Segerer's own anguish.

I continued to work every day with the road gang. Fortunately, Korff was able to understand a few words he remembered from his time at a technical institute in Stuttgart, so he acted as the conduit between the foreman and the rest of the men. On Christmas Eve the foreman informed us that it was customary in England to finish work early. Korff had told him that it was also the custom in Germany, but that it was also customary for the workmen to be given either a gift or a bonus by the boss. The foreman had laughed it off, saying that he had never heard of such a thing, but that we should ask the owner of the company for he would be coming out to see us that day. Sure enough, Mr Whitley, the owner, showed up just before noon. The foreman went over to him and said something which made the owner laugh. They continued chatting for a while longer, occasionally looking over in our direction and laughing again. Ten minutes later Mr Whitley got back into his car and disappeared without so much as a nod or a wave in our direction. We thought that was the last we had seen of him, but half an hour later he returned. He climbed out of his car and came over to where we working. He shook each of our hands, gave us all a packet of cigarettes and made a short speech, the only words of which I understood were the words 'Merry Christmas'.

We were dropped off at the camp gate that afternoon. Even though we had been promised a special meal the following day, I was not particularly looking forward to it. Men would inevitably be thinking of home and I couldn't help thinking that rather than having a day off, it might have been better for the men to have worked as normal so that they had something to occupy their thoughts. In Germany it is traditional to celebrate and exchange gifts on Christmas Eve, or Weihnacht as we call it, rather than on Christmas Day. I was therefore dreading the evening to come, for there were sure to be long faces around the dining room and in all the huts. It wouldn't be the first Christmas that I had spent away from home and I was immeasurably better off than the previous year, when there had been little to eat. However, for all the privations in Guernsey, we had at least been fighting the war and been expected to make sacrifices; but now the war was lost and we were just captives, with no desire to make further sacrifices and no idea when we would be allowed to return home.

Georg Segerer not only had to bear the pain of separation from his wife and children, he also had to bear the pain of not knowing what had happened to them or whether he would ever be able to see them again. He was not the only man from the eastern part of Germany, some of the other prisoners at Camp 8 came from Silesia and Brandenburg, from the Sudetenland and Pomerania; none of these men had received a single word from home. My own home and much of the northwest was in the British sector, while further south the Americans controlled Baden-Wurttemburg and Bavaria. Men from all these regions had received messages from home. Some were joyous and some were tragic: one man from Mannheim learned that his entire family had been killed when a bomb struck their house shortly before the end of the war, another learned that all three of his brothers had been killed during the fighting in France. Whether the news was good or bad, at least these men had received some news, they could give thanks to God or they could cry tears of sorrow, but at least they knew. The only thing that Georg Segerer and others from the eastern regions of Germany knew was that their homes and families were cloaked in an impenetrable wall of silence.

I began to receive regular letters from my father in which he described his many fruitless journeys to government offices in Soest and Lippstadt in an attempt to find some clue as to what had happened to Bernie. He also wrote that Beckum was a changed place. Although it had escaped any serious damage during the war, it was now full of refugees from the east who left their homes and possessions behind as they fled westwards to escape the advancing Russians. He also informed me that twenty-five men from the village had been officially listed as killed or missing, and that five families had lost two or more sons. It seemed an impossibly high number of casualties from just one small village and I wondered that if a tiny village like Beckum had suffered so grievously then how many lives must have been lost throughout the entire country.

Despite all that I had been through, after reading my father's letters, I was beginning to think that I had been lucky. I had survived the fighting in Normandy, the crash near St Malo and near starvation in Guernsey. I had made an almost complete recovery from my wounds and had recovered all my lost weight, and although I was now a prisoner, I had enough to eat and was being treated decently. With the exception of Bernie, who I was sure would turn up eventually, my parents and my younger brothers and sister were all alive and well. I reckoned that I had a great deal for which to be thankful.

48

Mile End was not the only prisoner of war camp in Shropshire; I discovered that there were many others and that some of them were quite close by. One of these camps was about five miles away in the small village of St Martins and it was to this camp that I was sent after spending nine months at Camp No 8 - Mile End. Some prisoners of war who had been captured by American and Canadian forces had initially been sent into captivity across the Atlantic, but they were now being sent to England and they needed the huts at Mile End to cope with these new arrivals. Prisoners who had already spent some time in this country and who had begun working outside the camps were therefore dispersed to smaller camps like St Martins.

The village of St Martins and the neighbouring colliery village of Ifton stand in rolling countryside to the north of Oswestry. The camp was on the edge of the village at a place called Bank Top, which stands on the windy crest of a hill looking west towards the Welsh hills. The camp was much smaller than Mile End and had once contained Italian prisoners, but they had since been repatriated and it now became home to three hundred Germans. My transfer coincided with a noticeable reduction in the level of security. At Mile End in the early days, the main gate was always guarded and prisoners were not permitted to leave the camp after 6pm, but now the rules had been relaxed, the gates were no longer guarded and we could come and go more or less as we pleased.

When I was sent to St Martins, I was once again split up from my friends. Korff, my last link with the Channel Islands, was transferred to a camp near Shrewsbury. He was the latest to join a long list of friends I had found and lost; Rudi in Normandy, Lenz and Reidle in Guernsey. It seemed that the system had been purposely created to divide comrades and friends and scatter them to different places. During the time we had all been together we had never bothered to exchange home addresses and I realised that it would be impossible to trace them when it was finally over. Perhaps it was just as well, home was another world and we had lived an existence apart from that, an existence that no one at home could possibly understand. The close bonds that are forged between men in times of war should not be subjected to the humdrum pressures and prosaic realities of normal life. It is sometimes better to remember those friendships in the fiery context in which they were made.

In the spring of 1946 my twenty-first birthday was rapidly approaching. I was at an age when young men are keen to find excitement, chase girls and have fun, yet the opportunity for such youthful pleasures had been denied me for the past three years. As the regime in the camps became more relaxed and we were allowed to leave the camp in the evenings, the possibilities at last arose of being able to lead something like a normal life and take part in more light-hearted pursuits. The younger men naturally headed towards the public houses and dance halls of local towns, but this still involved something of a risk as we were still in uniform and clearly stood out from the crowd. Most of the local people treated us with kindness, or at least aloofness, but memories of the war were still raw and our clothes clearly marked us out as the defeated enemy. The heady mix of alcohol and the testosterone-charged competition for the attention of young women meant that many of these forays into the local towns resulted in fights.

Helmut Luchinger occupied the bunk next to me in Hut No 7 at St Martins Camp. He was a year older than me and had been captured near Caen shortly after the Normandy landings. His home in Germany was only fifty miles from my own so we shared something in common, even though he was in the army and I was a paratrooper. One of my first outings was with Helmut Luchinger. One evening we went to a small town not far from the camp where we treated ourselves to some fish and chips, of which I had learned that the English were very fond. We were innocently walking along the high street when a middle-aged woman approached. At first I thought that she was going to ask a question, but when she came up close, she spat in my face, then her features contorted in fury as she shouted at Luchinger and me.

"You bastards killed my son."

She then continued indignantly on her way.

My knowledge of English at that time consisted of barely a dozen words but Luchinger, who had been in England longer than I, understood what she had said and he translated for me as the woman's spittle ran down my cheek and dripped on to my fish supper. Of course I hadn't killed her son, but someone wearing a uniform similar to mine obviously had. Although I was naturally angry, I could hardly chase after her. I'm sure that I had killed someone's son, the young American soldier in the jeep near St Malo – he must have been someone's son. The young man in the Resistance who had foolishly ambushed our train, he had a mother too. All the men who had died in that wretched, pointless war had been someone's son.

My transfer to the camp at St Martins had taken place as work on the road gangs was ending and I had no idea what my next work assignment might be. I had enjoyed the work and was sorry to see it end, especially as we had begun to be paid in real money rather than in camp vouchers. I had been at St Martins for two weeks when I received a notice from the camp commandant informing me that my next work assignment would be on a local farm. I remembered some of the men at Mile End complaining of the way they had been treated by some of the farmers and I wasn't keen to try it. Short of being allowed to return home, I wanted to work either on the roads or in some kind of construction, not spending my days milking cows and shearing sheep. I had never done any farm work since I was a schoolboy and didn't feel inclined to start now, so I took the letter to the commandant's office and told him that I was a skilled bricklayer and that I was not about to become a farm labourer.

The commandant told me that I had no choice in the matter and that it was the only job available. I asked him what would happen if I refused the assignment and he told me that I would be locked up and lose all my privileges. I was hard pressed to think what 'privileges' I enjoyed, but concluded correctly that the commandant had it within his power to make my life significantly more miserable.

He continued:

"And after you've cooled your heels in the lock-up, you'll go and work on the farm as directed."

I had no alternative. For a moment I had forgotten that I was a prisoner of war with no rights and few choices. In the end I would have to do whatever I was directed to do and go wherever I was directed to go.

The following day I was taken by lorry from the camp and dropped off two miles away at a canal bridge, with instructions to find the farm of a Mr Davies which lay somewhere across the fields. At this time, I was only able to speak and understand a few words of English, while the Welsh language was a complete mystery. Although I was in England, this borderland contained many places which had Welsh names, and one of these was the farm to which I had been assigned. It was called Pen y Bryn.

Following the directions I had been given at the camp, I began walking for some distance along the canal bank before cutting off along a rough track that curved up towards the crest of a ridge. As I made my way up the track I passed a young girl of about fifteen coming down the hill in the opposite direction. She appeared to be on her way to school, and though I smiled at her, she took one look at my uniform, and frowned before hurrying past without a second glance. As I reached the crest of the ridge an old farmhouse surrounded by ancient yew trees came into view. Dogs barked in the yard as I walked up to the front door of the old stone building.

I knocked and a few moments later a short, wiry woman in her late thirties, her dark hair pulled back into a bun, came to the door.

"Good morning," I announced in my best, rehearsed English, "I have come to see Mr Davies."

A small runny-nosed girl with black curly hair peered out suspiciously from behind the woman's skirts and I could hear the cries of another child within.

"Archie's in the cow-shed," she said, waving her arm in the direction of an old wooden barn on the other side of the yard. She said nothing else, just gathered up the little girl and closed the door. I walked over to the barn and inside found a man sitting on a small, wooden stool, busily milking.

"Morgen!"

"We say 'Good morning' around here," he replied, from the other side of a black and white cow.

"Ja .....Good morning," I replied, remembering my English.

"Grab that stool and give me a hand over here," he said, as if the formalities of greeting his new employee were already at an end. I didn't understand what he said, but he motioned towards another stool and I brought it over beside him.

He was inspecting the cow's udders which appeared raw and swollen.

"Ich...er....I'm from the camp," I said

"I know lad," he replied without looking at me, still studying the swollen teat, "I didn't think you'd swum all the way here from Germany."

"Mein name ist...er.... my name is Theodor TerHorst."

He looked up from the udders.

"Mine's Archie," he said, proffering a meaty paw.

"What did you say your name was?"

"Theodor TerHorst."

He rose to his feet, his inspection of the udder finished.

"That's far too complicated for me, you'll have to shorten it. I'll call you Horst if it's all the same to you, and you can call me Archie, then there'll be no confusion."

I looked him up and down. He was a tall man, a little over six feet tall with a handsome, weathered face and dark, wavy hair swept back from his forehead. I estimated that he must have been in his late thirties.

"Time for some breakfast. I'm half starved. Have you eaten?"

I stared at him in blank incomprehension. He sighed and made a motion of putting food into his mouth.

I smiled. Memories of being without food for so long were still painful and I seldom turned down the offer of a meal….and certainly not a free one. The cloudy morning had promised rain and a few drops began to fall as we walked across the farmyard. As we entered the house, I was aware of the delicious aroma of fried bacon and eggs wafting from the kitchen.

The small woman with the dark hair who had answered the door when I arrived was busy with the frying pan.

"This is Horst," Archie announced as he sat down at the large scrubbed table that stood in the middle of the room. The woman, whom I now realised was his wife, turned to look at me and nodded curtly before resuming her cooking. The little girl who had previously clung to her skirts eyed me warily from the corner where she was playing with some kind of rag doll. An older girl aged five or six sat at the table playing with a lump of bread, her lips and chin smeared with what looked like red jam.

Archie's wife took a plate from a large wooden dresser and began to fork huge rashers of bacon onto it. A couple of eggs completed the feast and she set the plate down on the table in front of her husband.

"Get a plate for the lad?"

"In here?" she said.

"Of course in here. Do you expect him to eat outside with the animals?"

Her shrug indicated that that was exactly where she thought I should be eating. She said nothing, but removed another plate from the dresser and forked some more bacon and eggs onto it, then brought it over and placed it on the table in front of me.

"Danke," I said, smiling my sweetest smile, but she merely turned away with no acknowledgement.

Archie winked at me as though this was some kind of family joke. I didn't give it too much thought, however, the smell of bacon and eggs was irresistible and I soon emptied my plate. After a hot mug of tea we went back outside and Archie showed me around the rest of the farm. I barely understood a word as he rambled on, showing me the fields and the chaotic jumble of barns and sheds crowded around the farmyard. Even though I understood little of what he said, I nevertheless got a fair appreciation of what kind of place this was, this farm on the hill called Pen y Bryn.

49

I would rise early each morning at the camp, shower and dress before walking the three miles following the course of the canal, and across the fields to the farm. Although I got out of bed at five, Mr Davies was already well advanced with the milking by the time I arrived at Pen y Bryn. I would help him finish, then herd the cows back into the fields before going into the farmhouse for breakfast. Mrs Davies seemed to become a little less frosty as she grew used to my daily presence at the breakfast table. I stopped eating breakfast at the camp altogether, preferring to wait until I could eat at the farmhouse. The delicious taste of sizzling bacon and eggs, together with some slices of freshly baked bread as I sat down to one of Mrs Davies's breakfasts in the kitchen, became the highlight of my day.

There always seemed to be young children in the house and I eventually calculated that they had three in all, a boy of eight, a girl of five and another girl of two, but it wasn't until I went to the farm one Saturday that I realised they also had an older daughter. I hadn't seen her at the farmhouse during the week because she was away at school in Oswestry and didn't return home until after I had left to return to the camp. When I eventually did see her, she turned out to be the girl who had passed me on the track as I walked up to Pen y Bryn on the very first day. She was just sixteen, pale-skinned and dark-haired like her parents, and whenever I saw her in the house or anywhere around the farm, she would studiously ignore me, refusing even to acknowledge my polite 'good mornings' or 'helloes'.

One morning, after I had been working at the farm for a week or so, I went into the kitchen with Mr Davies for breakfast as I usually did after the milking was finished and was surprised to find the eldest daughter sitting at the table. It was a Wednesday morning and I don't know why she wasn't at school that day, but when I sat down she suddenly got up and stormed out of the room. Mr Davies burst out laughing and then explained to me, although I couldn't understand every word, that his daughter had once told him that if he ever had a German prisoner of war working at the farm, she would shoot him. The look of surprise on my face upon hearing this amused him even more and he thumped the table, roaring with laughter.

After milking had been completed and breakfast eaten, I would work through the rest of the day before returning to the camp for my evening meal. Despite my initial reluctance to work on a farm, I found as the weeks passed by that I was enjoying the work; this was doubtless helped by the fact that it was springtime and it was good to be out in the fresh air. Most importantly, I was now being paid entirely in cash rather than as before with vouchers to be spent at the camp shop. By the end of May 1946, the number of prisoners at St Martins had dwindled to less than fifty and those that did remain were only using it as a place to sleep; it had ceased to be a place of detention.

The payment of proper wages in the strange English currency of pounds, shillings and pennies had begun because, as the camps were gradually being closed down, the shops were the first things to go. The authorities clearly found running the camps expensive and wished to shut down as many of them as possible. To speed up this process they encouraged farmers and other employers of prisoners to provide accommodation in addition to wages, and so it was that Mr Davies asked me if I would like to move into Pen y Bryn.

A man grows tired of living in a hut with other soldiers and I had lived such an existence for the past five years. The camaraderie that such living engenders during time of war rapidly disappears when men are merely kept as prisoners. Group solidarity in the face of a common enemy evaporates and the foibles of one's fellow man become nothing more than nuisances and irritations. The snoring and belching, the breaking of wind, the groans of nightmares and urgent sounds of furtive masturbation by young men deprived of other sexual release were things for which I had little tolerance. It was not a difficult decision to move into Pen y Bryn. Mr Davies had been very fair to me so far, and although his wife and eldest daughter were cold towards me, I decided that I could tolerate it. I was given a small attic bedroom that was nevertheless amply large enough for me and the few pitiful possessions I had brought from the camp. I was thrilled. Although I was still a prisoner unable to return to my own country, I was once more living in a family home, for the first time in over five years.

After two months at Pen y Bryn I was gradually beginning to understand a little more of the language. I had been in England for more than a year, but had barely spoken a word of English while living in the camps. It was only when I started working on the road gang and then at the farm, that I realised that apart from my fellow prisoners, no-one in this part of the world was likely to speak to me in German. I wished now I had made a greater effort to learn English at Mile End when they offered evening lessons, but then I was more interested in playing cards or football, and like many other men at the time, saw little point in learning a new language when we believed that we would soon be going home.

The Davies family would mock my poor command of English at every opportunity and this made me more determined to learn the language, but I didn't suspect that it would be the Davies's eldest daughter who would gradually take on the role of my tutor. She had continued to studiously ignore me after I moved in, and after what Mr Davies had told me, I half expected to see her coming towards me one day with a loaded shotgun. She gradually became less aloof now that I was living under the same roof; not that I saw that much of her because she was at school during the week, so I would only see her at the end of the working day or at weekends.

Joan Davies was the daughter's name and she had thick, dark hair that flowed like waves around her pretty face and onto her shoulders. At sixteen, she was five years younger than I was and only a young schoolgirl who had never been much further than the local town, while I had been a soldier, a man of the world who had seen and lived through things that no man should. Despite the difference in our age, I had been so starved of any kind of female company for so long, that I always made a point of being polite, and smiling at her in an attempt to thaw her frostiness. Over the next few weeks, I became aware that our paths were crossing more frequently than had previously been the case and I began to suspect that this wasn't entirely accidental. I would sometimes notice her playing outside with her younger brother and sisters, appearing to join in with their games, but always watching me intently.

One Saturday morning I was working out in the

cowshed, cleaning up after the milking when she walked in. I hadn't seen her earlier that morning when I'd had breakfast with Archie, so I greeted her;

"Gut Morning," I said in my best English accent.

She ignored the greeting and said, "I'm looking for my Dad. Have you seen him?"

"He's gone into town," I replied.

She turned on her heel without any sign of acknowledgement, but then paused and turned.

"It's *Good* not *Gut!*" she said.

"Bitte?"

"When you say *Good* in English, as in '*Good Morning*' you say '*goooood*,'" mouthing the word.

"Goooood," I repeated, slowly.

"That's it!" she smiled, "Good!" and went out into the yard.

I worked hard to improve my English, not just through conversation, but also by attempting to read the daily newspapers that were delivered to the farm. I especially liked to follow the illustrated articles because this gave me a clue to the topic and I found that I was better able to understand the story. The papers were full of news about the new free health service that the Attlee government was planning to introduce. Most German prisoners had been amazed when the British people had casually discarded Churchill in the election the year before. It seemed a poor reward for a man who had led his country to victory and who had been such a formidable enemy. The papers were also full of news about events in Nuremburg, where the high-ranking leaders who had survived the war had gone on trial. I remember seeing one photograph of Goering, sitting in the dock, looking as fat and arrogant as ever. I knew of course that Hitler and many others were dead, but it gave me some grim satisfaction to know that my ultimate commanding officer in the Luftwaffe had, like me, also ended up a prisoner. Perhaps there was some justice in the world.

I continued to exchange letters with my father. I told him of my change in circumstances and that I was no longer being held in a prison camp, but had begun working on a farm and was generally being treated well. His letters were always full of news about the family, how my younger sister and brothers were doing at school and how my mother was coping. He had still not been able to find out what had happened to Bernie, and though he always assured me that he was continuing to make every effort, it was very difficult. He would say that the family were missing me, but in reply to the question he always posed at the end of his letters, I could only write that I didn't yet know when I would be allowed to go home.

One day, after I had been at the farm for about six months, a postcard was delivered from the authorities stating that I had received a package from Germany that had to be collected from a place called Hawkstone Park near Shrewsbury. Hawkstone Park had become the main administrative centre for the remaining camps in the Shropshire and Wales area and all the prisoners' mail and parcels were sorted here. Only letters and cards would be sent to the outlying camps or the homes where prisoners were living; anything larger had to be collected in person.

I showed the card to Mr Davies, and because I had no way of getting there to pick up the parcel, he agreed to take me the twenty miles in his small Hillman van. Hawkstone Park was a grand country house set in acres of landscaped grounds. When we arrived I reported to the main office and handed the postcard to the duty guard who took it and disappeared into another room, returning a few moments later with a small cardboard box wrapped in brown paper and tied with string. I could see from the loose string and torn paper that it had already been opened.

I looked at the guard.

"All prisoners' packages are opened," he said, anticipating my question.

I removed the string and paper and looked inside the small cardboard box. There was a short note from my father in which he had written that he hoped that the few things he had been able to send would make my Christmas a little happier. The note went on to say that they would not be celebrating Christmas properly until both Bernie and I returned home. I placed the note in my pocket before checking the contents of the box. There was an empty bottle, a mouth organ, a cigarette lighter and a small framed photograph of my parents that I remembered had once stood on the table in the parlour.

"You have to sign for all this," said the duty guard.

I picked up the empty bottle and looked at him accusingly.

"That bottle contained pure alcohol and has been destroyed," said the guard abruptly. "It's not allowed to send such items through the prisoner mail service."

I knew that it must once have contained some of Beckmann's corn spirit because the familiar scent lingered on the cork that had been stuck back into the neck of the bottle.

"Likely bloody story," I muttered, "Which of you bastards drank it?"

"Now don't take that attitude with me, young man," the guard replied as he handed me a pen. "Sign here to say you've collected it."

I reluctantly signed the form, placed the contents back in the box and returned to Mr Davies's van. As we drove back to Pen y Bryn I looked at the things in the box; merely touching them and turning them over in my hands made me feel closer to home. The mouth organ and cigarette lighter, and even the empty bottle, the contents of which had doubtless been drunk by those bastards at Hawkstone Park, had actually been in my house. These ordinary objects confirmed that my family was not a figment of my imagination and that I had a real home to which I would one day return. It was a reality whose existence I had occasionally doubted during the long years of military and prison camp life.

50

By the beginning of 1947 there were no longer any restrictions on our movements and prisoners were more or less free to come and go as they pleased. As a break from life at Pen y Bryn, I would often rendezvous with some of my former fellow inmates, meeting with Luchinger in Oswestry on Saturday evenings when we would catch up with the latest news and rumours: what our respective employment conditions were like, whether we had met any girls, what news we had received from Germany, and of course the perennial topic of when we might be allowed to return home.

It was a relief to be able to speak German once again after spending the working week struggling with the English language, often spoken in incomprehensible accents. While in the local towns, I would often bump into other prisoners of war whom I hadn't previously known. Many had been held in other camps across the region, but were now working in Shropshire and I discovered that some were employed as miners at the local colliery at Ifton, barely three miles away from Pen y Bryn. Through these new-found friends, and their friends in turn, I was able to build up a network of contacts with whom I could share news and information and make life in a foreign land more tolerable.

The work at Pen y Bryn was hard and the hours were long, but to my surprise, I actually began to enjoy farm work. The farm itself was about sixty acres and although it was mainly pasture given over to sheep and cattle grazing, the soil was not so poor that it couldn't support crops of barley, kale and wheat. Mrs Davies was gradually overcoming her initial antipathy towards me, and the younger children treated me like an older brother. Archie in particular treated me almost like a son and I was never excluded from any family activities; if they went to visit relatives I was always invited along, if they had friends for dinner, I would always be given a seat at the table. Living with the Davies family at Pen y Bryn compensated in some measure for the enforced absence from my own family at home.

Although the war had been over for almost two years, many of its effects still lingered. Rationing was one of the most obvious legacies and there were still severe shortages of many items, particularly those things that could not be grown or produced locally and had to be imported. The Davies's however, never seemed to go short of anything, their dinner table was always laden with wholesome food of every kind. Had it not been for the fact that much of my work was physically demanding, I'm sure I would have had to return to the business of punching additional holes in my trouser belt, although on this occasion the additional holes would have been required to loosen rather than tighten it.

As I became more familiar with the workings of the farm and more conversant with the language, I realised that in addition to being a regular farmer, Mr Davies was carrying on a brisk trade in the black market. Farmers at that time were required to sell their produce to the Ministry of Agriculture for a fixed price, but everyone knew that eggs, chicken and milk could be sold at a far greater profit on the black market. I became certain that he must have been carrying on this trade throughout the war years, but probably on a smaller scale, for even the biggest rogues moderated their behaviour in times of national crisis. Now that the war was over, the continuing need for rationing was believed by many to be due to government incompetence rather than any state of emergency, and Archie Davies felt less need for restraint, save that degree which might protect him from prosecution.

As he became more confident of my trust, he began taking me with him on some of his nocturnal trips to sell his produce, usually chickens and eggs to people who lived in the vicinity. Some were local people who just wanted a little extra for a Sunday lunch or for some special occasion, but others were wholesalers and dealers who would in turn sell the produce on for a little extra profit. I was well aware that these activities were illegal, but I wasn't too concerned at being caught, as far as I was concerned it was Mr Davies who was breaking the law, I was merely a prisoner of war assigned to work on his farm and do as I was bid in exchange for two pounds a week and a roof over my head.

We would load his small van at night and drive off to deliver items throughout the Shropshire borders and occasionally, if it was a larger order, as far away as Llangollen and Wrexham. One regular port of call was a public house just over the Welsh border in a small village by the name of Sellatyn. Its proper name was the Cross Keys, but everyone in the area referred to it simply as the 'docks'. It had earned the name for good reason, operating like a commercial port with a steady stream of clients, both sellers and buyers who knew that there was a good possibility that a profitable transaction might take place. Mr Davies told me that business had been going on there throughout the war and that it would have been closed down years ago had the local policeman not been receiving regular bribes.

Safe in the belief that I myself would not get into trouble with the law, I began to actively encourage Archie in his illegal endeavours. Although he was good to me, he had a streak of greed within him, frequently boasting that he made more money from these illicit activities than from regular farm income, and even though he was now using me as his accomplice, he never saw fit to increase my wages. One autumn evening I had accompanied him to some rough pasture about a mile away to shoot rabbits. He knew there were quite a few burrows in that particular field and that the elderly farmer who owned the land wouldn't mind, but that chilly night the rabbits must have been keeping themselves warm in their burrows and after a fruitless hour he decided to call it a night.

"Why worry about shooting a few rabbits?" I volunteered as we trudged for home, "there's plenty of sheep in these fields."

I had said it more or less as a joke, but Archie looked at me with a gleam in his eye. The unsuccessful search for rabbits had certainly been a waste of two hours on a cold evening when we could have been warming our toes by the fire, but a sheep, that was something else. Stealing a sheep was rustling, but I could see him begin to calculate how much he might get for a whole sheep if it could be sold on to the right person. He stopped and was silent for a moment as he looked back across the pasture.

"Go and fetch the van," he said, suddenly.

I took off across the fields, running the mile back to Pen y Bryn where I jumped into the van which had, as usual, been left in the yard with the keys in the ignition. I drove rapidly back down the maze of lanes to where Mr Davies was waiting by the gate to the pasture, shotgun in hand. I got out, leaving the engine running.

"Go on then lad, see if you can catch a good plump one."

"Me?"

"It was your idea," he replied, "I'll wait here by the van."

I recalled the time when Lenz, Reidle, Korff and I had stolen the goat from under the noses of the Wehrmacht on Guernsey. Compared to that dangerous expedition this one would be relatively simple. There were no trip wires with alarm bells and no suspicious armed soldiers with itchy trigger fingers.

Archie opened the back door of the van, placed the shotgun inside and then climbed into the driver's seat. I jumped over the gate and looking across the field, faintly saw in the distance the white shapes of some sheep. I crept slowly towards them and as I came closer, I spotted one of the sheep lying down a little way off from the rest of the flock. I circled around before moving quickly towards it. When I got within a few yards, it must have heard me for with a frightened bleat it began to get to its feet, but I sprang forward and managed to grab it by the rear legs before it could take off into the darkness. It bleated and kicked furiously as I lifted it up, half carrying, half dragging it to the gate where the van was parked. Throwing the frightened animal over the gate, Mr Davies and I wrestled it into the back of the van, then I jumped in after it. After the door was shut, Archie immediately set off, throwing me from side to side in the back as he sped back through the twisting lanes.

Ten minutes later we arrived back at Pen y Bryn where Archie stopped the van in the entrance to one of the fields. We dragged the animal out of the van, quickly slit its throat and held it down on the ground while its life ebbed away in the darkness. We wrapped it in an old blanket and put it back into the van, where it would remain until the following morning when Archie would take it to the local butcher, who would be only too pleased to carve up some local mutton and sell it on with no questions asked. We didn't steal very many animals, but Mr Davies was clearly not above taking a few liberties when the mood took, him and as he increasingly took me into his confidence, I became more involved in his illicit activities.

Beyond the old farmhouse at Pen y Bryn, surrounded by its ancient yews, the land to the south gradually sloped down towards water meadows through which the Shropshire Union canal ran from east to west, forming the farm's southern boundary. In the distance beyond the canal the vast sweep of Welsh hills ran all the way south towards the Criggion Hill, topped with its obelisk, and then on to the rocky Stiperstones before ending with the Long Mynd. The farmhouse itself was very old, parts of it dating from the seventeenth century although there had been many additions and alterations over the years. Archie Davies didn't have much time for sentiment or tradition and he often talked about moving into a modern house, something that would symbolise not the past, but the future, the bright new future to which many of the citizens of a victorious post-war England aspired.

The house may have been old, but the family who lived in it were young and growing. Apart from Joan, the Davies's eldest daughter, there was ten-year-old John, then two more girls, seven-year-old Joy and little Desiree who was just a toddler, and from the expanding bump I could see beneath Mrs Davies's apron, another one was on the way. Space was clearly becoming tight and something would have to be done. Archie Davies was never one to spend a penny of his own money if he could possibly avoid it and though the house was badly in need of some modernisation, very little had been done to it in all the time he had lived there. He often talked of building a completely new house nearby, but always claimed that he couldn't afford to do it. I asked him one day whether the farmhouse was insured. He merely shrugged, but said nothing. However, just like the occasion when I had suggested stealing a sheep, I could see his mind ticking over as he thought of the possibilities. He slapped me on the shoulder as he repeated the word insurance.

He probably wondered why he hadn't thought of that himself. Perhaps there might be a little 'accident' and he would be able to afford a new house after all, and it wouldn't cost him a penny. I suspected that he might ask me to perform the deed and so it proved. Archie was well aware of his reputation as a bit of a rogue in those parts, and needed to establish a firm alibi so that when the 'accident' happened, he would be able to say with a clear conscience that he had not even been at the farm and therefore could have had nothing to do with it. What better alibi than to be seen at the cattle market in Oswestry when disaster struck at Pen y Bryn?

And so Archie schemed and plotted. He reckoned that the likeliest cause of an accident would be a fire caused by the old paraffin stove in the kitchen, which had seen better days and in the damp winter months was responsible for the noxious fumes liable to give anyone a headache if they spent too much time in the room. He mentioned his plan to me one day and seemed surprised when I refused point blank to do it. Stealing the odd sheep was one thing, but burning down a house was something else. What if someone was injured or even killed, I would be the one who ended up in jail. I could see that Archie was determined to carry out the plan so I agreed to help, but insisted that I would not be the one to light the match.

It was arranged for the accident to take place on a Wednesday morning. Archie would make sure that Mrs Davies and the children were out of the way, then he would light the fire and go into Oswestry to the cattle-market as he often did and ensure that he spoke to, and was seen by, as many people as possible. I would remain at Pen y Bryn and make sure that things went smoothly.

No-one else, not even Mrs Davies, knew of the plan, so in order to get them out of the way, Archie arranged for them to visit some neighbours that morning. I removed my few precious items from my bedroom, the photograph of my parents, my mouth organ and some clothes, and hid them in the barn. Fortunately the chosen day turned out to be dry and blustery. Archie dropped Mrs Davies and the children off at the neighbours' about a mile away and returned to Pen y Bryn.

He had rehearsed the plan well and went into the kitchen with a small jar of paraffin, which he sprinkled onto an old towel and placed on top of the old heater so that the end was left hanging in front of the flame.

"This would be a lot simpler if you just lit it when I was already at the market,' Archie said.

I merely smiled. I had no intention of doing so; if he wanted to burn his own house down, that was his business.

He muttered under his breath something about my ingratitude, but set to work putting the towel in place so that it would gradually heat up and eventually catch light. Satisfied that everything was at last in position, we left the kitchen. I made my way over to the milking parlour while he jumped into his van and drove at breakneck speed into town.

I certainly wasn't going to go back and check on his rudimentary incendiary device, but nevertheless kept looking over towards the house to see if I could see any sign of smoke or fire. Almost half an hour had elapsed before I saw the first wisps of smoke coming through the partially open kitchen window. As the smoke increased, I was alarmed to hear the sound of voices. For some reason Mrs Davies and the younger children had returned from the neighbours' house early. I ran out into the yard as they approached. I could think of nothing to do except throw out my arms and blurt out that the house was on fire and that they shouldn't go near. Mrs Davies and the children looked at me as if I had taken leave of my senses.

The smoke emanating from the kitchen window had now increased and I could now see that flames were licking against the curtains. She watched in horror and tried to get past me towards the house, but I held her back. She escaped my grasp and ran across the yard to the door, but I managed to catch her once again before she could enter.

"It's too dangerous!" I shouted, holding her tightly as she struggled once again to get free.

I was less concerned for her physical safety than the fact that she might well have succeeded in putting out the fire before it could spread to the rest of the house.

She continued to struggle as I held onto her to prevent her going inside. I could feel that the heat inside was becoming intense and I managed to pull her away from the door.

"Get the fire brigade," she shouted at last.

I must have looked at her blankly.

"For God's sake run to the neighbours and get them to phone the fire-brigade."

After warning them not to go anywhere near the house, I made a pretence of running to the neighbouring farm, but as soon as I was out of sight I stopped running and slowed to the pace of a leisurely walk. I reached the neighbouring farmhouse about thirty minutes later and asked them to call the fire brigade, but by then I could clearly see the smoke from Pen y Bryn billowing among the yew trees and drifting across the fields. It took the fire brigade another half hour to arrive from Oswestry and by then the fire had thoroughly taken hold of the old farmhouse. Even then, almost an hour after the fire had started, they were able to prevent the entire house from being destroyed, managing to contain the blaze to that half of the house where it had begun.

As the firemen were damping down and clearing up, Archie's van screeched to a halt in the yard. Feigning shock at the disaster that had befallen his home, he jumped out of the vehicle and ran over to his wife, hugging her and the children who had been running around in a state of high excitement and generally getting in the way of the firemen. In full view of the firemen and the neighbouring farmer who had summoned them, tears ran down Archie's cheeks in a performance of which a professional actor would have been proud. The fire had left the farmhouse a chaotic jumble of charred timber, collapsed masonry and pools of black, ash-filled water. Pen y Bryn had been saved, but only just.

For a few months after the fire the family went to stay at a neighbouring farm until things could be sorted out. Part of the house still remained habitable, although there was nowhere to cook or wash. Archie and I continued to live in the undamaged part of the house and a week later, after Archie had submitted the claim, the man from the insurance company came out to assess the damage. A faulty paraffin heater was deemed to be the cause of the fire and the insurance company duly paid out on the policy. Archie now had enough money to build a new house and reckoned that he could, with a bit of demolition here and a spot of repair there, also rehabilitate Pen y Bryn. It wouldn't be as spacious as before, but it would still make a perfectly comfortable smaller house.

The money went into Archie's bank account, but no work began on the new house. Pen y Bryn was repaired and the family eventually moved back in. The children had to double up, but I was able to re-occupy the attic room as I had before.

51

My reward for helping set the house on fire was an old
motorbike that Archie bought for me instead of giving me an
increase in my pay. The bike, an old 250cc Rudge had
clearly seen better days, but it had a good engine and by the
time I had finished polishing the chrome and touching up
the paintwork, it shone like new. That motorbike was my
pride and joy and it gave me a wonderful sense of freedom,
no longer would I have to rely on lifts from Archie or stand
in the rain for hours waiting for the bus, now I could go
wherever I pleased, whenever I pleased.

I was becoming reasonably fluent in the language
although my accent still occasionally caused some
confusion. My English had improved mainly because of the
efforts of Joan because night after night she would sit with
me after the evening meal and go through books, magazines
and newspapers making sure that I understood the words
and the grammar. We were spending a great deal of time
together and despite the difference in our ages, I felt closer
to her than anyone else in the family. Once I had the
motorbike I would often take her out on Sunday afternoons,
despite her mother's grave misgivings about the safety of
her riding on the pillion seat. We would roar off into the
mountains of Wales or sometimes up to the coast, visiting
Rhyl or Llandudno which were only a couple of hours ride
away from Pen y Bryn. The sight of the sea on those days

brought back memories of the last time I had seen it in Guernsey over three years earlier and before that in Cherbourg.

I enjoyed Joan's company and we had a great deal of fun whenever we were together, but I was gradually becoming aware that my feelings towards her were beginning to change. I had been living under the same roof for two years and it felt as if I were part of the family, treating her in much the same way as a brother might treat a younger sister, but I was not part of the family and Joan was not my sister, she was an attractive girl of almost seventeen, almost a woman and she seemed to me to get prettier by the day. Our relationship changed forever one night in September.

As they were up every morning before six, the Davies's were in the habit of going to bed early. The younger children were usually in bed by eight, but Archie and his wife would regularly go upstairs at ten o'clock leaving Joan and I downstairs in the parlour either talking, reading or listening to the wireless. I wasn't a big drinker, but Archie liked a couple of glasses of whisky in the evening and one night he had left an almost full bottle on the dresser. I decided to pour myself a glass and also a small one for Joan who was sitting on the floor as she often did. I handed her the glass, but as I did so, it slipped from her fingers and fell to the floor, spilling the contents down her dress. I grabbed a cloth and attempted to wipe it off, my hands brushing against her breasts. I had done it so spontaneously and un-self consciously that it wasn't until she gave me a look of surprise at my actions that I realised what I was doing. In my embarrassment, I dropped the cloth, quickly grabbed her in my arms and kissed her fully on the lips.

We both knew that a boundary had been crossed and that a return to our former relationship would be impossible. She had responded fully when I kissed her and I knew then that she too had the same feelings towards me. There could be no more pretence, no more playing at brother and sister and yet, as far as the rest of the world was concerned it had to appear that was the case for we instinctively knew that our relationship would have to remain a secret one. Things continued much the same as before, but we took extra care not to be seen too often together around the farm and though the English lessons continued as before, we rarely stayed up much later than her parents. The only time we could truly be together was on those occasions when we climbed on my motorbike for a Sunday outing where, beyond the watchful eyes of her parents and the other children, we could give full expression to our passion.

Living a lie was an exquisite form of torture. I wanted to be with her, to touch her, hold her, kiss her, but as we both went about our daily lives at Pen y Bryn for the most part I could only watch her. So conscious were we of hiding our true feelings that it must have seemed to everyone else in the house that we were more distant than normal, a little cooler towards each other, perhaps because of some kind of disagreement. Like a thief with a guilty secret I expected at any moment to be confronted by her parents. Each time Archie or Joan's mother spoke to me, I caught my breath wondering if this was the moment they had chosen to confront me with the revelation that they suspected what was going on.

52

The summer of 1948 drew to a close and I still met regularly with Luchinger and some of the other ex-prisoners in the Oswestry pubs where talk was of little else save the rumour that we would at last being allowed to visit our families in Germany. At first we had heard that we were being allowed to return home for good, but we later learned that this had been changed to a one month visit. We would be allowed to go, but only in exchange for a signed undertaking that we would return to our jobs in England afterwards.

It had been more than four years since I had last set foot in my homeland. Four years ago I had been a carefree eighteen year-old, eager to see the world and to play a small part in the victory that would surely be ours. Now at the end of 1948 I would at last be allowed to return, but the world had changed since I boarded the train for France what seemed to be a lifetime ago. The victorious German armies that had swept all before it, conquering territory from the Atlantic shores to the Russian steppes, had been shattered and broken. Divided up between the victors, Germany would be as unrecognisable from the place I had left as I was myself. I had done and seen things during those years that had turned me into a man and strangely, I was filled with trepidation about my return home which would surely be little more than a meeting between two strangers.

After weeks of speculation we finally received official

confirmation that we would be allowed home just after Christmas. We were to be allowed one month and would be provided with free transport warrants in exchange for a signed undertaking that we would return to our jobs in England. A few days after receiving the news Luchinger told me that he had run into Georg Segerer a couple of weeks earlier and that he was in a bad way. Word had got round that some prisoners of war would at last be allowed home to visit their families, but it had been difficult for him and the others from the eastern part of Germany now under Russian control to take. They had never received any letters from their families, no little parcels at Christmas as the rest of us had and now many of their comrades were going home. It must have seemed to them as if their previous lives had never been. There would be no happy homecoming for them.

I excitedly told Joan that I would soon be returning home to see my family, but I promised that I would return to see her at the end of the month regardless of whether or not I had given any written guarantee to the authorities. She appeared doubtful, but understood that I could not possibly pass up this opportunity to see my family once again. I duly collected my rail warrant for the special train that would be leaving three days after Christmas and signed the undertaking to return to England and my job at Pen y Bryn. I spent most of Christmas Day with the Davies family, but in the afternoon I met up with Luchinger and gave him a lift on my motorbike the five miles to Mile End to see some of the men who were still living there.

The place was eerily quiet. The guardhouse was deserted, the commandant's quarters and most of the huts lay empty and forlorn, weeds sprouting in profusion from the rusty guttering. Only fifty men still lived there, most had jobs outside, but for one reason or another had either been unable to find accommodation or had simply chosen to remain at the camp, one of these was Georg Segerer who worked at a sawmill in Oswestry. I had brought some slices of some of Mrs Davies's fruit cake for the men and when I found Segerer in his hut I gave him some of the slices. He seemed to have aged since I last saw him, he was only in his early forties, but his hair had turned completely grey and his eyes were little more than dull, cloudy pools. I couldn't help but notice that his collection of carvings had grown considerably. They were not only arranged on a table near his bed, but were distributed on various tables and shelves all around the hut, there were dozens of them and all were figurines. Most represented the Madonna though some were of Christ while others were figurines of various small children. All the figures were beautifully carved, the arms and legs smooth and polished, the folds of their robes exquisitely crafted, but the faces of all of them were filled with anguish and torment.

He asked me whether I was going back to Germany the following week with the others and when I replied that I was, he made me promise to come back upon my return and tell him about everything I had seen and asked me whether I could find out how things were in the east. Promising to see him the moment I returned, he pressed a small, carved wooden crucifix in my hand.

"Give it to your mother." He said

I left the hut to go and look for Luchinger, but I would never return to see Georg Segerer again for that night he hanged himself.

Joan and I said our private tearful farewells, despite my assurances, she was still not convinced that I would ever return to Pen y Bryn. Archie took me to the railway station at nearby Gobowen where I met up with the others and we boarded the train that took us the twenty miles to Shrewsbury where another special train was waiting to take all the ex-prisoners to Harwich. There must have been more than five-hundred men milling about on the station platform at Shrewsbury when I arrived, they had come from all over the Welsh Marches, from Cheshire, Shropshire, Herefordshire and various parts of Wales. Men who had not seen one another since they had lived in the same camps years before, shook hands and hugged each other. There was great excitement as men exchanged their stories and compared their varying degrees of fortune.

I walked up and down the platform among the swarm of men, searching for any familiar faces. As I neared the end of the platform, I felt a hand clasp me on the shoulder. I spun round. It was Korff. We embraced one another, excitement at the forthcoming journey heightened by our unexpected reunion. As the engine blew its whistle and vented a great cloud of steam, we climbed aboard. Luchinger, Korff and I found a compartment and settled down for the journey. We told stories; played cards, showed each other the gifts we had bought for our families and boasted of how many girls we had made love to while in England and how many more we would make love to when we reached home.

At Harwich we boarded the steamer, joined by hundreds more men who had arrived from different parts of England and Scotland. It was too much to hope that we might run into Lenz or Reidle, but Korff and I searched nonetheless, scouring every deck and cabin on the vessel from stem to stern. We had no success and concluded that it would have been typical of those lucky bastards to have been sent back to Germany right after the war, probably finding themselves cushy little jobs near their homes while we were left to rot in the prison camps.

The steamer eventually docked in Rotterdam and we boarded the train that would take us to Germany. The devastation in the port city was unimaginable, even three years after the war had ended, vast swathes still lay in ruins. A collective silence hung over the carriage as we looked out over scenes of desolation, whole areas of the city were little more than piles of rubble and if this were Holland then I wondered how much worse it must be in defeated Germany. The train left the ruins of Rotterdam behind and trundled onwards without stopping, steaming eastwards across the flat, dyke-filled terrain of western Holland which gradually gave way to the sandy, undulating wooded landscape closer to the German border. Night fell as we crossed into Germany, I was home at last. I peered out through the window, but all I could see was darkness and my own reflection in the window.

The train pulled into Munster at dawn. The station platforms were a chaotic mass of returning soldiers dragging cases and packs. Some men were moving swiftly towards the exits, but most were searching for connecting trains that would scatter them to the various parts of Germany. Luchinger bade me farewell as he moved off to find a train that would take him home to Duisburg, while Korff gave me his address in Stuttgart before disappearing into the crowd. He had told me on the boat that regardless of any undertaking, he couldn't face making the return journey and was fully prepared to accept whatever the authorities might do if he failed to return. I realised then that I might never see him again.

From Munster, the journey to my home was a relatively short one, Lippstadt lay only a couple of hours away by train and from there it was only a short hop to the village halt at Benninghausen where my family would be waiting. It was early afternoon when the train finally pulled into the small halt at Benninghausen. Feeling almost sick with excitement and anxiety, I climbed down from the carriage, dropped my case on to the platform and looked around. The place was deserted except for a man and two boys standing at the far end of the platform. I couldn't quite make out who they were from a distance, but picked up my battered case and walked slowly towards them. His hair was greyer, the small moustache had been shaved off and the worry lines were deeper, but as I approached I could see that it was my father. We approached one another then stopped for a moment, then finally ran towards one another for the final few yards and embraced as tears streamed down our cheeks.

The two boys looked on, embarrassed at the sight of their father crying and hugging this stranger on the station platform. When my father finally released me from his grip, I looked down at them. Heinz had been nine when I last saw him and Eugen just five, Heinz was now a gangly teenager and Eugen a tousle-haired boy of almost nine. They eyed me warily, their world for the past five years had not included any older brothers and now this stranger, considerably older than either of them, had suddenly arrived to interrupt the normal order of things. Doubtless my mother and father had often spoken of me, but they had probably also spoken of Bernie and he had not returned. In a child's mind where reality and imagination often blur, they must have wondered whether any of us existed at all, thinking perhaps that any older brothers were merely a figment of their parents' imagination.

Beckum is only a half hour walk from Benninghausen and the four of us proceeded to walk there on foot, Heinz and

Eugen taking it in turns to struggle with my case. We walked past the woods and fields where I had played as a boy, past my old school which Heinz and Eugen now attended and then past Brandt's which stood at the crossroads in the middle of the village. Everything was just as I remembered it, yet strangely everything seemed somehow smaller, the distances between places seemed shorter and what had seemed to be steep hills now seemed gentle. When I had left, I knew everyone in the village and everyone knew me and although I saw some familiar faces who called out to me and waved, there were many unfamiliar faces, more recent arrivals who had arrived from the east.

At last we arrived at the house. My sister Wilhemina was waiting on the front door step to greet me. Now a young woman of nineteen, she was unrecognisable from the scrawny teenager I had known. As we hugged and kissed, my mother came to the door. She had aged in my absence. Small and wiry as she had always been, her hair had turned completely grey and deep, dark lines furrowed her brow. When I embraced her tightly, she felt frail and insubstantial in my arms. She wiped away her tears and ushered me inside.

My mother had felt the loss of Hans who had died five years earlier, but she had been able to come to terms with the death of her eldest son. She had also accepted the fact that I was being held a prisoner for she knew that I was safe and well and would eventually return home. What she had not been able to accept was the continued absence of Bernie, it consumed her waking thoughts and made it impossible to enjoy her other blessings. For the past three years my father had written countless letters and made innumerable journeys to government offices in a vain quest for information. He had not been alone. The families of thousands of men who were also missing in action had also carried out a desperate search, seeking any scrap of information that might allow the nightmare of uncertainty to end. The effect of this on my mother was clearly visible; she was only forty-six, but looked a good ten years older.

Compared to many families the Terhorsts had survived the war fairly well. Our home had not been destroyed, my father still had a job and there were still four surviving children. My parents knew that they were fortunate compared to others, some families in the village had lost all their sons, yet grief knows no logic and the thought that someone has suffered a greater loss, does nothing to diminish one's own. There were many rumours that the Russians had failed to repatriate large numbers of German prisoners after the war had ended and that even now, thousands were toiling away in Siberian slave camps. Rumours such as these only served to aggravate a wound that would not heal.

Stories of the difficulties in the Russian controlled sector of Germany and the whereabouts of German soldiers taken prisoner during the war pervaded the country. It was increasingly apparent that the Russians wanted to make the partition of the country permanent for they had already tried to bring Berlin completely under their control by denying access via land to the British and Americans. No official communication ever came out of the eastern sector and there seemed little hope of re-uniting the families split by the Russian occupation and an impenetrable wall of silence greeted any enquiry about the whereabouts of soldiers who had served in the east. The Russians it seemed, would never forgive the German people.

Despite everything, it was still good to be home. My parents treated me like the prodigal son and spared nothing to ensure that I was as comfortable as possible. It seemed that my mother was preparing food every day in readiness for visits by aunts, uncles and cousins. Friends, neighbours and sometimes complete strangers were invited into the house for drinks to help the Terhorst family celebrate the return of their son. I spent my time relating my adventures in France and the Channel Islands, about how I had been treated as a prisoner in England and what I had been doing since my release from the prison camp. As my health was repeatedly toasted, I was wished well for the future and asked when I would be coming home for good. Though I told them that I had to return to England for the time being because of the regulations, I did not mention Joan, I wasn't even sure myself what might become of it, but I knew that despite the fact that I was once again back among my own people, I was missing her.

The month at home ended all too quickly, the days had been filled with parties and outings and the tearful farewells were never easy, but the time had come to go back. Returning to England was much easier for me than for some of the other ex-prisoners and I wondered how many would prove unable to tear themselves away from their families to make the return journey. As I sat on the train headed once more to Munster, I reflected on the past month, it had been good to be home in familiar surroundings, but there had also been the unfamiliar. The men of the village, the boys with whom I had gone to school, and played football in the Youth were no longer there and although physically intact, the scars of the village were clear for all to see. The pain was present in the faces of everyone who no longer had a son, a husband or a father. I had been welcomed home, but I had sensed the silent reproaches of those less fortunate who secretly cursed me for being alive.

53

By the time I returned to Pen y Bryn, it was early February and Archie seemed genuinely pleased and a little surprised to see me. He must have wondered whether or not I would actually return, but didn't say anything. I had no way of knowing whether he suspected that the real reason I had returned was not out of any sense of honour or because of the undertaking I had signed, but because of his eldest daughter. Joan was in the house when I got back, but it was many hours before I finally got the chance to see her on her own. She had feigned a certain disinterest in my return until that moment, but when we were finally alone, she poured out her heart with a young girl's anxiety, confiding that there had been times during the past weeks when she thought she might never see me again.

It had taken my return from Germany to confirm in her eyes that I was serious about her and although we had to continue with the pretence that our relationship was platonic while her family was around, it was becoming increasingly difficult to hide our feelings for one another. We would spend every free moment that we had together, going for walks across the fields or along by the canal. We talked to each other every single day and would remain sitting downstairs for hours after the rest of the family had gone to bed.

Women notice these things quicker than men and so it

was that three weeks after I had returned from Germany, Mrs Davies finally confronted her daughter with the accusation that she had been 'carrying on' with me. It would have been impossible to hide our feelings for one another for much longer and in truth I was surprised that it had taken either of her parents so long to notice that we had become much more than mere friends. Joan had denied it, but told me what her mother had said although surprisingly Mrs Davies never said a word to me. It was clear however that things could not continue as they had without some kind of confrontation and it was not long in coming.

One day while helping Archie with the milking he suddenly asked me about my intentions regarding his daughter. I was caught off guard and without stopping to think of the consequences, I blurted out that I was going to ask her to marry me.

The colour drained from his face. He stood up from his task as he digested what I had said.

"You're not going to have her!" he finally bellowed, the colour returning to his cheeks, which were now bright with anger and indignation.

I stood my ground even though he stood a good twelve inches taller than me.

"Don't you think I'm good enough?" I replied.

I could see that he was about to say 'no', but he hesitated.

"I didn't say that, but you aren't going to have her."

With that he turned on his heel and stalked out.

I finished the milking, washed myself off and went over to the farmhouse for breakfast as I normally did. I was greeted by a stony silence as I entered the kitchen. Archie had his head buried in the newspaper while Mrs Davies was busy at the stove. Joan wasn't there.

"She's upstairs packing." said Mrs Davies in reply to my

unspoken question and she put a plate of bacon and eggs in front of me.

"Packing?"

"That's right, packing. She's leaving."

"Leaving?… Where to?"

"Somewhere you won't be able to find her." Archie interjected, peering over the top of his newspaper.

"I'll soon find her." I said and got up leaving my breakfast uneaten. I went out into the yard and lit a cigarette. I was angry, but not surprised. I had been foolish to think that we could have kept our relationship secret, but I had suspected all along that they would have objections even though in many respects they had treated me with great kindness. For almost three years I had eaten with the family, played with the family and for the most part been treated like one of the family, but now I had become involved with their precious daughter, the true nature of the relationship was revealed. Now I was no longer a member of the family, I wasn't even as high in the pecking order as an ordinary worker; I was a German prisoner of war, the lowest of the low. I was merely cheap help on the farm and had no realistic prospect of getting any other job than a farm labourer, what's more I might well be deported and sent back to Germany at any time. Neither wonder they didn't see me as much of a catch for their precious daughter. I kicked the barn door in anger and frustration.

I lit another cigarette and pondered my next move, wondering whether to go in and argue my case with them or whether I should just pack my bags and leave. They clearly had better ambitions for their daughter than she should marry the likes of me. There were many wealthy farmers in the district with sons who might well have found a beautiful girl like Joan to their taste. Perhaps I had been stupid to return to England, I should have listened to my father and stayed at home in Germany. No doubt I would have soon forgotten all about Pen y Bryn, the Davies family and their daughter.

My thoughts were interrupted by the sound of raised voices and crying, I went across the yard to the side of the house just in time to see Mrs Davies bundling Joan into the back of their car. Archie threw a small suitcase into the boot, climbed in and, without so much as a glance in my direction sped off down the lane. When Mr and Mrs Davies returned later that evening without Joan, they barely spoke a word. Angry and upset though I was, I was determined not to give them the satisfaction of seeing me beg them to tell me where they had taken her. I was confident that I would find out sooner or later. It turned out to be much sooner than I thought, for later that evening when I went to bed I discovered a folded piece of paper under my pillow. As upset as Joan had been, she'd had the presence of mind to leave a message for me before she was taken away. The note said that she was being sent to stay with an uncle who lived on a remote sheep farm high in the Welsh hills some fifty miles away.

The following morning I began my work as usual, not returning to the house until breakfast time. Archie was once again buried in the morning paper while Mrs Davies was busy cooking breakfast.

"Morning!" I said, determined to act as normally as possible and not be the first to raise the subject of their daughter's absence.

"You'll not be seeing her again." Mrs Davies announced triumphantly as she put my breakfast plate on the table

"It's not all that far to her uncle's house," I replied.

She spun round.

"How...how do you know where she is?" she asked indignantly.

I just smiled and carried on eating.

"Well...well you won't be seeing her again." she blustered.

The meal was finished in complete silence then I got up and went to my room. I certainly wasn't going to remain in the kitchen with the two of them pretending that nothing had happened. I lay on my bed smoked a cigarette and thought the matter over, wondering what I should do, indeed wondering what I could do. I concluded that despite Archie Davies's undoubted cunning, he and his wife must be fools if they believed that sending her fifty miles away to her uncle could prevent me from seeing her again. I wondered what they proposed to do in the long term – surely they couldn't leave her indefinitely in the wilds of Wales. The most likely option was to quickly marry her off to someone else... or to get rid of me.

I went to bed that night plotting my strategy. I knew that I wasn't a good catch for their daughter, but the fact that they had taken her away so abruptly, concentrated my mind and made me realise just how strong my feelings for her were. I resolved either to make her mine or leave Pen y Bryn and leave England altogether, with or without permission, but first of all I had to see her again and this I planned to do the following Sunday when I would take my motorbike and ride into the Welsh hills. I had gone beyond the point of caring what her parents would think of my actions or indeed what they might do about it.

My plans proved unnecessary, for to my surprise and that of her parents, she returned to Pen y Bryn on Saturday afternoon. Her Uncle Pryce, Mrs Davies's brother had driven her home and Archie and his wife were less than pleased by this turn of events. I wasn't in the farmhouse when she arrived, but she told me later that an almighty row had broken out between her parents and her uncle who had taken pity on her and brought her home because she had been in tears for almost the entire week. Archie Davies had ranted and raved, but her uncle had refused point blank to take her back with him, insisting that the girl belonged at home and that if there were any problems they should be resolved there.

When I eventually saw her alone for a few moments later that evening, I explained that I had found her note and that I had planned to come and see her the next day. I also told her that I had made up my mind that if I could not have her, then I would leave Pen y Bryn forever. It was then that I told her that I wanted to marry her. Even though we both knew that she could not marry without her parents' consent she said yes and said she would wait no matter how long it might take. We waited to see what her parents intended to do next, perhaps they would send her away again, if not to her uncle then somewhere else, for they had many relatives elsewhere in Wales. I was well aware that there was also nothing to stop them from sending me away as well, but it seemed that I had little option other than to bide my time. During the following week, Joan and I stayed out of each other's way as much as possible, exchanging only smiles and a few words when no one was about.

During the following weeks, her parents' anger seemed to abate, perhaps they hoped that the shock of sending Joan away had brought us both to our senses and that any fanciful ideas we may have had about each other had disappeared. They clearly remained suspicious however and I felt that our every move was being watched, but on the few occasions when we did have the opportunity to talk, Joan and I re-affirmed our love for one another and our determination one day to get married, no matter what her parents or anyone else thought. After three weeks I decided that the time had come to act for it seemed likely that as soon as we stepped out of line then one of us would surely be sent away. My understanding of the language was still sketchy and my knowledge of the law in England almost non-existent, but I knew enough to know that seventeen year old girls were not free to marry without their parents' permission and that this wasn't likely to be forthcoming. I realised that something would have to be done to resolve the situation and that if Joan's parents were not going to take any action, then it would fall to me.

Bill Holland was a neighbouring farmer who had feuded with Archie Davies over many years. I had done a few odd jobs for him over the past two years and he had paid me generously. He had often told me that if I ever needed anything, I should go and see him and I decided that the time was now. I had no idea whether he could help me with my problem, but I knew that I could at least ask him without word getting back to Pen y Bryn.

Bill heard me out and then, as I suspected, advised me that it would be impossible for Joan to get married without her parents consent and furthermore she would not be able to marry without such consent for another four years. He offered to get me the necessary consent forms, but I couldn't imagine how Joan's parents would ever be persuaded to agree to sign them. It would be years until Joan would be old enough to marry without their consent and we both knew that we could never wait that long. I wrestled with the problem for days until I came to the conclusion that they could not be persuaded to agree and that left only one course of action open to me.

I was rapidly discovering that in love as in war there are no rules. Norms of behaviour are ignored in the name of expediency, men are forced by circumstance to take whatever action they need to survive and I knew that I could not survive unless I was with Joan. Bill Holland duly got the forms and helped me to fill them out. When they were complete with the exception of the all important signatures, I took them back to Pen y Bryn and hid them in my room. I told Joan what I had done and what I proposed to do. I awaited my opportunity that came late one evening when all the children had gone to bed and Archie and his wife were sitting at the kitchen table.

"I've got a form for you to sign." I said, entering the kitchen. I placed it in front of Archie. He picked it up and read it carefully; probably thinking it was something to do with my Aliens Order registration. His expression changed as he read the form and realised what it was.

"I'm not signing that!" he said, tossing the form back to me. I picked it up without saying a word and handed it to Mrs Davies.

"I'm not signing either." she sniffed, when she had finished reading it.

Their reaction didn't surprise me in the least, but I had wanted to give them both an opportunity to change their minds without resorting to coercion, but their intransigence strengthened my resolve.

Struggling to keep my anger under control, I gave them a piece of my mind;

"I came here to Pen y Bryn almost three years ago. I'm honest and I've worked hard and don't forget that it was you who invited me to live under the same roof. It seems that I'm good enough to share meals with you, good enough to look after the children, but not good enough to marry your daughter. I love your daughter and she loves me, so this is what's going to happen if you don't sign the form. Tomorrow morning I'm going to the police station and I will tell them all about your deals on the black market and the theft of your neighbour's sheep.

Mrs Davies glared at her husband.

"You wouldn't dare." Archie blustered. "You've got just as much to lose as I have."

"I have nothing to lose, the only thing I want from you is permission to marry Joan. If I don't have that, then I don't care what happens to me. Don't forget that I'm already a prisoner, I've been locked up before, so don't think for one moment that I wouldn't do it."

I pushed the form in front of him once again thrusting a pen into his hand, but still he hesitated.

"Then there's always the little matter of the fire and the insurance company." I said.

Archie looked horrified.

"What insurance?" Mrs Davies demanded.

"Nothing! Its nothing." Archie said, shifting uncomfortably in the chair.

He sat still for a few moments, twisting the pen in his fingers.

"Don't think I won't do it." I said.

"You'll go to jail too." he said.

I laughed. "I've been in prison camps and suffered things you can't imagine. Don't think for one moment that one of your jails holds any fears for me."

He knew he was beaten and scribbled his signature on the bottom of the form.

54

Blackmailing your future parents-in-law is not the ideal way to begin a marriage. The consent forms had been signed and we were now free to marry, but what Joan's father saw as my treachery, soured the atmosphere. Conversation was strictly functional and even the younger children were quieter than usual, their bubbling conversations curtailed by the tense, brittle air which pervaded the old farmhouse. Despite all this, I felt that a weight had been lifted from my shoulders, no longer would Joan and I have to hide our feelings in front of anyone, or steal away in order to enjoy a few snatched moments of intimacy.

Her parents were clearly in no mood to forgive us and the following weeks were filled with a series of rows between Joan and her father. Things finally came to a head after yet another row when Archie stormed out of the room and told her to pack her bags and leave. She came to me in tears to tell me what had happened.

"You'd better do as your father says!" I told her. "I know where we can go."

While she went up to her room to pack her suitcase, I threw a few of my things into a small bag then went downstairs and out through the kitchen door without even glancing at her parents. A squally wind rustled the branches of the yews around the farmhouse, blowing sheets of rain across the fields. I took her case, then her hand and we made our way up the lane, leaning into the wind until we reached the door of Bill Holland's house. When he came to the door and saw us standing on his doorstep, wet and bedraggled with bags in our hands, it didn't require a lot of explanation.

"Archie's thrown you out has he? He said, ushering us inside. "The stubborn old bugger. Well you two just come inside and dry yourselves off."

His wife came through into the hall to see who it was.

"You can stay as long as you like," said Mrs Holland , after we told them what had happened. She went to make us a hot cup of tea while I told Bill that I had managed to get the Archie's signature on the consent form.

"I don't know how you managed that, lad." he said

I thought it best not to go into great detail about my methods, the secrets of Archie Davies had stood me in good stead once and they might do so again.

Bill and his wife didn't have any children so there were plenty of spare rooms in the rambling old farmhouse and they offered us the use of two of them. I told him that Archie would go mad when he found out that Joan and I were staying there, but he merely laughed and slapped me on the back.

"Archie doesn't own this place, lad. He doesn't tell me who I can have to stay under my own roof. I'm not worried about him and neither should you be."

I think he was secretly pleased that we had arrived, for it was an opportunity for him to get back at his rival. It didn't however take Archie too long to work out where we had gone and on our second evening at the Holland's he turned up to remonstrate with Bill, but his neighbour was having none of it. He told Archie that it was none of his business who stayed in his house and that his daughter was free to return home any time she chose, reminding him that he had been the one who had thrown her out in the first place. Archie's appearance at his door gave Bill a splendid opportunity to tell his neighbour a few home truths, which he had evidently been bottling up for some time. He told him that it was about time he grew up and acted more responsibly towards his family, adding that he should be thankful that his daughter wanted to marry such a fine, hard-working young man.

Archie stormed off, but when he had gone Bill told me that he was in such a foul mood that he was capable of doing anything, possibly even going to the police and accusing me of abducting his daughter. As she was still a minor in the eyes of the law, he suggested that it would be a good idea if I went to the police first and told them what had happened. It made sense; for if I had learned one thing about Joan's father, it was that he was completely unpredictable and liable to act on impulse without thinking things through. If he did report me to the police, I might find myself in lot of trouble.

First thing the following morning I went straight to the police station in Oswestry and told the desk sergeant my story. He heard me out and then placed a call to the newly installed telephone at Pen y Bryn, asking Mr Davies to come down to the station as soon as possible. Archie appeared an hour later acknowledging me only with a glare and it appeared his mood was little better than it had been the day before. I was revelling in his discomfort for he was clearly uncertain why I had gone there and must have wondered whether I might have mentioned anything about his black market and rustling activities. He seemed somewhat relieved when the sergeant told him that the matter only concerned his daughter and that he wanted to ascertain that everything I had told him was true. He nodded that it was and the sergeant reminded him that he had certain responsibilities as a parent of a legal minor and that he should think about asking his daughter to return to the family home as soon as possible.

The sergeant added that if he didn't want his daughter to see me anymore then he shouldn't have signed the consent forms and terminated my employment rather than throw his daughter out of the house. Archie struggled to keep his temper. Yesterday he'd had a dressing down from Bill Holland and today he was getting one from the police sergeant...and it was entirely my fault. He nevertheless promised the sergeant that he would allow Joan and I to return, but having us back and being on speaking terms was quite another matter.

The following day Joan and I packed our cases once again, thanked Bill and his wife for allowing us to stay and also for his good advice before we walked the short distance back to Pen y Bryn. We decided that the best thing was to proceed with the wedding as soon as possible, for once the deed was done there could be no more arguments over it and things might return to a semblance of normality. Joan and I made our plans, any kind of traditional family wedding in church was completely out of the question, we would have to marry in the local registry office, so arrangements were made and the date was set.

The day of our wedding dawned cold and damp; mist enveloped the branches of the yews outside my bedroom window and hung thick over the lower fields down by the canal. I dressed in the only coat I possessed, an old checked sports jacket with leather patches on the elbows that I had picked up from a second-hand shop in Wrexham. A white shirt with a red and blue striped tie, a pair of beige, flannel trousers and some brown brogues completed my ensemble.

Joan wore a long brown coat with a fake fur collar over a pale blue dress that she had been given by an aunt.

Her mother had barely spoken a word to either of us since we had returned from Bill Holland's and she made it abundantly clear that she would have absolutely nothing to do with the wedding. Archie on the other hand seemed to have reconciled himself to what was about to take place although he too had told us that he would not be attending the wedding. My motorbike had unfortunately broken down earlier that week which meant that we would have to catch the bus into Oswestry. To my surprise, Archie agreed to take us in his car, but despite the pleas of his daughter, he refused to come in to the Registry Office

Bill Holland had agreed to be our best man and was already waiting for us outside. I would have liked Luchinger to perform this task, but realised that like me, he was subject to the provisions of an Alien Order and would not have been able to act as an official witness. In any case he had been transferred to another colliery some distance away and everything had been so hurried that I had not been able to get in touch with him to tell him about the wedding.

Joan clung tightly to my arm throughout the brief procedure. This was not what she or I could ever have envisioned our wedding day to be like. Instead of a church filled with smiling, familiar faces with our closest relatives looking on admiringly, all we had was a cold, virtually empty room and only the familiar face of the neighbouring farmer. We were duly declared man and wife by the registrar and then, as the pubs had just opened, together with Bill, we went along the road to the Golden Tankard where he treated us to a celebratory drink. He then drove us back to Pen y Bryn.

When we entered the house, Mrs Davies was busy in the

kitchen. Archie was nowhere to be seen. As we entered she turned round and said;

"I hope you're not expecting a wedding breakfast."

"I don't want anything from you." I replied and took Joan's arm.

"Come on, I'll not spend another moment of our wedding day in this house."

The fog had barely cleared as we walked up the lane to the crossroads to catch a bus into Wrexham. We held onto each other tightly as the bus nosed slowly through the damp murkiness of the foggy November afternoon. I had no plans when we arrived, but it was good to be with my new wife away from the stony silence of Pen y Bryn. We found a café and went in for a cup of coffee. There we talked of our plans and I told Joan that I would make up for this apology of a wedding day and that we might one day look back on our situation and laugh about it.

It was growing dark, but I was determined not to return to Pen y Bryn any earlier than necessary. It was only five o'clock, the café would be closing soon and the last bus didn't leave until nine. We finished our coffee and went outside, a light drizzle had begun to fall. Along the street, the lights of a cinema shone in the gathering darkness, as we walked past I saw the billboards advertising Gary Cooper starring in the 'Man who shot Liberty Vallance'. It wasn't the most romantic film to watch on a wedding day, but inside it would at least be warm and dry. I bought two tickets and we spent the next two hours holding hands and cuddling in the back row while Gary Cooper shot Indians on the big screen.

After the film had ended, I picked up a bottle of wine from an off-licence on the way to the bus station. It was past ten o'clock by the time we got back to Pen y Bryn and my new in-laws and the rest of the family had gone to bed. Joan and I went into the kitchen and opened the wine. I poured two glasses and then two more.

"Here," I said to Joan. "Take these up to those miserable buggers upstairs."

She disappeared with the two glasses and came down a few minutes later.

"They want us to go up and have a drink with them."

I almost dropped my glass in surprise. First of all they want nothing to do with the wedding and now they wanted to toast us, I found their behaviour completely baffling. When we entered their room they were sitting up in bed holding their glasses.

"Well, good health!" said Archie and we all raised our glasses and drank.

55

Now that we were married, we shared Joan's bedroom which was slightly larger than mine, but it was becoming increasingly clear that the house at Pen y Bryn was too small. With a large family there was little privacy for a newly married couple and I began looking around for somewhere else to live. Painfully aware that I had virtually no money and that buying a place of our own was completely out of the question, it would be a case of renting, but at that time very few houses were available.

Any thoughts that my financial situation might improve now that I was Archie's son-in-law had evaporated when I had asked him for a pay increase now that I was a married man. He had refused, saying that three pounds and fifteen shillings plus free board and lodging was more than enough for the work I was doing, so in addition to looking for alternative accommodation, I also began to look for alternative employment.

Although I had come to enjoy the outdoor life involved in working on the farm, there was clearly no future in it for me. In addition to Joan, Archie had four other children including two sons and it was clear to see where I fitted into the pecking order. Changing jobs however was not quite as easy as it might seem, under the provisions of the Aliens Order Act to which I was still subject, I couldn't just change jobs like anyone else. I had first to submit an application to the Home Office for an endorsement to my work permit that would allow me to move out of agriculture before I could actively seek another job. I sent away for the necessary papers, duly completed them and waited for two months before the endorsement was issued.

I might have been persuaded to stay on at the farm if Archie had agreed to pay me an extra five shillings a week. Joan had asked him to reconsider my wages now that I was part of the family, but he had told her that he saw no reason to pay more for the same amount of work and that she should have considered the low pay of an agricultural labourer before she married one. After that, I was determined that neither Joan nor I would ever ask him for more money again. Things moved faster than I could have imagined for within one week of receiving permission, I had managed to find both somewhere else to live and a new job. I had heard that a local building company called Jones Bros. were expanding and taking on additional men so I applied and was taken on as a bricklayer. I was looking forward to returning to my old trade though it seemed a lifetime since I last wielded a trowel back in Germany in the days before I was put into uniform. At last I would be out from under my father-in-law's thumb and earning four pounds a week more than I was receiving at Pen y Bryn.

That same week, Bill Holland let me know about Mr Naginton, an old man who lived in Meirion House, a large, rambling house in the village. His wife had died a few months earlier and he was looking for a housekeeper to cook his meals and keep the house clean. I went along to see him, explained that Joan and I wanted to move out of Pen y Bryn and that until we found a place of our own, suggested that we move in with him. Joan would do the cooking and cleaning while I went out to work, it wasn't a place of our own, but at last we were free of the stifling constraints of Pen y Bryn.

Life was easy at Meirion House, both Joan and I got on well with Mr Naginton and I was enjoying my work with Jones Brothers. What was entered into as a strictly temporary arrangement gradually became a normal existence and the weeks turned into months. The situation might have continued for longer, but for the fact that Joan became pregnant and knowing that the old man didn't want any children in the house, it gave renewed impetus to the search for a place of our own. Although I was earning more money working at Jones Bros, I still had little by way of savings and there was no possibility of buying a house as it was impossible for an alien to obtain either a bank loan or a mortgage.

One day I mentioned the problem to the foreman at Jones Brothers, telling him that Joan and I would soon have to move out of Mr Naginton's house and that so far I hadn't managed to find anywhere else. He thought about it for a few moments then told me that he'd heard that an old bus was being scrapped by a local transport company and that it might be available for any reasonable offer.

I laughed.

"An old bus! How could we possibly live in a bus?"

"Don't laugh," he replied. "Go and have a look at it, you'd be surprised how much room there is in a bus when all the seats have been taken out."

I said that I would give it some thought, but I confess that I didn't like the sound of it. At the end of another week of fruitless searching however, I decided that there would be no harm in at least taking a look at the old bus so I went down to the depot in Oswestry. I was directed to the far corner of the yard where a few ancient vehicles were parked against a wall. A green double-decker with spiral steps at the rear and flaking paintwork was the one for sale. It had clearly seen better days, the seats and engine had already been removed and when I climbed on board I discovered that there was indeed a surprising amount of space on both floors. I tried to visualise it with curtains and some furniture and decided that it might not look so bad after all. The depot manager said that if I wanted it, I would have to decide quickly because it was due to be taken away the following weekend by a scrap dealer.

"It's yours for fifty quid, including delivery!" said the manager.

I told him that I would need to get a site organised, but nevertheless shook on the deal. I returned straightaway to Pen y Bryn to ask Archie if he could give me a small parcel of land on which to put the bus. I was reluctant to ask him for anything, but I didn't have too much choice under the circumstances. When I told him that Joan was expecting a baby, he agreed to make available a small corner of a pasture a quarter of a mile from the farmhouse and overlooking a small wooded dingle. It was a pleasant enough spot and I set to work preparing a level base on which the bus would stand and digging a pit for the septic tank. The following week, the bus arrived on the back of a low loader. A crane arrived to lift the old vehicle onto the base I had prepared and I set to work converting it into a home for my wife and our first child which was kicking in her womb.

Every day when I returned from work, I would quickly finish my evening meal before going down to Pen y Bryn where I worked until late in the evening getting the old bus into shape. The upper deck made a spacious bedroom with ample room for a double bed and a cot, I partitioned the downstairs into a separate sitting room and kitchen and turned the drivers cab into a small pantry. I fashioned a door to enclose the platform at the rear then installed a gas stove for cooking and a couple of paraffin heaters for warmth. I cut a hole in the side of the bus and built an external brick chimney up the side so that we could have a coal fire. Joan made curtains for the many windows and I managed to get a second-hand sofa and armchair. I bought an old wooden garden shed that I placed behind the bus to house the toilet and although there was no running water, within two weeks we were able to move in to 'Dingle View'.

There is nothing quite like having a place of your own for the first time and even such a humble abode as a converted bus meant the world to Joan and I. After we moved in I set about giving it a fresh coat of paint, putting a picket fence around it to keep the grazing cattle away and even planting flowers and vegetables. The resulting crops of potatoes, carrots and runner beans would enable us to make some economies in the housekeeping budget and allow us to save a little more for the future. Joan couldn't have been happier if I'd bought her a palace, she was just nineteen and although heavily pregnant, did everything possible to make our new home a comfortable one. She made covers for the old chairs, knitted clothes for the baby and cleaned the old bus until it sparkled and shone.

Our son, Robert was born in June and like any proud father I thought he was the most beautiful and perfect thing ever created. Joan and I would spend hours studying him intently as he lay sleeping in his cot, watching his every move, marvelling at his perfectly formed fingers and toes and caressing the wisps of downy hair covering his head. I was now twenty-seven years old, I had a beautiful son, a place of my own to call home and I was happy, but far from content. I had no intention of living in a bus for the rest of my life, nor was I satisfied being a mere jobbing bricklayer working on building sites around the county.

I knew that my English would never be perfect, the farmers and bricklayers from whom I learnt were not scholars and I had picked up bad linguistic habits too numerous to mention. My grammar may have been poor, but I could understand virtually any conversation and could be described as fluent even though I would occasionally be ribbed for my spectacularly poor pronunciation. I knew that I was capable of achieving much more.

It seemed that I had spent my entire life obeying orders and working to the instructions of others, firstly at school, then in the Youth, the Arbeitsdienst, followed by the Luftwaffe, a succession of camp guards and finally those of my father-in-law at Pen y Bryn. Perhaps it was the sense of freedom and independence I now had, the desire to improve the lot of my young family or perhaps it was a desire to make up for the lost years of war and prison camps. Whatever the underlying reason, I decided that the only way I could better myself was to start up my own business. I had never been afraid of hard work and although I knew it would not be easy, I was determined for the first time in my life to be my own boss.

It was around this time that the Ministry of Agriculture had stipulated that all milking parlours had to be brought up to a certain standard in order for farmers to continue selling their produce. Many of the farms in the area had ancient milking sheds that had changed little during the past hundred years and it still wasn't unusual in the hill farms of Wales to see milking being done by hand. Farmers were given a certain amount of time to make their conversions, but I knew that there would be a lot of building work in the area as dairy farming was the main source of income for many farms. Seeing the opportunity I handed in my notice at Jones Brothers, used what little money I had managed to save to buy a van and other building tools and became T. Horst – Building Contractor. I had gradually stopped using my name in its full, hyphenated form, as it seemed to cause a great deal of confusion among the local population.

My first job was to install a new milking parlour at Pen y Bryn. I had given Archie a very competitive price, but typically he got a quote from another builder before giving me the job and equally typically, made me wait a considerable length of time before paying me. I then built one for old Bill Holland next and as word spread that I was doing good work at reasonable prices, I found that I was soon getting contracts from many other farmers in the area. As I became busier I had to hire more labourers and by the end of the year I calculated that I had made more money than I had in the previous four years put together. Joan and I celebrated the end of a successful year and the beginning of 1952 by attending a New Year's Eve party in the village, taking Robert with us in his carrycot. We danced the night away and drank more than was good for us, toasting our future. Frost sparkled and stars twinkled in the clear night air as we walked home down the lanes, but when we reached Pen y Bryn it was to discover that Dingle View had burnt to the ground.

I felt as if part of me had been destroyed. A mass of scorched, twisted metal and piles of ash were all that remained of our beautiful little home on which we had lavished so much care and where we had spent many happy months. As I tried to comfort Joan who sobbed uncontrollably and gazed at the remains of her home, I was reminded briefly of the truck in Normandy that had been hit by the American plane. No-one had been incinerated in this fire however and there would be no half-cremated bodies to bury in hastily dug pits. Instead of the new year heralding a time of optimism for the future, it seemed that once again fate had conspired to try and drag me down.

56

With our new home a pile of smouldering ashes, we had no alternative but to move back temporarily into the old farmhouse at Pen y Bryn. Archie had finally built a bungalow next door with the proceeds of the insurance and although I had patched the old place up, a number of rooms had been lost to the fire. It was nevertheless empty and there was enough room for the three of us, although we only intended to stay as long as it took to find another place. Our stay would turn out to be much longer.

My building business continued to prosper and the following year Joan presented me with a beautiful daughter. I was far from wealthy, but for the first time in my life I didn't have to watch every penny and was able to think about matters other than where my next meal was coming from. It was now 1954 and I hadn't returned to Germany since my visit almost five years earlier. Although I wrote to my parents and received occasional letters in return, I knew that I was growing increasingly remote from them. My parents weren't getting any younger while my sister had herself married and my brothers were now almost grown men. I reflected sometimes that as far as they were concerned, I might just as well have died during the war like Hans and Bernie. I was little more than a fading photograph on the side table in the parlour.

From the letters which we exchanged, they knew of my

life in England and of my new family, but I longed to show them off in the flesh, Joan was also intrigued by this German family of which she had heard so much, but had never seen. I decided that it was time I made the journey back to Germany and so I closed the business down for the month of July and loaded up my recently purchased first car, an old Morris, with the things we needed for our expedition. It took eight hours to reach Harwich in Essex where we stayed overnight in a hotel before driving down to the docks the following morning. I removed our belongings and left the car on the quayside where it was winched aboard the ship by crane.

As I leaned on the guardrail watching the English coast slip away, I cast my mind back to the last time I had made this crossing four years earlier, when hundreds of returning prisoners had been my fellow passengers. Some had returned to England, but many had not, Korff being one of those who stayed on in Germany as he had promised. I had lost touch with Luchinger, allowing him to drift out of my life like so many others with whom I had shared horror and deprivation. Perhaps it was better this way. There was no point in dwelling in the past, what was done was done and it was time to look to the future.

After a long drive through Holland and northern Germany, we eventually arrived in my home village. The journey had taken almost three days and we were tired, but relieved that we had arrived and that the old car had not let us down. Joan and I were feted by family and friends, there were parties and outings, visits to relatives, barbecues in the garden and long summer evenings spent talking and drinking. My parents wouldn't put their first grandchildren down, constantly picking them up and showering them with kisses, nothing was too much trouble for them as long as the little ones were contented. I think it was the first time my mother had been genuinely happy since Hans had died ten years earlier. My parents hadn't changed a great deal since I had last seen them, but my two younger brothers and sister had changed almost beyond recognition. Heinz was now eighteen, Eugen fifteen and Wilhemina a married woman of twenty-five.

It was a wonderful month spent in the bosom of my old and new families, a warm, idyllic summer of endless parties and reunions. I met people I hadn't seen since I was last at home and others that I hadn't seen since I was a boy, but I was conscious too that there were many others whom I had known and would never meet again, their unseen presence just as real as those who were there in the flesh. The missing were an unspoken void which no-one wanted to discuss. I would occasionally ask an innocent question about what happened to so and so and there would be silence, an unspoken rebuke. How could I have asked such a stupid question?

The stonemasons had transformed the small war memorial in the village. It had first been erected at the end of the Great War when half a dozen names had been inscribed upon a simple granite slab. A few extra names might have been accommodated on the original, but the masons had not envisaged the need to add a large number of names to those that had perished in the 'war to end all wars'. The names of the more recent dead had required an entirely new polished, granite slab. Beneath the phrase 'Gott Mit Uns' Hans's name was inscribed and further down, under the more hopeful and less final sounding 'Vermissen' was carved the name of Bernie.

Although the war still cast a long shadow, things had otherwise changed in a multitude of ways. The reforms of

Chancellor Adenauer were beginning to bring real prosperity to the people and the recovery was visible. Roads were full of Volkswagens and everywhere new buildings were being erected, autobahns being constructed and ruined bomb sites being cleared. It seemed as though the people were attempting to rebuild and repair as quickly as possible in order to erase the painful past and create a shiny, new Germany which could hold up its head, reborn and unsullied by the past.

I had been teaching Joan to speak a little German ever since I moved into Pen y Bryn and although she was a little unsure of herself, she soon began to feel quite at home and I was pleased at the way she handled herself. She coped easily with family and friends who were curious to meet this 'Englander' whom I had married.

One day I happened to meet up with Rainer, an old friend from the days when I was an apprentice at the building company in Lippstadt. We sat drinking in Brandt's telling each other of our experiences since we had last met. He told me that he had served in Italy and that he survived a number of scrapes before finally being captured by the Americans who had kept him in a camp in the Italian Alps for eighteen months. He had heard that I had survived the war and was now living in England so he asked me how things were. I told him that things were fine, that I had married a local girl and was now running my own business.

The talk eventually turned to money and he told me that as a self-employed builder doing contract work for larger firms he was able to earn far more than I was. He went on to tell me of the severe labour shortages that were badly affecting many trades and professions in Germany and how the building industry in particular was under such pressure that wages were skyrocketing. There was even talk of importing workers from countries such as Italy and Turkey to cope. He painted such a glowing picture of the riches that were available to anyone with skill and an appetite for hard work, that after a few more beers, I was beginning to think that perhaps my future might lay back in Germany after all.

When I returned to my parents' house, I related the conversation to Joan. I thought that she would be against the idea of moving to Germany, but when I told her about the need for people and the high wages on offer in the construction industry, to my surprise she said that she would follow me wherever I wished to go. I had no need to ask my parents if they approved of the idea, as they had never made any secret of their desire for me to return, they had two other sons and a daughter, but I think they felt that my return might in some small way compensate for the loss of Hans and Bernie.

By the end of the holiday I had made up my mind, it was too good an opportunity to miss. I would be able to earn more in one year than three in England building milking parlours for skinflint farmers who would quibble over the bill for months before paying me. We would go back to England, sell up and return to Germany, staying initially with my parents until we could find a place of our own. At the end of July, we returned to Pen y Bryn and informed Joan's parents that we were moving to Germany. I completed a few outstanding jobs before giving all the men one month's notice, sold the van and packed up all our belongings.

It was October by the time we arrived back in Germany. The long warm days that we had enjoyed in the summer had gone and a chill easterly wind carried with it the promise of a cold winter. We moved into the spare bedroom of my parents' house and Joan and the children soon settled in. I began working with Rainer and three other builders who were also self-employed and working a colossal number of hours each week. At first things went well and the money was everything that I had imagined, but the hours were extremely long and I was expected to join in the lengthy drinking sessions which took place at the end of the day. I had never been afraid of hard work, but would often not return home until late at night, exhausted and worse for drink and it seemed that the only time I saw my son and daughter was when they were fast asleep. I could only kiss them gently on the forehead before I fell into bed myself and sometimes I was too tired even to do that, falling asleep in the chair downstairs.

Joan never complained, but I could tell that she was unhappy and I knew that it wasn't because she was away from home or that she didn't get on with my parents for they treated her like their own daughter. The problem was me. I only saw my family on the occasional Sunday when I was not working and even then I was often too tired to think about doing anything. I hadn't even had time to look for a house of our own, although I had found time to put down a deposit on a spanking new Volkswagen.

One evening in Brandt's, I was sitting having a drink with Joan and my father when a friend of his, an elderly man from a neighbouring village came in and sat down by us. We were having a few drinks and talking about old times when he turned to me;

"I don't know how you've done it, Theo." he said, slapping me heartily on the thigh

"What do you mean?" I asked.

"Well, we might have lost the war, but you still managed to get to England and what's more, you came back with some booty." he winked first at me, then at Joan.

Everyone within earshot laughed at his joke, but I hadn't

thought about my situation in quite that way before. The old man had meant it in jest, but it was nevertheless true. No matter what I had gone through during and immediately after the war, I had eventually landed on my feet. I had a lovely wife, a beautiful son and daughter and now I was back in Beckum earning good money and apparently flaunting my good fortune in the faces of those who continued to suffer. I had returned to Germany to please my parents as well as for financial reasons, but I now began to read the signs of jealousy and disapproval in the faces of their neighbours and others in the village for whom there would be no homecoming sons, no grandchildren and no sparkling new cars parked outside their homes.

As the months went by, I became more conscious of eyes burning into me, the twitching of curtains as I walked through the village, the polite, but distant greetings. It had taken me six months to notice, but now the awful realisation dawned upon me that many of the people in my home village, the place in which I had grown up, the place I had craved to see for so many years, probably hated me.

57

We returned to England the following year. My parents were naturally disappointed at my decision, but they understood the reasons. My mother found it hard to accept that her entire family would never be near to her again, but she understood what many other families already realised; that although the war had long since ended, it would never really be over.

When we moved back once again into the old farmhouse at Pen y Bryn, I knew that this country against which I had once fought would forever be my home. I re-started my building business, buying equipment and hiring men. The pace of life in this rural corner of England was much slower than the frenetic activity in the booming economy of Germany, but it provided a good living for my family and more importantly, I was able to spend time with them. My second son was born in the following year, at about the same time that Joan's father decided to buy a larger farm about thirty miles away.

Pen y Bryn was put up for sale and we finally had to move out of the old farmhouse. Archie sold me a parcel of land in one of his fields on which I built my own house. With every spade full of earth I dug for the foundations I felt as though I was planting myself deeper and more firmly in my adopted land. From the house which I built, I could see across the fields to Pen y Bryn, surrounded by the stand of ancient yews and could also see the spot where our first home, the converted bus with the grand name of Dingle View once stood.

And so it was that I took root in this place. I am now eighty years old and have spent sixty of those years living here. I have lived in England for so long now that it is sometimes difficult for me to remember living anywhere else. Germany exists for me as a place for summer holidays and family visits, but it is this corner of rural England that now holds almost a lifetime of memories, it is the place I have come to love and the place I call my home. Times have changed of course, the old prisoner-of-war camp at St Martins still stands although these days the huts which once housed men, house the businesses and offices of a small industrial estate.

Now that I am retired I have time to think of the past, to remember some of those with whom I came into contact during those mad years when my life was changed forever. Rudi who saved my life in Normandy, Lenz, Reidle and Korff who helped me to survive the horror of slow starvation in Guernsey. The anguish of Georg Segerer who hanged himself at Mile End when the rest of us returned to Germany and Luchinger who accompanied me on my first tentative expeditions outside the camps. I am not the only ex-prisoner of war living in this part of the world, many like me stayed because they married local girls, some because they were unable to return to their homes in the east, while others just somehow forgot to go back, the course of their lives changed forever by war.

About thirty thousand German prisoners never returned home after the war and remain in England to this day. Although I was offered British nationality in the 1950's, I still possess a German passport. I never bothered to take up the offer though I appreciated the gesture and it barely seems to make any difference these days when we're all classed as European citizens. The only thing I have not been allowed to do over the years, is vote in general elections which I confess, has not caused me too much concern and I don't think that my inability to cast a vote has unduly affected the course of history.

My eldest son, Robert is buried in the small churchyard in St Martins, taken with an attack of asthma when he was just fifteen. I had seen and experienced some terrible things during the war, but to bury my own son was the hardest thing I ever had to bear and I understood how my parents felt when Hans died and of how much they grieved over the unknown fate of Bernie. Although a part of me died that day, I had not lost everything, my daughter and youngest son grew to become healthy adults and they now have children of their own. I'm sure that my three grandchildren never give a thought to the fact that they have some German blood running through their veins. They think of themselves as being as British as the next person and they regard me merely as their elderly grandfather with an odd name and a funny accent.

Many histories of the Second World War have been written. They usually speak of political leaders and military commanders, of invasions, victories and defeats, painting grand pictures of a war that ravaged Europe and profoundly altered the destinies of people and nations. In these pages I have merely recounted what happened to one ordinary young man from a small village in northern Germany who was caught up in those extraordinary times.

EPILOGUE

Theodor ter Horst passed away in January 2009. He is fondly remembered by his family and friends both in England and in Germany.